HANDBOOK ON
MECHANICAL PROPERTIES OF ROCKS

Series on Rock and Soil Mechanics
Vol. 2 (1974/75) No. 1

HANDBOOK
ON
MECHANICAL PROPERTIES OF ROCKS

– Testing Techniques and Results –
Volume I

by

V. S. Vutukuri

Department of Mining Engineering
Broken Hill Division
University of New South Wales

R. D. Lama

Institute of Soil and Rock Mechanis
University of Karlsruhe

S. S. Saluja

Department of Mining Engineering
Banaras Hindu University

First Edition
1974

TRANS TECH PUBLICATIONS

Distributed
in the USA and Canada by
TRANS TECH PUBLICATIONS
411 Long Beach Pkwy.
Bay Village, Ohio 44140
USA

and worldwide by
TRANS TECH S. A.
CH-4711 Aedermannsdorf
Switzerland

Copyright© 1974 by
TRANS TECH PUBLICATIONS
Clausthal, Germany

International Standard Book Number
ISBN 0-87849-010-8

Library of Congress Catalog Card Number
LC 74-82971

Printed in Germany

FOREWORD

Like a sculpturer, a construction engineer must know best his material with which or in which he has to work.

The rock, as a construction material, is the most complicated and most difficult to describe and define with which an engineer has ever to deal with and still it is the most commonly used building material. We have built in it and over it right from our appearance on the earth and still it is the material about which we know the least. It is absolutely necessary to understand it and control it so that the tragedies of Vajont, Malpasset, Langarone do not repeat themselves.

The problems of excavation and construction in rock, whether for mining of deeper or poorer quality minerals or for underground storage reservoirs, deep foundations, water storage dams or high speed transportation facilities, have become more complicated and wide spread requiring more stringent economic controls, technical planning and designs requiring an exact knowledge of the behaviour of immediate rock in particular and the surrounding rock in general.

The need for a handbook or a reference book containing an overall view of the material properties as well as the behaviour of the geologic-body and the methods to determine it had long been felt. This aspect of the field of rock science has grown so big that not many can keep an overall view of it. Therefore, this book by these authors who have spent considerable energy in describing the behaviour of the rock material and rock masses, is all the more welcomed. This work containing a rich review will be useful in determining the safety and economic viability of construction work in rock; an aspect in which there is nothing more important than the knowledge of the rock behaviour.

With satisfaction one could state that the book contains not only the mechanical properties of the rock substance in small hand specimens but also that of the composite rock mass which is built out of an assembly of such

FOREWORD

elements. The details of the important methods of investigation described in the book and the analyses of the results obtained are important for a man in practice.

Without approving any premature standardisation of the methods of testing, it is hoped that this treatise will particularly give an impulse to the various attempts of rock mass classification and the unification of the understanding of the testing techniques.

It is for this purpose I wish this book a wide dissemination.

Prof. Baurat h.c. Dr.-Ing. Dr. mont. h.c.
Leopold Müller – Salzburg
Division of Rock Mechanics
Institute of Soil Mechanics and Rock Mechanics
University of Karlsruhe

Preface

The knowledge of mechanical properties of rocks is essential in any rock mechanics investigations connected either with mining, tunnelling, drilling, blasting, cutting or crushing. After predicting the state of stress, strain or stored energy from the analysis of loads or forces being applied to the rocks, the behaviour, i.e., fracture, flow, or simply deformation of the rock can be estimated from these mechanical properties.

The mechanical properties of a rock depend primarily on its mineral composition and constitution, i.e., its structural and textural features. They also depend upon the condition it is in when tested (e.g., temperature, water content).

In reviewing the factors which influence the mechanical properties, it is helpful to work progressively from the scale of the single mineral to that of the rock mass. The properties of a single mineral are a function of its chemical composition, lattice structure (which determines glide systems), and lattice defects such as vacancies and dislocations. They also depend on its orientation relative to the applied stress field and on the mode of load application.

In bulk specimens of intact rock the mechanical properties depend not only on the properties of the individual minerals, but also upon the way in which the minerals are assembled. The relevant information is given by a full petrographic description, which includes the mineral composition of crystals, grains, cementing materials and alteration products and also the structure and texture, including size, shape, distribution and orientation of crystals, grains, pores and cracks. The degree of isotropy or anisotropy is also important and varies with the size of the body of rock under consideration. For example, in schist, gneiss, and other foliated rocks, the constitutive properties vary with direction even at the microscopic scale, and to the extent that the mechanical properties even of a small specimen are affected. However, in sedimentary rocks, which are generally laminated, the rock within a lamina may be relatively isotropic, whereas, at a scale that includes the separation between lamina, the same rock may be relatively anisotropic. On the other hand, other rocks may be strongly anisotropic even within very thin sheets. Primary anisotropy, brought about by preferential orientation during crystallisation, or by recrystallisation during sedimentation or metamorphic processes, may be distinguished from secondary anisotropy, brought about by geologic deformation of the rock.

The rock mass contains planes of weakness that affect its mechanical properties, making it mechanically anisotropic.* These planes of weakness may be joints, faults, fractures, partings between beds, or in bedded or laminated rock, layers of lower strength rock. The mechanical properties of a rock mass depend upon the following factors:

1. The mechanical properties of the individual elements constituting the system.

2. The sliding characteristics of the planes of weakness.

3. The configuration of the system with respect to the directions of loading.

4. The operating stress field.

The size or scale of the rock body that is being considered is an important factor in deciding the testing program for the determination of the mechanical properties of rock. From an engineering standpoint, if bodies of rock are being considered at a macroscopic scale, planes of weakness generally are not a point of concern. Operations such as crushing, grinding, and drilling occur at this scale. However, at a megascopic scale, e. g., in the excavation of large underground openings, in large open pit mines, planes of weakness generally dominate the failure process. This conclusion is borne out by the observation that the larger part of fracture surfaces created by underground or slope failures occurs on planes of weakness rather than through fresh rock.

Virtually all data on the mechanical properties of rock have been obtained from tests at a macroscopic scale, i.e., on specimens of rock, hand size or larger, but specifically below a size that would include planes of weakness of geological origin, e. g., joints, bedding planes, etc.

As yet, data are meager on the mechanical properties of large bodies of rock, i.e., from tests at a megascopic scale. The requirement for this information has been realised for some time, but the problems of preparing in situ test specimens and developing equipment for applying loads of the required magnitude have been slow in materialising. Several investigators have studied the effects of mechanical defects such as joints and bedding by testing

---

* This anisotropy is in addition to that due to mineral fabric (schistosity, etc.) that may be present both on macroscopic and megascopic scales.

specimens containing either real or simulated planes of weakness in the laboratory.

Various testing techniques (both laboratory and in situ) have been developed for the determination of mechanical properties and the results obtained are often dependent on many factors.

Probably because of the relative importance of this subject, a large amount of literature is available from a great number of papers scattered over many engineering and scientific periodicals and texts, and the proceedings of several conferences and symposia on the subject of rock mechanics, rock pressure, mining, etc.

The purpose of this handbook is to present a detailed treatment of the subject from the widely scattered literature in a simple, clear and logical form.

Volume 1 contains five chapters and an appendix dealing with 1. Specimen preparation for laboratory tests; 2. Compressive strength of rock; 3. Tensile strength of rock; 4. Shear strength of rock; 5. Strength of rock under triaxial and biaxial stresses; and Stiff testing machines. Volume 2 would contain Static and Dynamic elastic constants of rock, Rheological properties of rock, Mechanical behaviour of jointed rock, Large scale testing of rocks, Classification of rock and Miscellaneous properties of rocks (for details see Contents in this book).

It is hoped that this handbook will serve students, research workers, designers, practising engineers and members of the teaching staff in equal measure in the fields of mining engineering, civil engineering, geological engineering and petroleum engineering.

ACKNOWLEDGEMENTS

The authors gratefully acknowledge the inspiration given by the many authors from whose publications materials have been liberally drawn for the preparation of this book.

Permission to reproduce figures from their publications was kindly given by various publishers and authors. The author express their thanks to them. The authors offer their most grateful thanks to Professor *Müller* – Salzburg, University of Karlsruhe for his continuous inspiration, support and his emphasis on the subject of rock testing and its importance in practice and suggestion in writing of this book. The authors are thankful to him for kindly going through the book and writing a foreword.

The authors are deeply indebted to the following specialists for reviewing the manuscript (either in whole or in part) and offering many valuable comments, suggestions and criticisms:

1. Dr. Z. T. *Bieniawski,* Head, Geomechanics Division, National Mechanical Engineering Research Institute, South African Council for Scientific and Industrial Research, Pretoria, South Africa.

2. Prof. S. *Budavari,* Professor of Rock Mechanics, University of Witwatersrand, South Africa.

3. Mr. P. G. *Chamberlain,* Head, Property Determination Research Support, Fundamentals of Rock Failure, Twin Cities Mining Research Centre, U.S. Bureau of Mines, U.S.A.

4. Mr. L. A. *Endersbee,* Civil Engineer, Civil Design Division, Hydro Electric Commission, Tasmania, Australia.

5. Prof K. W. *John,* Departments of Geology III (Geotechnique), Institute of Geology, University of Bochum, West Germany.

6. Dr. J. A. *Hudson,* Tunnels Division, Transport and Road Research Laboratory, Department of the Environment, London, England.

7. Prof. E. *Hoek,* Golder Hoek and Partners, London (formerly Professor of Rock Mechanics, Royal School of Mines, University of London) United Kingdom.

8. Prof. T. *Ryncarz,* Institute of Underground Mining, Academy of Mining and Metallurgy, Cracow, Poland.

9. Prof. Dr. W. *Wawersik,* College of Engineering, Department of Mechanical Engineering, University of Utah, Salt Lake City, U.S.A.

The authors wish to express their sincere gratitude to the University of New

South Wales and the Institute of Soil and Rock Mechanics, University of Karlsruhe for facilities provided and wish a special word of thanks to Professor A. H. *Willis,* Pro-Vice-Chancellor, University of New South Wales for his encouragement in this work.

The authors gratefully acknowledge the assistance provided by the Management of North Broken Hill Limited in drafting of figures.

The authors are indebted to many colleagues in the preparation of the manuscript. Among the many others, the authors wish to mention especially the following:

Professor J. E. *Andersen,* Director, Broken Hill Division, University of New South Wales, for his interest and for providing various facilities.

Dr. R. K. *Asthana,* Mr. S. *Bhandari,* Mrs. M. *Browne,* Mr. R. E. *Byrne,* Mr. R. *Burkett,* Mr. W. M. *Dowd,* Mr. C. A. *Jenson,* Mrs. K. *Lynch,* Professor K. O. *O'Brien* and Mr. B. *Olds* for help in one form or the other.

Mesdames C. J. *Bright,* M. *Considine,* S. A. *Nejaim,* M. E. *Perry,* P. *Reece,* L. R. *Tweedie* and L. *Watson* for the arduous job of typing the manuscript.

Mrs. L. F. *Black,* Mrs. L. *Bollen,* Mr. K. J. *Murray,* Mr. L. *Separovich* and Mr. M. P. *Singh* for preparing figures and photographs.

The authors wish to express their deep appreciation and their profound gratitude to their wives for their patience and understanding during the preparation of the manuscript.

CONTENTS

CHAPTER 1

Specimen Preparation for Laboratory Tests

1.1. Introduction

Proper sampling of the rock mass and preparation of specimens require considerable care and effort. The samples collected must truly represent the parent body. The preparation of specimens takes up much of the time allocated for tests. Often the results are widely scattered. This poses the problem as to how many specimens are required for the test. These various points are dealt with in this chapter.

1.2. Sampling

Sampling should be proper because the samples collected must truly represent the rock mass, the properties of which are to be determined. Rock masses, in general, are non-homogeneous and the properties of the samples taken from one portion of the rock mass may be altogether different from those taken at another location.

The averages calculated from test results would be affected if certain portions of the deposit are not sampled. This leads to the important conclusion that samples should be collected from all portions of the deposit.

To ensure proper sampling, lithological studies of the deposit are made and regions which differ markedly in their mineral composition, nature of the cementing material, texture and degree of alteration are marked on the cross-section of the deposit. Very often, changes in the colour of the mineral, reflectivity and bands help in delineating these regions on the spot by visual examination.

In bedded deposits, bedding planes are important lines of demarcation which can be easily recognised. In coal seams, the petrographic properties of different constituents vary greatly and seams can be easily divided into different sections by visual examination.

The presence of cleavage planes, joints, cracks and other discontinuities is also taken into account. Along the cross-section of the deposit, these planes are separately marked out for the collection of samples.

Rock properties greatly vary in the regions of faults, dykes and folds. The presence of such structures is also kept in view.

Samples are usually collected from the field in the form of large blocks. In the case of softer rocks such as coal, shale and salt, they are cut from the parent body with appropriate machines. In the case of harder rocks, they are excavated by drilling closely spaced holes touching each other. Very often the help of cleavage planes and other planes of weakness is used.

Sometimes large blocks are collected after blasting. These blocks, however, have been subjected to high intensity stress waves from blasting which might have induced some fine cracks or extended preexisting cracks.

When it is necessary to test the properties of rock from inaccessible regions, diamond drilling is carried out to obtain cores.

In cases where irregular specimen testing is practised, small size samples may be collected from the run-of-faces worked by conventional methods of mining. The collection of such samples is least laborious but there is one inherent defect in that the weaker portions would have been broken into smaller pieces and samples collected would usually consist of those portions of the deposit which are comparatively stronger. Besides, it is very difficult to say which sample corresponds to which portion of the deposit. Moreover, samples collected have already been subjected to high stresses developed during winning of the mineral. Some of these disadvantages can be overcome if the samples are obtained by breaking one or more large blocks manually.

The samples collected are marked on the map to indicate their original positions and orientations relative to identifiable boundaries of the parent rock mass.

During the transportation of the samples, care is taken so that they are not subjected to excessive jolts which might induce fresh cracks or cause extensions of pre-existing cracks. They are also protected from the effects of weathering and are properly stored in a suitable place.

1.3. Preparation of Specimens

Test specimens may be divided into three categories:

> Regular specimens – Cylindrical
> Prismatic or cubic
> Irregular specimens
> Special-shape specimens

1.3.1. Regular Specimens

Most mechanical property test specimens are cylindrical. Typical specimen diameters are 2.5 to 5.0 cm (1 to 2 in) although facilities are usually provided for preparing specimens of diameters from 1.3 to 15.0 cm (0.5 to 6.0 in). Length-to-diameter ratios commonly used for some tests are listed below:

> Compressive strength test – 2.5 to 3.0
> Bending test   – 3   to 7
> Brazilian test   – 0.5 to 1.0
> Punch test   – 0.20 to 0.25

For making these specimens, cores obtained from drilling in underground excavations or exploration drilling are preferred since these require less preparation and can be protected easily from weathering by waxing, spraying or wrapping in polyethylene bags or sheet.

The specimens are prepared by cutting the cores into required lengths by disc saws.

When the sample is available in the form of a large block, it is first cut into small ones either on a machine or manually. Then, cores are drilled out from these blocks using either modified workshop drills or small quarry drills, A lathe utilising a coring bit can also be used for this purpose (ROWLANDS, 1967).

For the preparation of prismatic specimens, disc saws are employed. Blocks are first cut into plates, the plates into bars and the latter into prisms. If rocks are very brittle and of low strength, cutting by the saws often presents difficulties due to the shearing off of the material at the end of the cuts. In such cases, samples may be embedded in hard wax and then subjected to cutting.

Finishing of the specimen ends to certain standards before testing is important because the ridges and hollows at the specimen ends form points of stress concentration and cause failure at a relatively low load. Stronger rocks are more sensitive to end roughness than weaker rocks. The standard deviation of the results also increases with increased surface texture variation for all rock types.

Finish is given on a lathe, a surface grinder or a lapping machine. If lathe or surface grinder is used, final touching on a lapping machine is required.

If the sides of specimen are rough, they should be smoothened. This finishing is particularly important when electrical resistance strain gauges are to be used for strain measurements. Cylindrical specimens are finished on either lathe or surface grinder while prisms or cubes are finished on surface grinder or lapping machine.

Ideally, specimen ends should be parallel to each other and normal to the axis of the specimen. Surface grinding the specimen ends is the best method that will provide ends that are perpendicular to the core axis and parallel to each other within acceptable limits.

The tolerances on dimensions of cylindrical specimens for compressive strength test suggested by International Society for Rock Mechanics (I.S.R.M.) Committee on Laboratory Tests (1972) are given below:

1. The ends of the specimen shall be flat to 0.02 mm (0.0008 in).

2. The ends of the specimen shall be perpendicular to the axis of the specimen within 0.001 radian (3.5 minutes).

3. The sides of the specimen shall be smooth and free of abrupt irregularities and straight to within 0.3 mm (0.012 in) over the full length of the specimen.

Very often, during drilling, cutting and finishing operations it is necessary to use a coolant to dissipate the heat generated which otherwise may damage the specimen as well as the tool. Water is most commonly used for this purpose. In case of rocks affected by water, compressed air may be used as a coolant, but in such cases the operation has to be slow, the tool has to be withdrawn quite often to allow for adequate cooling of the tool and the rock and dust extraction facilities have to be incorporated.

1.3.2. Irregular Specimens

The preparation required on the samples collected for tests on irregular specimens is blunting the sharp edges by slight taps of a small hammer. The dimensions of the specimens are calculated from their weights.

1.3.3. Special-shape Specimens

Special-shape specimens are sometimes required, particularly for tensile tests, due to the problems in gripping of specimens.

WUERKER (1955) used specimens of the shape of cement-mortar or lignite briquettes (Fig. 1-1) for tensile strength tests. To obtain this shape, soft rocks, which cannot be core-drilled, are hand-cut whereas medium-hard to hard rocks are core-drilled as shown and cut to form a suitable specimen using a template.

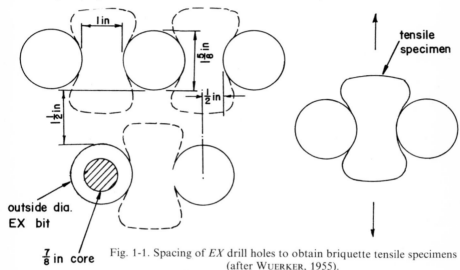

Fig. 1-1. Spacing of *EX* drill holes to obtain briquette tensile specimens (after WUERKER, 1955).

The tensile test specimen used by the Rock Mechanics Division of the National Mechanical Engineering Research Institute of South Africa is given in Fig. 1-2 (HOEK, 1964). Such specimens are prepared by grinding with a high speed water-cooled diamond wheel. The grinding attachment is carried on the tool post of a lathe and the profile of the specimen is generated by a profile and follower device actuated by the lead screw of the lathe.

Rings have also been used for tensile strength tests. The ends of the cores are first cut perpendicular to the longitudinal axis with disc saw. Then the required diameter holes are drilled along the longitudinal axis at the centre of the cores with a carbide drill on lathe. These cores are then cut into rings of the required thickness with a disc saw.

Hollow cylindrical specimens are sometimes preferred in triaxial strength tests. These are prepared by drilling blocks successively with two water-flushed diamond coring bits, the larger one being used initially to give the outside diameter (HOBBS, 1962). They may also be prepared by drilling first the inner hole and then by using specially-made overcoring bits with a central guide fitting to the inner diameter hole (PERRIN and SCOTT, 1964) or by using double-tube thin wall coring bits (MAZANTI and SOWERS, 1965). The hollow cylinders obtained are then cut to the required length using disc saws.

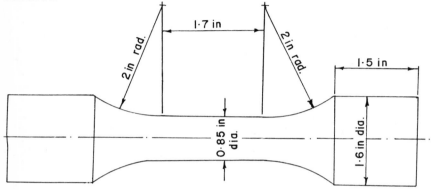

Fig. 1-2. Details of a tensile specimen used by N.M.E.R.I.
(after HOEK, 1964).

The spherical specimens have also been used in certain cases. They are particularly useful in measuring some of the properties in various directions. The U.S. Bureau of Mines recently developed a new technique for sphere preparation that reduces preparation time to nearly half that required by the former procedures (VICKERS and THILL, 1969).

The new sphere making technique requires a core having a diameter 0.16 to 0.32 cm ($\frac{1}{16}$ to $\frac{1}{8}$ in) larger than that of the desired sphere. After cementing the core on its side to a board, it is core-drilled in a direction perpendicular to the axis of the core (A in Fig. 1-3). This process is repeated again in a third direction, orthogonal to the other two drilling axes (B in Fig. 1-3). Edges or corners of the specimen are ground by hand until the specimen is roughly spherical (C in Fig. 1-3). The specimen is then ground in the sphere grinding machine (Fig. 1-4) in several stages using progressively finer grinding compounds until finished (D in Fig. 1-3).

In order to identify the initial orientation of specimen throughout the sphere preparation process, a system of rectangular coordinates is designated in the specimen, by drilling two very small holes of different diameter at right angles to each other.

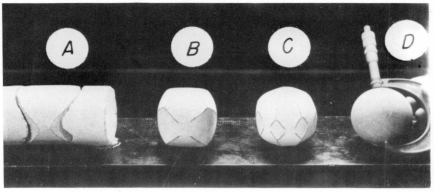

Fig. 1-3. The specimen is shown at several stages, A–D, of the new sphere making technique (after Vickers and Thill, 1969).

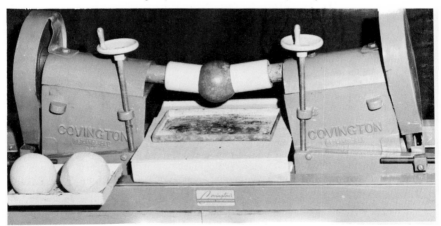

Fig. 1-4. The sphere cutting unit
(after Vickers and Thill, 1969).

1.4. Number of Specimens to be Tested

As pointed out earlier in section 1.2, the results obtained by testing of individual specimens are not representative of the parent body. Theoretically, it is not possible to obtain an absolute value, but results would be nearer the absolute the larger the number of specimens tested. But to limit the testing costs without sacrificing the reliability of results, it is necessary to ascertain the minimum number of specimens to be tested.

In determining the number of specimens to be tested, account must be taken of the variability of test results and the desired accuracy and reliability of the mean value. Variation depends upon the nonhomogeneity of the rock and the size of specimens. The smaller specimens show larger variation. As small specimens are tested in laboratory tests, the number of specimens should be large.

The following relationship can be used for the determination of the number of specimens, n, to be tested:

$$p = \frac{\left[100 + \dfrac{kV}{\sqrt{n}}\right]}{\left[100 - \dfrac{kV}{\sqrt{n}}\right]}$$

where V = coefficient of variation and
$\quad\quad p$ = a number.

The coefficient of variation, V, is determined by preliminary systematic experiments of say N specimens from the equation

$$V = \frac{s}{\bar{x}} \times 100\%$$

where $\bar{x}$, the mean value $= \dfrac{\Sigma x_i}{N}$ and

s, standard deviation $= \sqrt{\left\{\dfrac{\Sigma_i(x_i - \bar{x})^2}{N-1}\right\}}$

The value of k (Table 1) depends upon the desired confidence interval and the number of specimens tested in preliminary experiments, N. PROTODYA-KONOV (1961) chose 2 for the value of k. This coefficient relates to a confidence interval of 95% with large number of specimens (over 30).

The value of p depends upon the permissible deviation. If the permissible deviation is $\pm 20\%$ of the mean value, p would be 1.5.

In compressive strength tests, the coefficient of variation ranges from 15 to 30% while in tensile strength tests it is higher. Most frequently, the number of specimens for homogeneous rocks such as marble may be 2–3, for shales 5 and for sandstones 5–10. This number is still higher for coal.

Recently, YAMAGUCHI (1970) analysed this problem by using a statistical technique "Decision of the sample number" after carrying out experiments for compressive and tensile strengths on three kinds of rock, granite, andesite and sandy tuff. He concluded that ten or more specimens are required to determine the strength of rock.

TABLE 1

Values of k

Degrees of freedom (N - 1)	Level of probability (Confidence interval)		
	90%	95%	99%
1	6.31	12.7	63.7
2	2.92	4.3	9.92
3	2.35	3.18	5.84
4	2.13	2.78	4.60
5	2.02	2.57	4.03
6	1.94	2.45	3.71
7	1.89	2.36	3.50
8	1.86	2.31	3.36
9	1.83	2.26	3.25
10	1.81	2.23	3.17
11	1.80	2.20	3.11
12	1.78	2.18	3.05
13	1.77	2.16	3.01
14	1.76	2.14	2.98
15	1.75	2.13	2.95
16	1.75	2.12	2.92
17	1.74	2.11	2.90
18	1.73	2.10	2.88
19	1.73	2.09	2.86
20	1.72	2.09	2.85
25	1.71	2.06	2.80
30	1.70	2.04	2.75
∞ standard or deviation known	1.64	1.96	2.58

1.5. Summary and Conclusions

After conducting lithological and structural studies of the rock mass, sufficient samples should be collected from all markedly different portions of the rock mass. All samples should be marked to indicate their original positions and orientations relative to identifiable boundaries of the parent rock mass.

Cylindrical specimens are most common. The end faces of the cylindrical specimens must be strictly parallel to each other and perpendicular to the cylinder generatrix. The faces must be ground to close tolerances. The following standards have been suggested by I. S. R. M. Committee on Laboratory Tests (1972) for compressive strength test: –

1. The ends of the specimen shall be flat to 0.02 mm (0.0008 in).
2. The ends of the specimen shall be perpendicular to the axis of the specimen within 0.001 radian (3.5 minutes).
3. The sides of the specimen shall be smooth and free of abrupt irregularities and straight to within 0.3 mm (0.012 in) over the full length of the specimen.

Where special-shape specimens are warranted, they should be prepared even if they take more time for preparation.

The number of specimens to be tested depends on the variability of the results and the desired accuracy and reliability of the mean value. Ten or more specimens are preferable to determine the strength of rocks.

References

1. Hobbs, D. W.: The strength of coal under biaxial compression. Coll. Eng., Vol. 39, 1962, pp. 285–290.
2. Hoek, E.: Fracture of anisotropic rock. J. S. African Inst. Min. Metall., Vol. 64, No. 10, May, 1964, pp. 501–518.
3. I.S.R.M. Committee on Laboratory Tests: Suggested methods for determining the uniaxial compressive strength of rock materials and the point load strength index. Document No. 1, Oct., 1972, 12 p.
4. Mazanti, B. B. and Sowers, G. F.: Laboratory testing of rock strength. Proc. Symp. Testing Techniques for Rock Mech., Seattle, Wash., 1965, pp. 207–227.
5. Perrin, J. R. and Scott, J. J.: The White Pine 1. v. d. t. biaxial borehole deformation gauge. Proc. 6th Symp. Rock Mech., Rolla, Missouri, 1964, pp. 749–768.

6. PROTODYAKONOV, M. M.: Methods of studying the strength of rocks, used in the U.S.S.R. Proc. Int. Symp. Min. Res., Rolla, Missouri, 1961, Vol. 2, pp. 649–668.

7. ROWLANDS, D.: Preparation of specimens for rock mechanics research. Min. and Minerals Eng., Vol. 3, No. 11, Nov., 1967, pp. 428–430.

8. VICKERS, B. L. and THILL, R. E.: A new technique for preparing rock spheres. J. Sci. Inst., Series 2, Vol. 2, 1969, pp. 901–902.

9. WUERKER, R. G.: Measuring the tensile strength of rocks. Min. Eng., Vol. 7, No. 2, Feb., 1955, p. 157.

10. YAMAGUCHI, U.: The number of test-pieces required to determine the strength of rock. Int. J. Rock Mech. Min. Sci., Vol. 7, No. 2, March, 1970, pp. 209–227.

CHAPTER 2

Compressive Strength of Rock

2.1. Introduction

The procedure commonly used in the determination of compressive strength involves the use of a cylindrical specimen of rock loaded axially between platens in a testing machine. The stress value at failure is defined as the compressive strength of the specimen and is given by the relationship

$$\sigma_c = \frac{F}{A} \qquad (2.1)$$

where σ_c = compressive strength of the specimen
$\quad F$ = applied force at failure and
$\quad A$ = initial cross-sectional area transverse to the direction of force.

In concept, compressive strength determination is extremely simple, but in practice it is far from being so. In addition to the internal factors, mineralogy, grain size and porosity, the following external factors affect the test results significantly :–

(a) Friction between platens and end surfaces

(b) Specimen geometry :– (i)   Shape
                                              (ii) Height-to-diameter ratio
                                              (iii) Size

(c) Rate of loading

(d) Environment.

These factors must be recognised and interrelated and unless the nature of the specimen and the conditions of test are defined, the results may be misleading and virtually useless. These factors are dealt with in this chapter.

Recently, the importance of the determination of the mechanical behaviour of the failed rock termed as the post-failure behaviour of rock has been recognised. As it is not possible to obtain the post-failure curve in a normal testing machine, attempts have been made to increase the stiffness of the loading machine. More recently the servomechanism has been successfully used. A section on Post-failure Behaviour of Rock in Compression is included in this chapter.

Further, indirect methods for estimating compressive strength are also included in this chapter.

2.2. Stress Distribution in Specimens under Compression

The commonly used testing procedure is somewhat unsatisfactory because the stress distribution in specimens is non-uniform due to the end-effects associated with the elastic mismatch between the rock and testing machine. The result obtained is not a property of the rock alone, but is dependent upon the characteristics of both the rock and the testing machine.

When a specimen is compressed between the platens of a testing machine, it tends to expand laterally (both radially and circumferentially) as it shortens because of the 'POISSON's effect'. On the other hand, frictional constraint at the planes of contact between the specimen and the testing machine tends to prevent expansion. As a result, the specimen is not in a state of uniaxial compression in this region.

A number of investigators calculated the stress distribution within elastic cylindrical specimens under compression, assuming different boundary conditions. A summary of their results is given below.

FILON (1902) made a theoretical analysis assuming the following boundary conditions:–

(a) A resultant axial force acts across the ends of the cylinder, the distribution of which is not known.

(b) The end cross-sections of the specimen which are in contact with the platens remain plane.

(c) The stress acting across the curved surface of the cylinder is zero.

(d) The perimeter of the specimen ends remains fixed.

PICKETT (1944) presented a solution to the problem assuming the same first three boundary conditions of FILON but his fourth boundary condition is that ends do not expand at any point, i.e., there is no slipping. He used the FOURIER method and encountered the difficulty that the series was converging slowly for points near the outer edges of the cylinder and was unable to calculate definite values for stress at the outer edges of the cylinder. Using the lattice-analogy method, D'APPOLONIA and NEWMARK (1951) obtained the results, assuming the same boundary conditions as of PICKETT.

A more general problem was solved by BALLA (1960) using a combination of polynomial, FOURIER and BESSEL functions to satisfy boundary conditions. He considered the height-diameter ratio and a roughness factor also.

GIRIJAVALLABHAN (1970) solved this problem by finite element method and observed that his solution agreed very well with PICKETT's solution.

PENG (1971) also solved this problem by experimental and theoretical analyses.

All these solutions, however, produced different results. In Fig. 2-1, is given a comparison of stress distributions at the end surfaces of specimens with a height-diameter ratio of 1 for perfect confinement according to different investigators.

The axial stress distributions obtained by PICKETT, D'APPOLONIA and NEWMARK, BALLA and PENG agree in form but differ in numerical values to some extent. FILON's solution differs in form, possibly due to the fact that he did not consider that the ends do not expand at any point. The axial stress concentration is maximum at the corners of the specimen; 1.7 being for FILON's and D'APPOLONIA and NEWMARK's solutions, 1.6 for BALLA's, 1.9 (by extrapolation) for PICKETT's and 1.3 for PENG's.

The shear stress (τ_{rz}) distributions also show maximum values at the corners, with 1.1 for PICKETT's, 0.66 for D'APPOLONIA and NEWMARK's, 0.42 for BALLA's, 0.6 for PENG's, while FILON's solution, on the contrary, gives zero concentration at the corners and rises to a maximum of 0.52 at $r/R = 0.6$.

The radial (σ_r) and circumferential (σ_θ) stress concentrations differ very much from investigator to investigator. In many cases (i) circumferential stress is greater in magnitude than radial stress near the corners and (ii) the difference between circumferential and radial stresses becomes smaller toward the centre. They finally become equal near the centre. The radial stresses calculated by FILON and BALLA are zero at the corner, while those calculated by D'APPOLONIA and NEWMARK and PICKETT are 0.62 and 0.6, respectively. PICKETT's solution gives the same radial and circumferential stress concentrations at all points on the end surface, except those near the corners. PENG's values are undulating.

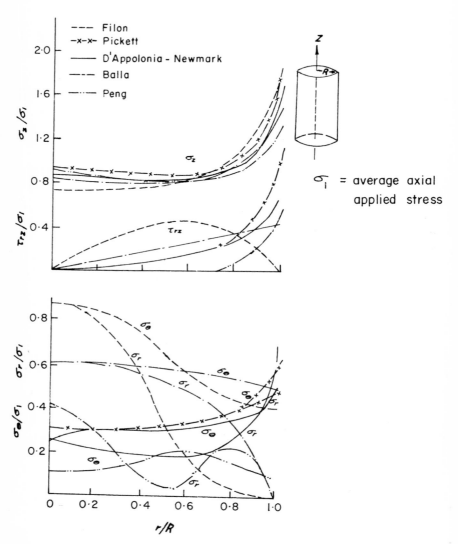

Fig. 2-1. Comparison of stress distributions at the end surfaces for perfect confinement, according to different authors (after PENG, 1971).

GIRIJAVALLABHAN plotted axial stress distributions at midplane of the cylinder. Along with his results, he included the results of PICKETT and D'APPOLONIA and NEWMARK (Fig. 2-2). All solutions indicate that the axial compressive stress is maximum at the centre of the specimen on mid plane.

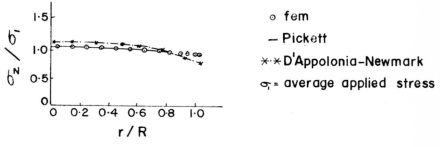

Fig. 2-2. σ_z stress at middle of cylinder
(after GIRIJAVALLABHAN, 1970)

The radial and circumferential stress concentrations are not available for mid-vertical-plane of the specimen from all the investigators. FILON's solution indicate that circumferential tensile stresses exist across the full width of the specimen and the maximum is -0.032 times the average axial compressive stress at the curved boundary. PENG also gave values for mid-plane in case of specimens with height-diameter ratio of 2. At the mid-plane, all radial stresses are tensile. The maximum radial tensile stress is -0.06 at the centre, and decreases on both sides to a value of zero on the cylindrical surface. The largest tensile circumferential stress concentration is -0.055 and occurs at the mid-plane, at a distance of about $R/2$ from both sides of the specimen.

KOTTE, BERCZES, GRAMBERG and SELDENRATH (1969) also solved this problem for a specimen with height-diameter ratio of 2, assuming FILON's boundary conditions. Their results are given in Fig. 2-3. This figure clearly indicates that triaxial compressional stresses are present up to a certain depth from contact surfaces in the rock specimen. Also there are tensional radial as well as circumferential stresses in the central region.

PENG also solved the problem for a height-diameter ratio of 2. His results are given in Fig. 2-4. These results also show similar trends.

BORDIA (1971) developed a stress concentration model based on PRANDTL's theory of localised plastic deformation for rock-platen contact surfaces of finite rock specimens and his solution is given in Fig. 2-5. The specimen section is divided into two major regions; one containing biaxial compressional

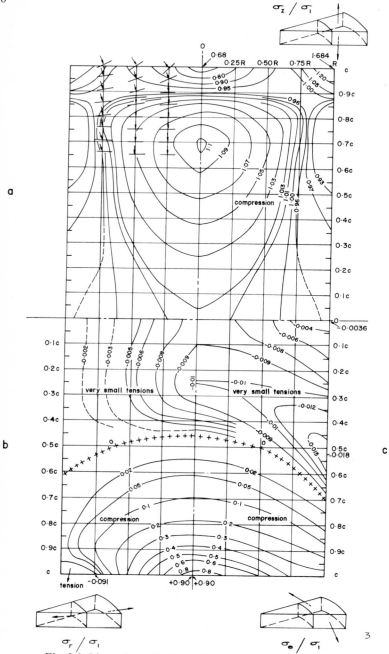

Fig. 2-3. Lines of equal principal stress under uniaxial loading
(after KOTTE, BERCZES, GRAMBERG and SELDENRATH, 1969).

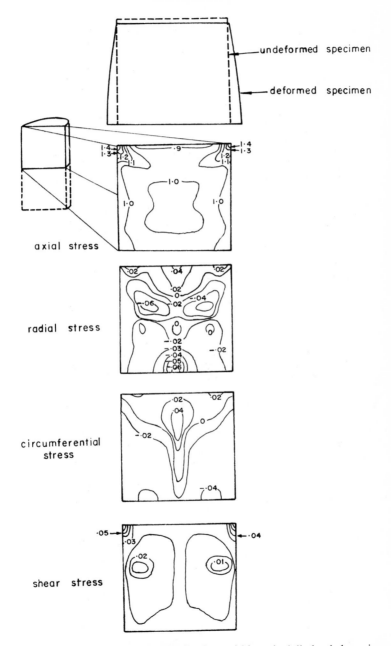

Fig. 2-4. Contour map of stress distributions within uniaxially loaded specimen (perfect confinement) (after PENG, 1971).

stresses (strains) near the contact surfaces and the other containing tensile stresses (strains) in one axis. The radial shear lines originate from the ends such as B. The biaxial compressional stresses (strains) induce a strengthening effect, while tensile stresses (strains) have a weakening effect on the strength.

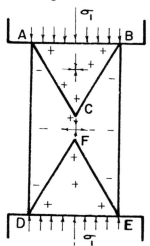

Fig. 2-5. Stress-strain distribution in a cylindrical specimen compressed between two metal surfaces (after BORDIA, 1971).

From a practical point of view also, circumferential tensile stresses must exist. With the application of force, lateral expansion takes place throughout the length of the specimen. The continuity of the specimen demands that the segments expand in a circumferential direction by an amount that is proportional to the distance from the geometrical centre of the specimen. This means that elemental volumes located around the outer circumference of a compression test specimen are required to exhibit more expansion in the circumferential direction than is allowed by POISSON's effect, so that circumferential tensile stresses must exist.

Also, tensile stresses are generated in the vicinity of the cracks, grain boundaries, etc. by the applied compressive forces.

In actual compression tests, however, a slight amount of radial as well as circumferential expansion of the ends will be expected so that the stress distribution will tend towards greater uniformity than the above solutions indicate.

Some other workers also suggested stress distribution patterns based upon their experimental observations.

TRUMBACHEV and MELNIKOV (1964), while discussing the distribution of stresses in the intervening pillars from photoelastic model tests on gelatine, mentioned that at mid-plane the axial stress is a little greater at the centre than at the edge of the pillar. Near the end planes, the axial stress is greater towards the edge of the pillar. Regarding the lateral stresses, they mentioned that there is compression at the ends and tension in the middle zone.

ZNANSKI (1965), from his experimental observations, however, suggested that the axial stress distribution on the end surfaces of the specimen is undulating with maximas at the ends and the centre (Fig. 2-6). LAMA (1966), from the study of failures of various specimens tested, suggested the existence of higher stresses at the centre of specimens than at the periphery. He found that failure of specimens with low height-diameter ratio occurs with the development of radial cracks radiating from the centre (Fig. 2-7). When an unhardened stainless steel platen was used, a concave cavity was formed in the lower platen supporting the above configuration of stress distribution. These deductions are contrary to the results referrred earlier.

PENG (1971) found the stress distribution in specimens to be a function of the platen configuration. Platens of the same diameter as the specimens gave more uniform stress distribution than platens which were larger than the specimens.

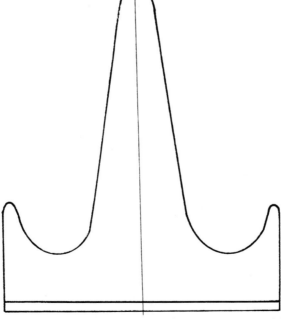

Fig. 2-6. Stress distribution on specimen ends compressed between rigid platens (after ZNANSKI, 1965).

Fig. 2-7. Failure of a specimen of size 10.0 cm × 10.0 cm × 2.5 cm
(3.940 in × 3.940 in × 0.985 in) with radial cracks diverging from the centre showing
the existence of high stresses at the centre
(after LAMA, 1966).

In summary, it may be said that at the contact surfaces, the effect of friction introduces a triaxial state of stress. This region extends into the specimen in the shape of a cone and beyond a certain distance stress distribution is more uniform. The strength of rock in the contact region increases many folds. Tensional (lateral) stresses exist at the mid-region of the specimen. The stress distribution in test specimens appear to be not only a function of specimen height-to-diameter ratio but also the platen configuration as well. Platens of the same diameter as the specimens are recommended.

Since the non-uniformity of stress distribution is due to friction and con-straint, some investigators tried to reduce friction by introducing paraffin or by placing capping materials such as rubber sheet, teflon, neoprene, thin copper or lead sheets, wood-fibre plates, treatex, masonite, cardboard, leather, blotting paper, etc. in between the specimen ends and platens. Some of these are not efficient enough to eliminate friction and ensure uniform stress distribution; some induce lateral tensile stresses and some give more or less uniform stress distribution.

HAST (1943), from his experiments, concluded that a layer of paraffin placed between the specimen ends and press platens induces compressive stress which is fairly linear, diminishing from the middle towards the edge (Fig. 2-8). Also, lubrication of the ends of the specimen produces lateral tensile stresses across the entire width of the ends of the specimen as a result of lubricant being squeezed out towards the edges. Besides, if the rock is porous, these lubricants may enter into the specimen and change its properties.

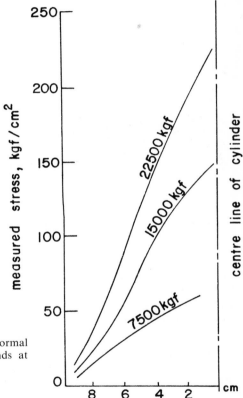

Fig. 2-8. Distribution of normal stress near the specimen ends at different load values (after HAST, 1943).

Some of the capping materials also develop lateral tensile stresses across the specimen ends. JENKINS (1958) revealed, from photoelastic studies, that when a specimen is loaded with sheets of rubber between the ends of the specimen and platens, high tensile stresses are developed throughout the whole height of the specimen. With a thin sheet of rubber and copper on each loaded surface, he found the lateral tensile stresses to be about half the applied axial compressive stress. BRADY (1971), after a three-dimensional finite element investigation, also reported that the use of a low-modulus insert such as rubber develops large lateral tensile stresses (of the order of one-half the applied axial compression near the specimen insert boundary) within the specimen. He also mentioned that the magnitudes of the induced stresses are very sensitive to both the POISSON's ratio/modulus of elasticity, v/E and height/diameter values of the insert material. The strength of rocks when tested by using such capping materials will thus be reduced and he concluded that insert materials with v/E values larger than the v/E value of the specimen should be avoided in laboratory testing of specimens between rough end-platens.

TRUMBACHEV and MELNIKOV (1964) also mentioned that if a soft layer is introduced at the roof line, transverse tension is induced at the top of the pillar. In addition, the transverse compressive stress concentration at the bottom of the pillar towards the edge is increased when a soft layer occurs at the top.

HAST (1943) reported that porous wood-fibre plates, treatex, masonite, etc. give more or less uniform stress distribution. He supported this by actual measurements using 13 mm (0.5 in) thick porous fibre plates on the ends of a concrete specimen of 4.0 cm (1.6 in) height and 12.4 cm (4.9 in) base. LUNDBORG (1968) reported the use of capping pieces of cardboard, leather, etc. of low POISSON's ratio to reduce the end effects. PENG (1971) obtained uniform loading in specimens of h/d ratio of 2 ($d = 3.18$ cm (1.25 in)) when steel inserts of height and diameter equal to the specimen diameter were placed between the specimen and the platens.

KARTASHOV et al. (1970) used a low-modulus stressed insert (Polyamide-56 plastic) in contact with the specimen in a rigid metal yoke to obtain a virtually uniform stressed state in the specimen. The scheme of the apparatus is given in Fig. 2-9. The specimen 1 is placed with its end faces in contact with inserts 2, each of which is located in the enclosed space of the cylindrical yoke, consisting of a container 3, a punch 4 and a casing nut 5. The specimen is introduced into the orifice of the yoke, leaving a small gap. Both yokes are placed in the body 6, which prevent their misalignment during the tests. The following dimensions were used in their apparatus: – Thickness and diameter of insert 7.5 mm (0.3 in) and 50.0 mm (2.0 in), respectively; and gap between insert and cylindrical yoke 0.5 mm (0.02 in).

Before testing, the inserts are compacted in the testing machine (using a washer with a diameter equal to that of the specimen, and a height equal to the thickness of the bottom of container 3) under a load greater than the breaking load, and pressed under this load by the casing nut. After compaction the surface of the insert is checked by a dial gauge and, where necessary, ground to the required accuracy. Thus, before testing, the inserts are under stress.

The following are some of the other methods suggested to overcome the influence of end friction: –

(a) By providing a dummy specimen above and below the test specimen and in contact with the platens of a testing machine. Lateral restraint will occur between the dummy specimen and the platen, while the test specimen will be free from restraint (SHOOK, 1963). The stress distribution will be more or less uniform in the test specimen though it may be highly non-uniform in the dummy specimen. However, this arrangement may not be suitable if the dummy specimens fail first.

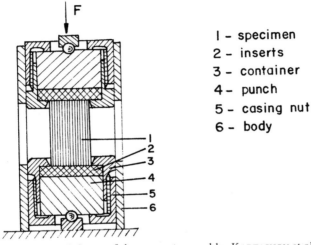

1 – specimen
2 – inserts
3 – container
4 – punch
5 – casing nut
6 – body

Fig. 2-9. Scheme of the apparatus used by KARTASHOV et al.
(after KARTASHOV et al., 1970).

(b) By shaping the platens of the testing machine so that the included angle of the cone in contact with the specimen is $(180-2\phi)$ where ϕ is the angle of friction. In this way, the effect of friction is compensated by the wedging action and uniform compression is obtained (SHOOK, 1963).

(c) By forming a double cone test specimen containing a gauge length between the narrower ends of the cones. If the cone angle approaches that of the same material exhibiting typical conical fractures, the compressive stress distribution across the area of the gauge section would be uniform. CHAKRAVARTY is reported to have confirmed by photoelastic coating technique that stress distribution is uniform in the double cone specimens and recommends this shape for compression tests (ROBERTS, 1964).

In routine testing, steel inserts of the same diameter as the specimen are recommended. The overall length of the platen should be at least equal to the diameter of the specimen (PENG, 1971).

Although HAST (1943) and LUNDBORG (1968) reported the use of capping pieces of cardboard, etc. to reduce the end effects, they are not recommended because they may produce tensile stresses at the interface and considerably reduce the load bearing characteristics of the specimen (GROSVENOR, 1963).

The other arrangements, double cone test specimens, special shaped platens, KARTASHOV et al. set up can be used for special investigation purposes.

2.3. Mode of Failure of Specimens in Compression

In compression tests, the pattern of failure may be either axially symmetric or random. Three types of failures are observed in specimens subjected to compression tests.

(a) The first consists of a general crumbling by development of multiple cracks parallel to the direction of applied force at mid-height of the specimen near the surface and its extension to the ends and into the centre of the specimen; when the specimen collapses, conical end fragments (free from cracks) are left, together with long slivers of rock from around the periphery (Fig. 2-10).

Fig. 2-10. Failure of a specimen of size 5 cm × 5 cm × 10 cm (1.97 in × 1.97 in × 3.94 in) (after LAMA, 1966).

(b) The second type of failure occurs with development of one or more major cracks parallel to the direction of application of force resulting in a series of columns (Fig. 2-11). This type has been termed slabbing (FAIRHURST and COOK, 1966), axial-cleavage fracture, vertical splintering (RINEHART, 1966) or splitting (PAUL and GANGAL, 1966).

Fig. 2-11. Slabbing failure in a specimen (after LAMA, 1966).

(c) The third type is the shearing of the test specimen along a single oblique plane.

Occasionally, all three types may appear to be present.

The first mode of failure is the most common. The conical wedge-shaped end segments of the failed specimen are due to the end constraints by the loading platens, and not necessarily to the intrinsic characteristics of rock. If specimens are too short, the resultant end cones may have a height approximately equal to the specimen half-height, and the apex half-angle, sometimes taken as the "fracture angle" of the rock, becomes a function of specimen height.

The second mode of failure is observed in some cases, particularly when the end constraint is eliminated.

The third type of failure has also been observed widely. But this is likely to be due to either platen rotation or lateral translation of the platens relative to each other, i.e., this type of failure is characteristic of the loading system (HAWKES and MELLOR, 1970).

2.4. Failure Mechanism of Specimens in Compression

The mechanism explained by PAUL and GANGAL (1966) is given here. Rocks contain a network of randomly oriented cracks. When a specimen is subject to an increasing uniaxial compressive stress, σ_1, a stress σ_1' will be reached such that the fracture of the cracks lying in the most unfavourable direction* will produce branch cracks which, in turn, may again branch, etc., but this branching effect will finally terminate as these cracks become oriented in the direction of the applied stress. Further fracture can take place only by attacking cracks which are less vulnerable than those already "removed". This can be done by raising σ_1 to a higher value, σ_1''. All branch cracks so formed will propagate a short distance and also align themselves with the applied stress. This process will continue for successive groups of cracks oriented at less unfavourable orientations until ultimately a sufficiently intermeshed network of cracks has been formed for macroscopic failure to result.

The cones generally formed in uniaxial compression are accounted for by assuming that the platens produce a lateral constraint within the hatched zone in Fig. 2-12, and that this lateral stress inhibits crack growth. Thus, initial fracture extension should start near the centre of the specimen, where the axial stress is greatest and the lateral constraint is a minimum. The areas outside the hatch zone should develop an intermesh of branching cracks oriented mostly in the axial direction, but, because of the inhibiting effect of the radial constraint, these cracks should not penetrate the hatch zone but, rather, contribute to total fracture along lines more or less intersecting the diagonals of the specimen.

FAIRHURST and COOK (1966) reported that, if the bearing plates used in uniaxial compression testing have the same diameter as the rock specimen, cylindrical specimens will fracture in a vertical direction rather than form the cones characteristic of this type of testing. This effect can be accounted for by assuming that this type of bearing plate reduces lateral constraint; hence, cracks should develop in the direction of σ_1. These rocks tend to split the specimen into columns which, in their opinion, ultimately buckle under the applied stress.

---

* For an elliptical crack the most unfavourable orientation is 30° to the applied compressive stress, and the new crack should initiate normal to the point where the tangent to the ellipse makes an angle of 30° to its major axis. For a crack of zero thickness the most unfavourable orientation is 45° to the applied compressive stress, and the new crack should initiate in a direction at 45° to the compressive stress. For either type of initial crack, the new crack will extend toward the direction of the applied stress.

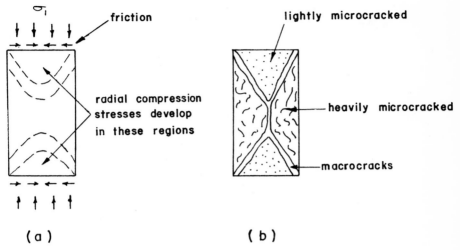

Fig. 2-12. Fracture in compression specimens with unlubricated ends;
(a) Stress pattern,
(b) Conical failure,
(after PAUL and GANGAL, 1966).

2.5. Friction between Platens and End Surfaces

As already discussed, the stress distribution in specimens with and without friction at the ends is quite different and it is obvious that compressive strength so determined will also be affected and will depend upon the co-efficient of friction between the specimen ends and platens.

The coefficient of friction between different materials is not constant and is also dependent upon the nature of the contact surfaces (i.e. roughness) and the condition of the material (i.e. dry or wet). BROWN and POMEROY (1958) studied friction for a range of coals sliding on steel and brass and reported that the coal-steel friction coefficient increases as the coal surface becomes polished and decreases as the normal applied load to the matting surfaces increases (Fig. 2-13).

MEIKLE and HOLLAND (1965) determined coefficients of friction between coal specimens and precisely machined faces of especially prepared steel platens at three levels of interfacial condition. Their results are given in Table 2. The coefficients were obtained by determining the tangential force necessary to move the normally loaded specimens on the plane surfaces of the platen.

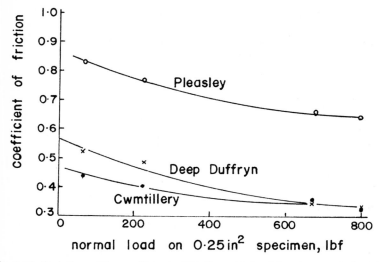

Fig. 2-13. Variation of the coefficient of friction with load for three typical coals sliding on steel (after BROWN and POMEROY, 1958).

TABLE 2

Coefficients of friction

between coal specimens and steel platens

(after MEIKLE and HOLLAND, 1965)

Number of specimens tested	Friction level	Conditions	Coefficient of friction
20	High (1)	Unlubricated coal specimen on "rough steel" platen (roughness 1.5 μm (60 μin))	0.30 ± 0.0006
20	Medium (2)	Coal specimen lubricated with thin graphite layer on "smooth" steel platen (roughness 0.13 μm (5 μin))	0.15 ± 0.002
20	Low (3)	Coal specimen lubricated with a thin graphite layer and a thin layer of graphite laden grease on "smooth" steel platen	0.04 ± 0.003

HOLLAND and OLSEN (1968) presented the results of their studies on the coefficients of friction between coal and sandstone, limestone and shale under wet and dry conditions. The average coefficient of friction for all the dry tests is 0.47 and for all the wet tests is 0.43.

The results of compressive strength tests of MEIKLE and HOLLAND (1965) are given in Fig. 2-14; they correspond to the equation

$$\sigma_c = C(d/h)^n \tag{2.2}$$

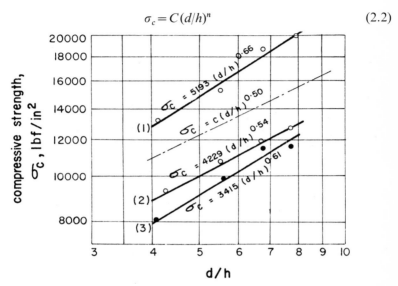

Fig. 2-14. Relationships between d/h and compressive strength of test specimens when tested at three levels of friction
(after MEIKLE and HOLLAND, 1965).

The values of C and n for the three levels of friction are

1. for unlubricated $\qquad C = 5193$ and $n = 0.66$

2. for graphite lubricated $\qquad C = 4229$ and $n = 0.54$

3. for graphite grease lubricated $\qquad C = 3415$ and $n = 0.61$.

In Fig. 2-15, the values of C are plotted against the coefficients of friction.

ZNANSKI (1954) carried out compressive strength tests on Cannal shale specimens with h/d ratio of 2, with and without friction at the ends of specimens. He found compressive strength, with friction, to be 107 MPa (15 630 1 b f/in^2) while without friction it was reduced to 50 MPa (7 295 1 b f/in^2). He also reported that the failure of specimens was violent when loaded with friction at their ends while specimens without friction at the ends failed rather mildly.

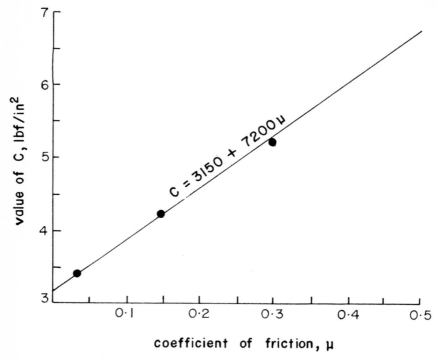

Fig. 2-15. Value of C as influenced by the coefficient of interfacial friction, μ (after HOLLAND and OLSEN, 1968).

2.6. Specimen Geometry

2.6.1. Shape

Test specimens may be cylindrical, prismatic or cubic. Of these, cylindrical specimens are preferable because their preparation is less time consuming and stress distribution is symmetrical in them about the axis.

As far as the effect of shape on the compressive strength of rocks is concerned, conflicting results have been reported. GROSVENOR (1963) reported that the strength of cylindrical specimens is usually higher than that of square prisms for height-diameter (width) ratios near 1 : 1 and lower for height-diameter ratios near 1.5 : 1. The strength values are about the same when the ratio is 2 : 1 and remain constant beyond this point for cylindrical specimens. On the contrary PRICE (1960) stated that unit cubes have greater strength than unit cylinders (i.e. height-diameter ratio of 1).

ALEKSEEV et al. (1970) reported results of their tests on 11 cubic and 11 cylindrical specimens of argillite at average constant factors height-diameter ratio $= 1$, volume $= 40\,cm^3$ $(2.4\,in^3)$ and rate of deformation $= 0.26\,mm/s$ (0.1 in/s). Their results show that the shape of the specimen has no effect on its strength.

Laboratory work at the Colorado School of Mines showed that square prisms give less variation in strength as the height-diameter ratio changes than do the cylindrical specimens (GROSVENOR, 1963).

As h/d ratio of 2.5–3.0 is recommended for compressive strength tests (see next section), cylindrical specimens are preferable.

2.6.2. Height-to-diameter Ratio (h/d Ratio)

The ratio of the height to the diameter of the specimens influences the test results. Stress distribution in specimens with small h/d ratio tends to be triaxial and they exhibit very high compressive strength. Specimens with large h/d ratio fail due to elastic instability. Specimens with h/d ratio in the medium range (2.5 to 3.0) are elastically stable and stress distribution in specimens is rather more uniform.

Compressive strength falls rapidly with increase in h/d ratio up to one, and with any further increase in h/d ratio the reduction in strength is very small (GROSVENOR, 1963, HOBBS, 1964b and LAMA, 1966). However MOGI'S (1966) precise measurements (Figs. 2-16, 2-17 and 2-18) show this trend at h/d ratio of 2.5.

Several investigators gave relationships between strength and height-diameter ratio. BUNTING (1911), after testing small anthracite specimens, gave the following equation for the strength of anthracite:

$$\sigma_c = 700 + 300 \left(\frac{d}{h}\right) \qquad (2.3)$$

where $\sigma_c =$ compressive strength, 1 bf/in^2
$d =$ least lateral dimension of the specimen, in and
$h =$ height of specimen, in.

BECKMAN (1963), after testing potash specimens with h/d ratios 0.5, 1.0, 2.0 and 4.0, gave the following equation:

$$\sigma_c = a \left(\frac{d}{h}\right)^b + c \qquad (2.4)$$

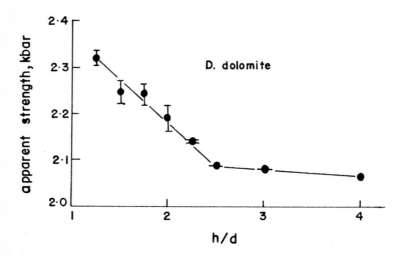

Fig. 2-16. Relation of apparent compressive strength to height/diameter ratio in Dunham dolomite (after MOGI, 1966).

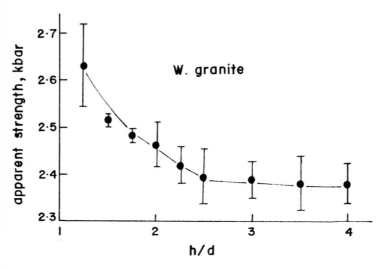

Fig. 2-17. Relation of apparent compressive strength to height/diameter ratio in Westerly granite (after MOGI, 1966).

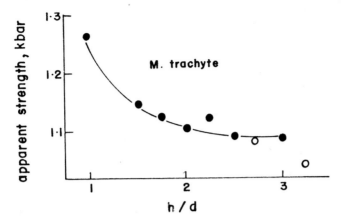

Fig. 2-18. Relation of apparent compressive strength to height/diameter ratio in Mizuho trachyte. Open circle: accompanied by bending (after MOGI, 1966).

where $a=$ constant, 900–2400, 1 b f/in^2
        $b=$ constant, 1.1–2.1 and
        $c=$ constant, 2200–3700, 1 b f/in^2.

STEART (1954) tested coal specimens of square cross-section of 23 cm (9 in) in width with 4 different heights, namely, 10 cm, 23 cm, 46 cm and 69 cm (4 in, 9 in, 18 in and 27 in). His results can be represented by the equation

$$\sigma_c = \frac{C\sqrt{d}}{h} \qquad (2.5)$$

where $C = \vee$ constant.

HOLLAND (1964) and others conducted experiments extensively on the strength of coal, keeping the height of specimens constant and only varying the base dimensions. They suggested that the strength of specimens can be represented by the equation

$$\sigma_c = K\sqrt{(d/h)} \qquad (2.6)$$

where $K =$ constant.

LAMA (1966) tested coal from two seams. He used prisms with h/d ratios varying from 0.2 to 3.0. His results, for h/d ratios 0.5 to 3.0, follow the relationship given below.

$$\sigma_c \propto \left(\frac{h}{d}\right)^n \tag{2.7}$$

For specimens with lateral dimensions 5 cm × 5 cm (1.97 in × 1.97 in)

$n = 0.368 \pm 0.075$ for seam A
$n = 0.349 \pm 0.060$ for seam B

For specimens with lateral dimensions 10 cm × 10 cm (3.94 in × 3.94 in)

$n = 0.360 \pm 0.024$ for seam A
$n = 0.342 \pm 0.020$ for seam B

For rectangular specimens, EVANS and POMEROY (1966) reported that a change in height affects the strength to a much greater extent than a change in lateral dimensions. They summarised their results as follows:

1. The compressive strength decreases with increasing height for a given cross-section.

2. The strength of specimens of height greater than 1.27 cm (0.5 in) shows no consistent trend with increase in lateral dimensions.

3. The strength for specimens of 1.27 cm (0.5 in) height increases with increase in minimum lateral dimensions.

They also reported that base dimensions appear to be important when the height is less than the minimum lateral dimensions. In such cases compressive strength increases slightly with base dimensions. This effect seems to be associated with friction between specimen and platens. When friction is largely eliminated by lubrication, this effect disappears. The strength of rectangular blocks of height greater than the minimum lateral dimension depends on the height and not on the length or width of the specimen.

BIENIAWSKI (1968b) reported that the average strength of rectangular coal specimens 8.9 cm × 5.0 cm (3.5 in × 2.0 in) cross section and 5.0 cm (2.0 in) in height is about 22.5% higher than that of 5.0 cm (2.0 in) cube specimens.

The A.S.T.M. standard for compressive strength tests on natural building stones (1942) suggested the following equation for calculating the compressive strength of the stone specimen with h/d ratio of 1:

$$\sigma_{c1} = \frac{\sigma_c}{0.778 + \dfrac{0.222}{\left(\dfrac{h}{d}\right)}} \tag{2.8}$$

where σ_{c1} = compressive strength of the specimen with h/d ratio 1
σ_c = compressive strength of the specimen with h/d ratio greater than 1
d = diameter and
h = height of the specimen.

OBERT, WINDES and DUVALL (1946) recommended the use of the same equation for other rocks also.

PROTODYAKONOV (1969) recommended the use of the following formula for calculating the compressive strength corresponding to h/d ratio of 2:

$$\sigma_{c2} = \frac{8\sigma_c}{7 + 2\dfrac{d}{h}} \qquad (2.9)$$

where σ_{c2} = compressive strength corresponding to standard specimen with
$\dfrac{h}{d} = 2$
σ_c = measured compressive strength
d = specimen diameter and
h = specimen height.

KARTASHOV et al. (1970) reported some interesting results. They tested marble, coarse sandstone and brick specimens with different h/d ratios for three different end conditions. In one series, paraffin-impregnated paper was used; in another, straight testing was done and in the third series, specimens were tested in specially designed apparatus with stressed inserts to ensure uniform loading of the specimen. Their results are given in Figs. 2-19 and 2-20 for marble and sandstone respectively. The strength of specimens with lubricated end faces increased with the h/d ratio (curve 3), but decreased in the case of end-face friction (curve 1). In the case of stressed inserts, (line 2), the strength was constant in the h/d range from 0.5 to 2.5–3.0.

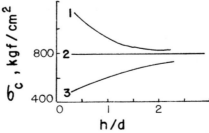

Fig. 2-19. Relation of compressive strength to height/diameter ratio in marble (after KARTASHOV et al., 1970).

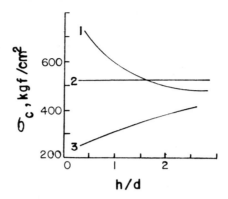

Fig. 2-20. Relation of compressive strength to height/diameter ratio in sandstone
(after KARTASHOV et al., 1970).

These results indicate that, for marble, the strength at h/d of about 3 (extra-polation of curve 1 in Fig. 2-19) represents the strength obtained in the uniformly loaded tests; for sandstone this ratio is about 1.7.

On the basis of the results discussed in section 2.1 and this section, h/d ratio of 2.5–3.0 is recommended for the determination of compressive strength. I.S.R.M. Committee on Laboratory Tests (1972) also suggested the same ratio.

For weak and friable rocks, it is difficult to obtain specimens having this height-to-diameter ratio. In such cases, it is recommended to compute compressive strength for this ratio by extrapolation inserting the data into one of the equations discussed earlier in the section.

2.6.3. Size

The strength of specimens usually decreases with increase in their size.

GADDY (1956) tested small cubes of coal in sizes of 5 to 23 cm (2 to 9 in) and gave the following relationship:

$$\sigma_{c1} = c/d^{0.5} \qquad (2.10)$$

where d = edge dimension
      c = coefficient representing the physical characteristics of the coal bed

SKINNER (1959) tested model pillars of anhydrite with sizes varying from 0.38 cm × 0.38 cm × 0.11 cm (0.150 in × 0.150 in × 0.045 in) up to 25.4 cm ×

$\times$ 25.4 cm $\times$ 15.2 cm (10 in $\times$ 10 in $\times$ 6 in) and observed decrease in compressive strength with increase in size.

MOGI (1962) tested marble prisms with a height-width ratio of 2 and heights of 4 cm, 6 cm, 8 cm, 12 cm and 20 cm (1.6 in, 2.4 in, 3.2 in, 4.7 in and 7.9 in). He fitted his results, given in Table 3, as follows:

$$\sigma_c = \sigma_{c0} d^{-0.092} \qquad\qquad (2.11)$$

TABLE 3
Effect of size on compressive strength of marble specimens (n/d = 2.0)
(after MOGI, 1962)

Lateral dimension of	2	3	4	6	10
prism, d cm (in)	(0.8)	(1.2)	(1.6)	(2.4)	(3.9)
Compressive strength σ_c, MPa (lbf/in^2)	12.8 (88272)	12.7 (87291)	11.8 (81112)	11.4 (78758)	11.6 (79935)
σ_c/σ_{c0}, %	100.0	99.0	91.9	89.2	90.6

EVANS and POMEROY (1966) tested two types of coal finding a decrease in the strength with an increase in the size of cubical specimens. Their results fitted the following relationships: –

$$\sigma_{c1} \propto d^{-0.32 \pm 0.02} \qquad\qquad (2.12)$$

$$\sigma_{c1} \propto d^{-0.17 \pm 0.02} \qquad\qquad (2.13)$$

where d = edge dimension of the cube.

LUNDBORG (1967) tested granite cylinders of the same height and diameter (2 cm, 3 cm, 4 cm and 6 cm) (0.8 in, 1.2 in, 1.6 in and 2.4 in) and observed a decrease in strength with increase in size. His results are given in Fig. 2-21. He also reported the results of BURKARTZ and KREUGER on cubical specimens of granite, sandstone and limestone (1968). Fig. 2-22 shows these results, again indicating a decrease in strength with increase in size.

BIENIAWSKI (1968 a) tested cubical specimens of norite with side lengths from 1.3 to 17.8 cm (0.5 to 7.0 in). He found a reduction in strength from the 1.3 to 12.2 cm (0.5 to 5.0 in) sizes and concluded that there would be no strength reduction thereafter.

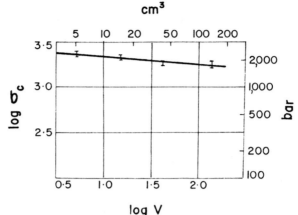

Fig. 2-21. Compressive strength, σ_c – size, V relationship for granite (after LUNDBORG, 1967).

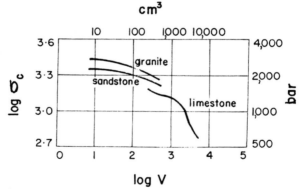

Fig. 2-22. Compressive strength σ_c – size, V relationship for cubical specimens of different rocks (after LUNDBORG, 1968).

The decrease in strength with size could be due to the increasing probability of flaws in the specimen. Depending upon the density of flaws, a decrease in strength with increase in the size of the specimens would be expected. It could also be expected that with sufficiently large specimens so that flaw distribution would not be affected by size, strength would not be affected with further increase in size.

Another factor that might influence strength would be the surface imperfections created either during the cutting of the specimen from the parent material, the machining of the surface or by the natural reaction of the rock minerals to the free surface. As the surface area per unit volume of specimen, for a constant shape, decreases with increase in size, strength would be expected to decrease with size. Besides, with sufficiently large specimens, the influence of this mechanism could be expected to be insignificant.

HOSKINS and HORINO (1969) reported interesting results concerning the influence of the specimen diameters (keeping height-diameter ratio 2) on the compressive strength of limestone, marble, sandstone, granite and plaster of Paris (Figs. 2-23–2.27). Figs 2-23–2-26 of compressive strength versus specimen diameter show that all 2.5 cm (1 in) diameter specimens have lower strengths than the 5.0 cm (2 in) specimens of the same rock type. The maximum compressive strength occurs either with a 5.0 cm or a 7.5 cm (2 in or 3 in) diameter specimen. It appears that the compressive strength decreases with further increase in specimen diameter. Fig. 2-26 shows a maximum compressive strength value at the 5.0 cm (2 in) diameter specimen (though not distinct). Although there are only three points for the granite in Fig. 2-27, the maximum compressive strength would appear to occur at 2.5 cm (1 in) or less.

They believe that the two diameter-size compressive strength relationships are due to the reasons discussed above. The volume effect is shown by the decrease in compressive strength with the increase in specimen diameter or volume. The surface flaws effect is shown by Figs. 2-23–2-26. Since the specific surface area is inversely proportional to the volume, the specimen with the smallest diameter (2.5 cm (1 in) in these tests) having the largest specific area should be the weakest, provided that surface flaws are the dominant control. Fig. 2-27 of the granite, would indicate, for the diameter sizes tested, that volume effects and not surface effects are the dominant control.

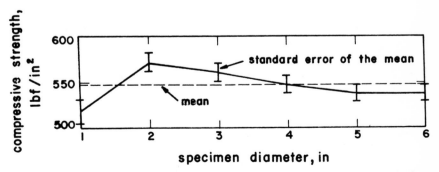

Fig. 2-23. Effect of specimen diameter on compressive strength of plaster of Paris (after HOSKINS and HORINO, 1969).

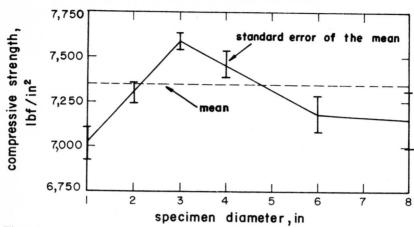

Fig. 2-24. Effect of specimen diameter on compressive strength of Kansas limestone (after HOSKINS and HORINO, 1969).

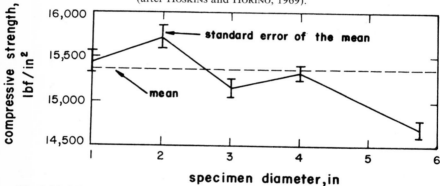

Fig. 2-25. Effect of specimen diameter on compressive strength of Carthage marble (after HOSKINS and HORINO, 1969).

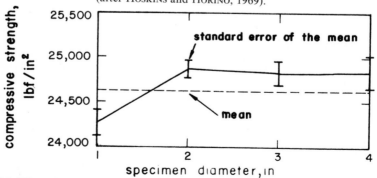

Fig. 2-26. Effect of specimen diameter on compressive strength of Longmont sandstone (after HOSKINS and HORINO, 1969).

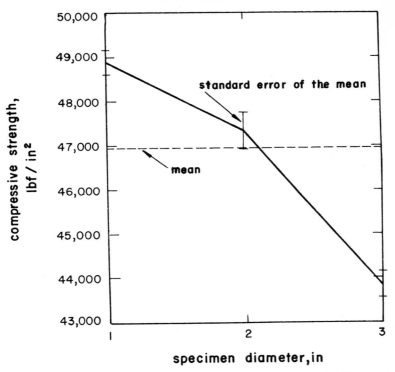

Fig. 2-27. Effect of specimen diameter on compressive strength of Salida granite
(after HOSKINS and HORINO, 1969).

Recently, some workers put forward a thesis that the variation in strength
with size is due to the non-uniform stress distribution in the specimen.
HODGSON and COOK (1970) found no evidence of size effect in compression
tests on quartzite and shale cylinders of up to 15 cm (6 in) diameter after
taking special precautions to ensure that the specimens were subjected to
uniform compression.

ALEKSEEV et al. (1970) tested a large number of specimens of argillite both
perpendicular and parallel to the stratification. These results revealed that
the volume of the specimen has no effect on the compressive strength
parallel to the stratification but when crushed perpendicular to the stratification, there is scale effect (Fig. 2-28).

From the results discussed in this section, it can be concluded that the size
of specimen has variable effect on the compressive strength. It is better to
test as large specimens as possible. The restrictions are: (i) the capacity
of the testing machine (ii) preparation equipment for large specimens and

(iii) the number of specimens that can be prepared from a particular sample. Theoretically, the size of the specimen should depend on the size of grains. The diameter of the specimen should be related to the size of the largest grain in the rock by the ratio of at least 10 : 1. But, in practice, many other factors get into picture, such as, flaws, surface defects, non-uniform stress distribution, direction of loading in respect to planes of weakness, etc. From the convenience point of view, 2.2 to 6.6 cm (0.87 to 2.60 in) diameter specimens are recommended for compressive strength tests. I.S.R.M. Committee on Laboratory Tests (1972) suggested cylinders having a diameter preferably of not less than NX core size, approximately 54 mm (2.13 in).

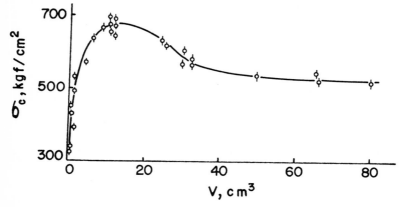

Fig. 2-28. Volume of argillite specimen versus strength perpendicular to stratification at constant h/d ratio and rate of deformation (after ALEKSEEV et al., 1970).

2.7. Rate of Loading

The compressive strength of rocks usually increases with increase in the rate of loading of specimens. The compressive strength at high rates of loading such as in impact and sonic tests may be several times the compressive strength obtained at slower rates of loading such as in laboratory testing machines.

FILCEK and KLECZEK (SALUSTOWICZ, 1965) conducted interesting experiments to study the effect of various strain rates on the compressive strength of Cannal coal (Fig. 2-29). They reported that with lower strain rate, the stress-strain curve followed the line 0–1 and compressive strength was smaller (σ'_c) and the specimens failed without violence. With increase in rate of straining, the paths followed by the stress-strain curve were 0–2, 0–3, 0–4, etc. and the compressive strength values were σ_c'', σ_c''', σ_c'''', etc. respectively. The compressive strength increased considerably with higher rates of straining and the specimens failed abruptly and violently.

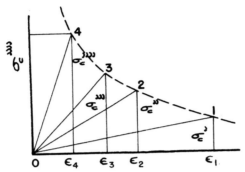

Fig. 2-29. Effect of strain rate on compressive strength of Cannal coal
(after SALUSTOWICZ, 1965).

HOUPERT (1970) investigated the effect of the loading rate on compressive strength of granite. His results (Fig. 2-30) also reveal an increase in strength with increase in loading rate.

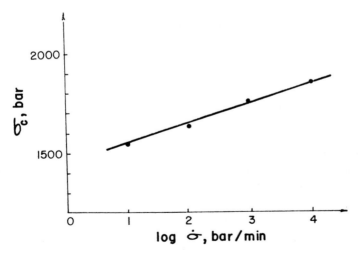

Fig. 2-30. Variation of compressive strength σ_c with loading rate $\dot{\sigma}$.
For each $\dot{\sigma}$, σ_c is the mean value of 6 tests; diameter of test specimens = 5 cm
(after HOUPERT, 1970).

PERKINS, GREEN and FRIEDMAN (1970) reported their results (Fig. 2-31) on porphyritic tonalite. These results also show increased strength with increasing strain rate.

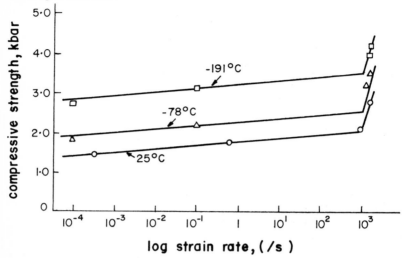

Fig. 2-31. Compressive strength – log strain rate for specimens loaded parallel to the core axis (after PERKINS et al., 1970).

KOBAYASHI (1970) also measured the compressive strength of various rocks under different loading rates which ranged from 9.6 kPa/s to 7.8 MPa/s (1.4 1 bf/in²/s to 1136.0 1 bf/in²/s). Low-speed loading tests were conducted in a hydraulic testing machine whereas high-speed loading tests were conducted in a newly developed high-speed compressive testing machine using an underwater explosive. A schematic diagram of this testing machine is given in Fig. 2-32. This design eliminates the shock waves so as not to expose the specimens to the impact loading.

Fig. 2-33 shows the relationship between the compressive strength and the strain rate of rocks. From this figure it can be seen that an increase in strain rate increases the compressive strength of rocks. In the case of Akiyoshi marble, the rate of increase is 2.6 in respect of the ratio of the high-speed compressive strength to that of the low-speed. In this case, the average loading rates of the high-speed tests are about $2.45 \sim 2.74$ TPa/s ($35.7 \sim 39.8 \times$ $\times 10^7$ 1 bf/in²/s), and the average loading rates of the low-speed tests are about 9.6 kPa/s (1.4 1 bf/in²/s).

Further, the results given in Fig. 2-34 show that the increment of the compressive strength between the strain rate of 10^{-4} cm/cm/s (in/in/s) and that of 10 cm/cm/s (in/in/s) increases as the porosity of the rocks decreases. Because of this strain-rate effect, he suggested that the effect of the pores, which exist in the rock, should be considered contributing to the strain-rate effect.

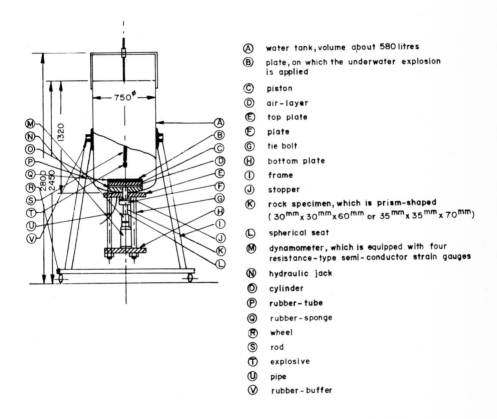

Ⓐ water tank, volume about 580 litres
Ⓑ plate, on which the underwater explosion is applied
Ⓒ piston
Ⓓ air-layer
Ⓔ top plate
Ⓕ plate
Ⓖ tie bolt
Ⓗ bottom plate
Ⓘ frame
Ⓙ stopper
Ⓚ rock specimen, which is prism-shaped ($30^{mm} \times 30^{mm} \times 60^{mm}$ or $35^{mm} \times 35^{mm} \times 70^{mm}$)
Ⓛ spherical seat
Ⓜ dynamometer, which is equipped with four resistance-type semi-conductor strain gauges
Ⓝ hydraulic jack
Ⓞ cylinder
Ⓟ rubber-tube
Ⓠ rubber-sponge
Ⓡ wheel
Ⓢ rod
Ⓣ explosive
Ⓤ pipe
Ⓥ rubber-buffer

Fig. 2-32. Schematic diagram of high-speed compressive testing machine (after KOBAYASHI, 1970).

OBERT, WINDES and DUVALL (1946) conducted compressive strength tests on various rocks for rates of loading of 0.69 MPa/s, 1.38 MPa/s and 2.76 MPa/s (100 1 bf/in²/s, 200 1 bf/in²/s and 400 1 bf/in²/s). They reported that the rate of loading has no significant effect on the compressive strength and recommended the application of load at the rate of 0.69 MPa/s (100 1 bf/in²/s) in their standardized procedures.

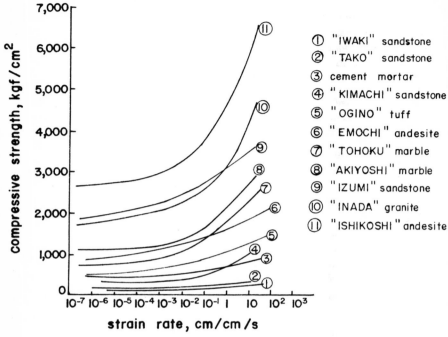

Fig. 2-33. Variation of compressive strength with strain rate
(after KOBAYASHI, 1970).

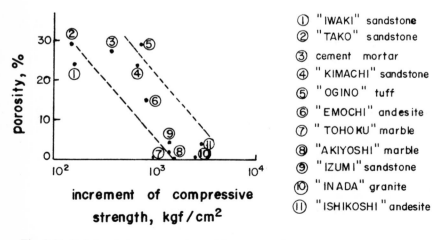

Fig. 2-34. Relation between porosity and increment of compressive strength (strain
rate of $10^{-4} \sim$ that of 10 cm/cm/s)
(after KOBAYASHI, 1970).

ALEKSEEV et al. (1970) reported a different relationship. Their results on argillite are given in Fig. 2-35 in which a plot of the rate of loading, parallel to the stratification $\dot{\Delta} l$ in mm/s versus specimen strength σ_c in kgf/cm² at a constant value of $\dfrac{h}{d}$ ratio is given.

$$\sigma_c = \sigma_0 - 220 \, \dot{\Delta} l \tag{2.14}$$

where $\sigma_0 =$ the initial compressive strength under the given conditions.

Even after plotting the points with varying $\dfrac{h}{d}$ ratio, the character of the relation is unchanged, but there is a marked increase in the scatter of the points, the boundaries of which are denoted in Fig. 2-35 by the dot-dash line.

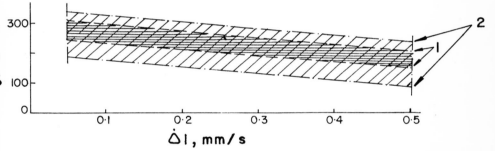

Fig. 2-35. Rate of application of load parallel to the stratification versus argillite
strength and limits of its variation:
1. with constant h/d ratio;
2. with variable h/d ratio
(after ALEKSEEV et al., 1970).

From the results discussed here, it can be concluded that the rate of loading also has variable effect on the compressive strength. For applications to situations under rapid loading (e.g. drilling, crushing, blasting) high rates of loading (comparable) are recommended for tests. If facilities are not available, the results should be extrapolated according to one of the relationships given earlier in the section.

For static purposes, the rate of loading is restricted within certain limits so that time required for conducting tests is reasonable. 0.1–1.0 MPa/s (14–140 1 bf/in²/s) can be recommended as a standard (HORIBE, 1970). I.S.R.M. Committee on Laboratory Tests (1972) suggested the stress rate within the limits of 0.5 to 1.0 MPa/s (70 to 140 1 bf/in²/s).

2.8. Environment

2.8.1. Moisture

Moisture has a varying effect on the compressive strength of rocks.

OBERT, WINDES and DUVALL (1946) studied the effect of moisture on different types of rocks and found that the effect is not pronounced (Table 4). For the rocks tested, the average increase in strength for oven-dried rocks is about 6% and the average decrease in strength for those in a saturated state is about 12%.

TABLE 4

Effect of moisture content on compressive strength

(after OBERT, WINDES and DUVALL, 1946)

Moisture condition	Ratio of oven-dried and saturated compressive strength to air-dried compressive strength						
	Marble	Limestone	Granite	Sandstone 1	Sandstone 2	Slate	Average
Oven-dried	1.01	1.03	1.07	1.01	1.18	1.06	1.06
Air-dried	1.00	1.00	1.00	1.00	1.00	1.00	1.00
Saturated	0.96	0.85	0.92	0.90	0.80	0.85	0.88

PRICE (1960) conducted tests on certain sandstones with different percentages of moisture (saturated, air dry and completely dry) and reported a significant decrease in strength with increase in moisture content (Table 5). For Pennant sandstone, he determined the strengths when water occupied 38% and 62% of the pore volume and found the values to be 144.8 MPa (21 000 1 bf/in^2) and 131.0 MPa (19 000 1 bf/in^2) respectively.

KJAERNSLI and SANDE (1963) indicated that with syenite the decrease in strength after saturation amounts to 94%; a further decrease, down to 85%, takes place if the specimen is tested submerged. They explained these results as follows: In the first case the surface tension of the water menisci on the air-water contact increases somewhat the strength (all-round capillary pressure) opposing thus the adsorption effect dominating after the full submergence of the specimen.

ZARUBA (1965) found the compressive strength for saturated specimens of massive epidiorite and schistose epidiorite to be 81–86% and 85–90% of dry strength respectively.

TABLE 5

Effect of moisture on compressive strength of sandstones

(after PRICE, 1960)

Rock	Porosity, %	Air-dry pore-water content as % of pore-volume	Relative compressive strengths for various pore-water contents expressed as percentages of completely dry rock		
			Completely dry	Air-dry	Saturated
Markham sandstone	6.0	22 ± 5	100%	57%	Not determined
Parkgate rock	10.0	9 ± 1.5	100%	68%	45%
Pennant sandstone	2.5	42 ± 3	100%	51%	45%
Darley Daly sandstone	19.5	3 ± 1	100%	80%	45%

SALUSTOWICZ (1965) stated that moisture may decrease the strength of sandstones by 40% and of shales by 60%.

COLBACK and WIID (1965) carried out exhaustive experiments under controlled conditions of moisture. They reported that the compressive strength of quartzitic shale and quartzitic sandstone under saturated conditions (submerged in water) is of the order of 50% of that under dry conditions (dried over $CaCl_2$ or P_2O_5) (Figs. 2-36 and 2-37).

The results of FEDA (1966) on schist and gneiss are given in Table 6.

RUIZ (1966) conducted tests on various types of rocks (Table 7). In cases 2, 8, 10, 12, 16 and 22 strengths in the saturated condition were higher than in dry condition. This was interpreted by RUIZ as due to the heterogeneity of the rock and to the small number of specimens tested.

BORETTI-ONYSZKIEWICZ (1966) determined the compressive strength of sandstones perpendicular and parallel to stratification in both air-dry and water saturation conditions. Results are given in Table 8.

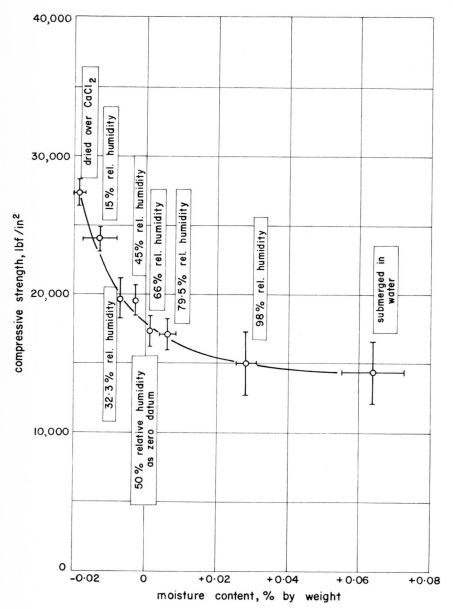

Fig. 2-36. Relationship between compressive strength and moisture content for
quartzitic shale specimens
(after COLBACK and WIID, 1965).

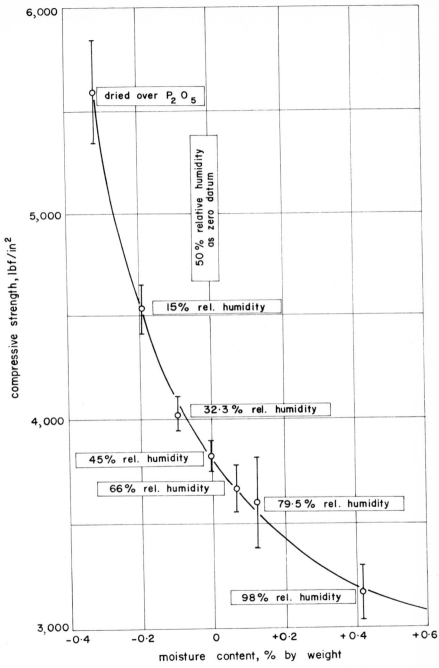

Fig. 2-37. Relationship between compressive strength and moisture content for
quartzitic sandstone specimens
(after COLBACK and WIID, 1965).

TABLE 6
Compressive strength values
for dry and saturated conditions
(after FEDA, 1966)

Type of rock	Dry MPa	Dry (lbf/in^2)	Saturated MPa	Saturated (lbf/in^2)	Saturated in % of dry strength
Schist	28.8	(4175)	13.9	(2016)	48.4
Gneiss 1	16.8	(2442)	9.9	(1434)	58.8
Gneiss 2	26.1	(3791)	10.5	(1519)	40.0
Gneiss 3	29.4	(4260)	10.5	(1519)	36.0

TABLE 7
Compressive strength of rocks
for dry and saturated conditions
(after RUIZ, 1966)

Case	Type of rock	Dry MPa	Dry (lbf/in^2)	Saturated MPa	Saturated (lbf/in^2)
1	Basalt 1	106.4	(15435)	102.1	(14811)
2	Basalt 2	191.3	(27747)	223.3	(32390)
3	Basalt 3	154.1	(22351)	111.8	(16216)
4	Basalt 4	168.5	(24438)	84.8	(12297)
5	Basalt with sandstone	64.7	(9386)	28.4	(4118)
6	Pyroclastic basalt	142.9	(20732)	63.6	(9230)
7	Diabase 1	158.0	(22919)	145.1	(21044)
8	Diabase 2	137.9	(19994)	173.1	(25106)
9	Dolomite	114.6	(16614)	95.0	(13774)
10	Granite 1	97.9	(14200)	113.6	(16472)
11	Granite 2	118.5	(17182)	103.8	(15052)
12	Porphyritic granite	86.4	(12524)	95.2	(13802)
13	Tourmaline granite	157.6	(22862)	106.7	(15478)
14	Granulite	151.3	(21939)	82.2	(11928)
15	Gneiss 1	133.2	(19312)	131.2	(19028)
16	Gneiss 2	155.5	(22550)	174.7	(25333)
17	Gneiss 3	113.1	(16401)	100.4	(14550)
18	Gneiss 4	137.1	(19880)	136.8	(19837)
19	Gneiss 5	96.0	(13916)	91.1	(13206)
20	Granitic gneiss 1	105.7	(15336)	71.5	(10366)
21	Granitic gneiss 2	158.6	(23004)	135.1	(19596)
22	Limestone 1	83.2	(12070)	97.9	(14200)
23	Limestone 2	85.2	(12354)	48.0	(6958)
24	Limestone 3	73.4	(10650)	61.7	(8946)
25	Quartzite	256.5	(37204)	205.6	(29820)
26	Sandstone	81.3	(11786)	73.4	(10650)

TABLE 8

**Compressive strength of sandstones
in MPa (lbf/in²)**

(after BORETTI-ONYSZKIEWICZ, 1966)

State	1		2		3		4		5	
	Perpendicular to stratification	Parallel to stratification	Perpendicular to stratification	Parallel to stratification	Perpendicular to stratification	Parallel to stratification	Perpendicular to stratification	Parallel to stratification	Perpendicular to stratification	Parallel to stratification
In air-dry state	150.2 (21783)	137.3 (19908)	125.6 (18219)	88.4 (12823)	93.9 (13618)	99.4 (12965)	93.5 (13561)	83.2 (12070)	69.2 (10039)	54.5 (7909)
After water saturation	103.7 (15038)	92.5 (13419)	87.9 (12752)	76.5 (11090)	63.4 (9202)	53.5 (7753)	81.4 (11800)	65.1 (9443)	55.2 (8009)	50.3 (7299)

BURSHTEIN (1969) studied the effects of moisture on the compressive strengths of standstone and argillite. Fig. 2-38 gives the compressive strength versus moisture content for sandstone (curve 1) and argillite (curve 2). With an increase in moisture content of 4%, the stronger sandstone (curve 1) loses half of its compressive strength; in the case of argillite (curve 2), an increase in the moisture content of 1.5% reduces the strength to a third of its initial value.

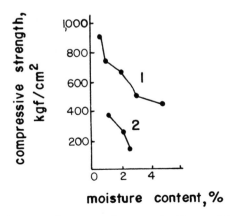

Fig. 2-38. Compressive strength versus moisture content for sandstone (1) and argillite (2) (after BURSHTEIN, 1969).

KROKOSKY and HUSAK (1968) tested small cylindrical specimens $\left(0.56 \text{ cm}\right.$ (0.22 in) and $\frac{h}{d}$ ratio $\left.3\right)$ of basalt rock in compression in four types of environment.

1. Specimens tested in air.

2. Specimens subjected to bakeout and tested in air (after a 24-hour bakeout at 260 °C (500 °F), specimens were allowed to sit approximately 10 minutes in room atmosphere).

3. Specimens subjected to bakeout and tested in moderate vacuum and

4. Specimens subjected to bakeout and tested in ultra-high vacuum.

The evacuation was accomplished in about 10 minutes. The bakeout of specimens was done to ensure reliable comparisons, since all operations performed on specimens tested in air should be the same as those on the specimens tested in vacuum.

Their results show a significant (50%) increase in strength by the bakeout process itself. This difference has been explained by the evacuation of water vapour from the small pores and capillaries. The mean strength versus pressure for groups 2, 3 and 4 is given in Fig. 2-39. Evacuation of the water vapour is almost completely accomplished at moderately low-vacuum levels, and so the major increase in strength is realised in the low-vacuum ranges. A further decrease in pressure has an almost negligible effect on strength since water vapour remaining in the specimens tends to a steady value at pressures below 0.5 to 1.0 torr (mm Hg).

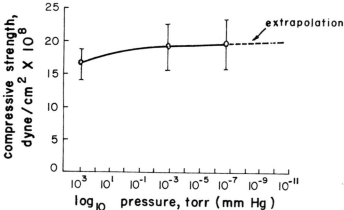

Fig. 2-39. Compressive strength versus pressure for groups 2, 3 and 4 (after KROKOSKY and HUSAK, 1968).

In summary, it can be said that moisture in the rocks has very significant effect on compressive strength in many instances. Unless the values to be used for design purposes are corrected to in situ conditions, catastrophic failures can occur. Many times, saturated specimens are recommended for tests so that the values obtained are conservative. It is best to test the specimens under natural environment. Because the moisture content changes while preparing the specimens, they have to be conditioned to bring them back to original state. This is all time consuming and I.S.R.M. Committee on Laboratory Tests (1972) suggested that the prepared specimens shall be stored prior to testing for 5 to 6 days in an environment of $20 \pm 2\,°C\,(68 \pm 4\,°F)$ and 50% humidity. This moisture condition shall be reported with the results in accordance with "Suggested method for determination of the water content of a rock sample", Method 1, I.S.R.M. Committee on Laboratory Tests, Document No. 2, Final Draft, November, 1972. For other conditions, extrapolation of the results in established relationships of similar rocks is recommended.

2.8.2. Liquids

COLBACK and WIID (1965) also tested the quartzitic sandstone in various liquids. Their results (Fig. 2-40) show that compressive strength is inversely proportional to the surface tension of different liquids with which the specimen is saturated.

STREET and F.-D.-WANG (1966) reported the effect of different liquids on the compressive strength of standstone (Fig. 2-41). The specimens used were 1.9 cm (0.75 in) × 3.8 cm (1.50 in) long cores. The figure shows the importance of pH on the compressive strength of this silica rock. Strength appeared to be minimum at a pH of approximately 7.

SIMPSON and FERGUS (1968) studied the effects of various liquids on the compressive strength of diabase. The actual environmental conditions are given in Table 9, and the results in Fig. 2-42. The compressive strength of water soaked diabase is about 60% of that of diabase dried at temperatures greater than 190 °C (374 °F). Of the solutions used, water decreased the strength to a maximum.

The effect of moisture and liquids on the strength of rocks may be explained as follows:

Certain minerals decompose when they come in contact with liquids and are dissolved, creating more liquid-filled voids. The factor which contributes most in decreasing the strength of rocks seems to be the attack of liquids

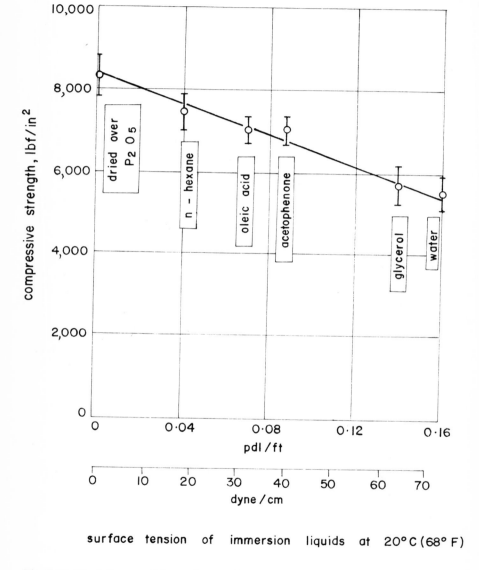

Fig. 2-40. The influence of the surface tension of immersion liquids on the strength of
quartzitic sandstone specimens
(after COLBACK and WIID, 1965).

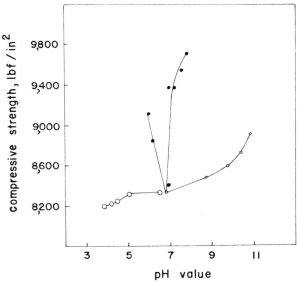

Fig. 2-41. Compressive strength – pH, sandstone. Closed circles, dodecylammonium chloride, small open circles, sodium carbonate, large open circles, aluminium chloride (after STREET and F.-D.-WANG, 1966).

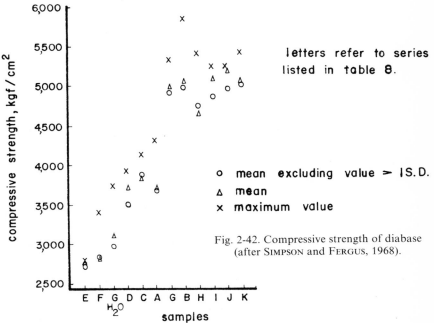

letters refer to series listed in table 8.

o mean excluding value ≻ IS.D.
△ mean
× maximum value

Fig. 2-42. Compressive strength of diabase (after SIMPSON and FERGUS, 1968).

TABLE 9

Test conditions

(after SIMPSON and FERGUS, 1968)
(Refer to Fig. 2–42)

Sample	Temperature °C	(°F)	Conditions
E	27	(80.6)	Immersed in destilled water for 15 days
F	27	(80.6)	Immersed in 6 parts water/1 part cutting oil for 15 days
D	27	(80.6)	Air dried for 15 days
C	27	(80.6)	Dried under vacuum* over magnesium perchlorate for 15 days
A	110	(230.0)	Air dried for 15 days
G	190	(374.0)	Air dried for 14 days
G-H$_2$0	190-27	(374.0-80.6)	Air dried at 190°C (374°F) for 13 days, then cooled and immersed in water at 27°C (80.6°F) for 1 day
B	345	(653.0)	Air dried for 15 days
H	345	(653.0)	Air dried for 5 days
I	345	(653.0)	Air dried for 1 day
J	200	(392.0)	Air dried for 8 days, cooled over SiO$_2$ gel, then immersed in CC1$_4$ at 27°C (80.6°F) for 1 day
K	200	(392.0)	Air dried for 8 days, cooled over SiO$_2$ gel, then immersed in ethylene glycol at 27°C (80.6°F) for 1 day

*The vacuum was periodically drawn to about 100 μ/Hg.

on crack tips, dissolving the material and increasing the stress at the apex, thereby helping in their propagation. It is also possible that liquids influence the surface energy of the rocks and since creation of new surfaces during the process of fracturing is dependent upon the surface energy of the rock, its strength will depend upon the decrease or increase in the surface energy under the influence of the liquid. Liquids which wet the surfaces of the rock invariably decrease the surface energy of the rock and hence the strength.

From this short discussion, it can be concluded that the compressive strength of rocks is influenced by liquids contained in them. This brings to a point that in the preparation of specimens for testing, cutting oils should be avoided. Only use of plain water is recommended for specimen preparation.

2.8.3. Temperature

The results of SIMPSON and FERGUS (1968) also give an idea of the effect of temperature on the compressive strength of diabase. A series of specimens air dried at 27 °C, 110 °C, 190 °C and 345 °C (80.6 °F, 230.0 °F, 374.0 °F and 653.0 °F) show a pattern of increased strength with an increase in drying temperature. A series vacuum dried over magneium perchlorate show slightly greater strength than the air dried series at 27 °C (80.6 °F). They explained the results in terms of moisture content.

BRIGHENTI (1970) studied the effect of cryogenic temperatures on the compressive strength of two limestones and two sandstones. His general conclusions are that (1) the rocks tested do not show notable strength decreases on account of ageing at cryogenic temperatures; (2) compressive strength of dry and saturated rocks increases, generally speaking, when the temperature decreases.

Normally, tests are conducted at room temperatures. If the in situ conditions are different, the tests should be conducted in simulated atmosphere. Very little work has been done on the effect of temperatures on the compressive strength of rocks and more investigations are needed.

2.9. Mineralogy, Grain Size and Porosity

The mineralogy, grain size and porosity are the intrinsic properties controlling rock strength. The rocks containing quartz as the binding material are the strongest followed by calcite, ferrous minerals; rocks with clayey binding material are the weakest. In general, the higher the quartz content, the greater is the strength (PRICE, 1960). The strength of rocks is greater for finer grained rocks (BRACE, 1961). Compressive strength decreases with increase in porosity (PRICE, 1960; KOWALSKI, 1966; SMORODINOV et al.,1970).

2.10. Post-failure Behaviour of Rock in Compression

The behaviour of rock subjected to compression, i.e., the complete load-deformation curve obtained till the rock has lost its strength completely can be given by Fig. 2-43. At different stages, when the rock specimen is unloaded, it follows typical hysteresis curves and the locus of the load-deformation curve in the post-failure region can always be traced either by recycling the load or by continuously deforming the rock specimen. The mechanical behaviour of the failed rock follows one of these reloading

curves and is located such as if the load-axis was shifted from its initial
(zero deformation) position to some point of A on the deformation-axis.

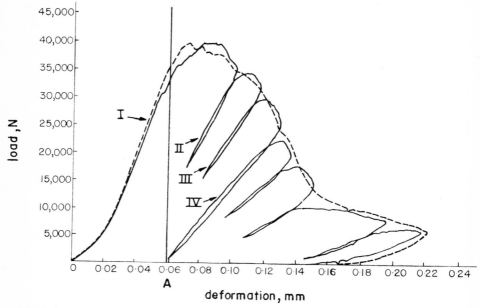

Fig. 2-43. Comparison of deformational behaviour of two identical sandstone specimens
in uniaxial compression, one subjected to gradually increasing load and the other to
cycling load after strength failure
(after BIENIAWSKI, 1969).

In a normal testing machine, it is not possible to obtain the post-failure
curve for, as the peak strength is just exceeded, rapid failure occurs due to
the release of the excess energy from the testing machine. Hence the earlier
attempts have been to increase the stiffness of the loading machine. More
recently, the use of servo-mechanism where the deformation of the specimens
is controlled, has been successfully used to obtain the complete load-
deformation curve for rocks under load.*

The stiffness of the testing machine influences the load-deformation curve
such that the unloading characteristic of the specimen at the stage where
failure occurs is a function of the unloading characteristic of the machine.
SPAETH (1935) suggested that when the real behaviour of the material can be
represented by Fig. 2-44 (a) the apparent behaviour is represented by

---

* Details regarding the stiff testing machines and servo-mechanism are given in Appendix.

Fig. 2-44 (b). The form of the curves between the displacement δ_1 and δ_2 is dependent upon the stiffness of the machine and as the stiffness of the machine increases, the material behaviour obtained approaches its real behaviour.

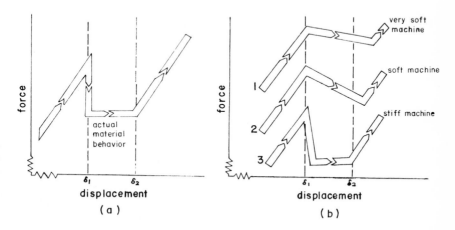

Fig. 2-44. Influence of the testing machine stiffness on the precise form of the force-displacement curve during plastic deformation of iron
(after SPAETH, 1935).

WAWERSIK (1968) made a detailed analysis of the post-failure behaviour of rock in compression. The results obtained by him for a number of rocks, Charcoal Grey granite, Indiana limestone, Tennessee marble, Solenhofen limestone, basalt are shown in Fig. 2-45. It is seen that though the rocks have more or less a similar pre-failure behaviour, the post-failure behaviours are strikingly different. The post-failure behaviour of the rocks can be divided into two classes (Fig. 2-46).

The class I behaviour can be described by a stable fracture propagation which means that when the maximum load bearing capacity of the specimen is exceeded, still some external work has got to be done for further destruction of the specimen and for lowering its load-bearing capacity. Such rocks retain their strength (partially) even when their maximum load carrying capacity has been exceeded.

In the class II behaviour, unstable fracture propagation takes place such that the amount of energy stored in the specimen at the moment when its maximum load carrying capacity is just exceeded is sufficient to maintain the growth of crack and its propagation throughout the specimen. In such cases, fracture propagation can be arrested only when the strain energy is

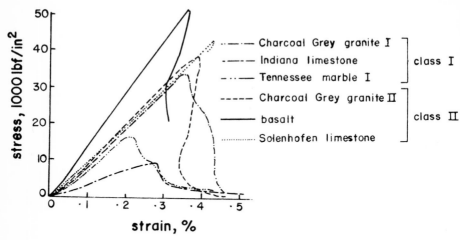

Fig. 2-45. Complete compressive stress-strain curves for various rocks
(after WAWERSIK, 1968).

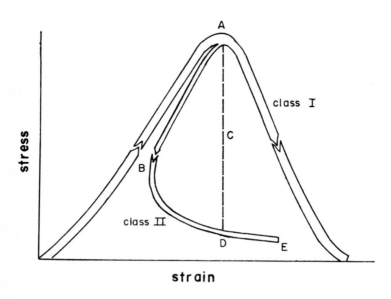

Fig. 2-46. Classification of rock failure behaviour in uniaxial compression
(after WAWERSIK, 1968).

extracted from the specimen. The dividing line between the two classes of rocks is the perpendicular line ACD which represents the case when the stored energy is just sufficient to produce total breakdown of the specimen.

Studies of BROWN and HUDSON (1971) have shown that the type of behaviour is dependent upon the structure of the rock. In highly porous, clastic sedimentary rocks like sandstones, limestones, etc. the fracture process starts with the collapse of the porous structure resulting in constant increase in their anisotropy. They have post-failure behaviour curve of class I type. Similar behaviour also occurs in some crystalline rocks. With ultra-fine grain size the failure is due to inter- and intra- granular sub-axial cracks. The curves obtained are dependent upon the grain size. With rocks of small grain size, the curves tend to be steep and fall into the class II category. In dense ultra-fine grained rocks e.g. Solenhofen limestone, where the structural breakdown process is instantaneous, they give rise to the class II curves.

It is possible that the post-failure behaviour of a rock may change from one class to the other depending upon the strain rates. At higher strain rates the rocks that have class I behaviour may change to class II behaviour.

When a specimen is unloaded and reloaded from any point in the post-failure region, it follows a loop which is very common to that usually observed in rocks subjected to repeated cycles of loading and unloading (Fig. 2-43). On reloading the specimen achieves the load value slightly less than the value at which it was unloaded. This slight decrease is because of the time-yield at the high stress almost equal to its failure load. The deformation modulus of the rock in the post-failure region continuously decreases (curves I, II, etc.) which is a measure of the degree of disintegration of the specimen.

The post-failure curves of the rocks may be strikingly repetitive as have been observed by WAWERSIK and BRACE (1971) or may vary from specimen to specimen. For homogenous specimens prepared and tested under carefully controlled conditions, repetitive results can be obtained (Fig. 2-47).

The post-failure curves, in general, may be characterised by regions of sudden drop in load bearing capacity followed by more gentle slopes when tested in uniaxial compression.

The fracture pattern of specimen can be divided into 8 distinct regions (WAWERSIK and BRACE, 1971). The regions I–III (Fig. 2-47) are marked with closure of pre-existing cracks as well as a combination of random crack formation, crack growth and sliding on existing crack surfaces. In the region IV, a small number of small fractures are formed more or less parallel to the direction of loading which grow in the subsequent stages of the post-failure curve with almost no change in their orientation. The cracks that appear at the centre of the specimen height lead to spalling of the material resulting in the decrease in the cross-sectional area of the specimen. This spalling begins at the beginning of the region V, continues in the region VI followed by small steeply inclined shear fractures which grow rapidly in the region VII. The region VIII is a loose mass of the broken material held together by friction (compare this with section 2.4).

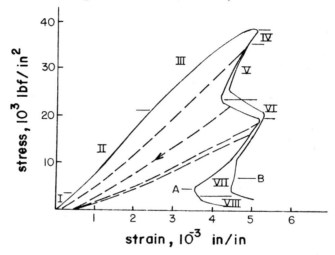

Fig. 2-47. Bounding uniaxial stress-strain curves for 25 samples of Westerly granite (after WAWERSIK and BRACE, 1971).

The reduction in the load-bearing capacity of the specimen in the post-failure behaviour is, therefore, due to the cracking of the specimen resulting in the decrease of the effective cross-sectional area. BRADY, DUVALL and HORINO (1971) tested specimens of Mt. Airy granite, Pikes Peak granite, Texas granite and marble. The specimens were deformed to preselected position along the post-failure curve of the specimen. These were then sectioned, polished and impregnated with fluorescent dye and the area of the specimen which had remained solid (at mid-height) was calculated. They found close agreement between the strength calculated from the reduced area and the peak strength of the specimen before failure.

The post-failure behaviour of the rock is also dependent upon the specimen geometry.

The stiffness of a specimen at the just initiation of post-failure region depends upon its diameter and height and can be given by

$$k_s = \frac{\pi}{4} d [h/d]^{-1} \times \frac{d\sigma}{d\varepsilon} \tag{2.15}$$

The stiffness of the machine k_m is also dependent upon the specimen diameter because of the platen indentation effects, but is essentially independent of the specimen height.* Since the shape of the post-failure curve is altered depending upon the relative stiffness of the machine and the specimen, it is obvious, that the post-failure curves so obtained shall be specimen geometry sensitive.

With the development of fractures in the post-failure region, the effective area at the centre of the specimen slowly decreases. The relative decrease in cross-sectional area is greater for the specimens of greater (h/d) ratio because of the different conditions of stress distribution in the specimen resulting in rapid decrease in the value of k_s. As such the post-failure curves of specimens with higher (h/d) ratio will be steeper. Results obtained by HUDSON, BROWN and FAIRHURST (1971) confirm this (Fig. 2-48). Similar results have also been obtained by BIENIAWSKI (1969). The post-failure stiffness of marble specimens as a function of specimen geometry is given in Fig. 2-49.

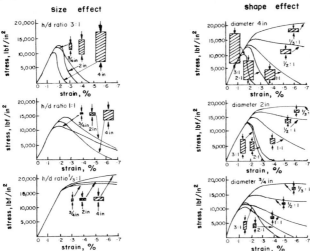

Fig. 2-48. Influence of the specimen size and shape on the complete stress-strain curve for marble loaded in uniaxial compression
(after HUDSON, BROWN and FAIRHURST, 1971).

* See Appendix.

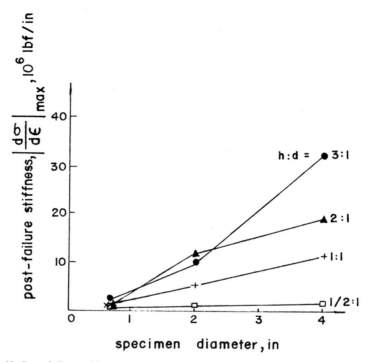

Fig. 2-49. Post-failure stiffness of Georgia Cherokee marble in uniaxial compression as a function of specimen diameter for various height/diameter ratios (after HUDSON, CROUCH and FAIRHURST, 1972).

2.11. Indirect Methods for Estimating Compressive Strength

The determination of compressive strength by testing regular-shaped specimens becomes very difficult when rocks contain gross cracks and flaws or when they break down by water or otherwise during preparation (e. g. mudstones and shales). Besides, the method is very time- and labour-consuming. In recent years, attempts have been made to determine the compressive strength by alternative methods.

2.11.1. Testing of Irregular Specimens

The estimation of compressive strength from tests on irregular specimens can be useful in the case of weaker rocks from which preparation of regular-shaped specimens is extremely difficult. It is also useful in the case of very strong rocks which may require special machines for the preparation of regular-shaped specimens. This testing also has direct relevance to the degradation of coal during the process of transportation.

The work on this method was initiated by PROTODYAKONOV and followed by other Russian scientists (PROTODYAKONOV and VOBLIKOV, 1957; TOKH-TUYEV and BORISENKO, 1958; MELEKIDZE, 1959; PROTODYAKONOV, 1960 and ILIVITSKII and NICKOLIN, 1961). International Bureau for Rock Mechanics (1961) recommended egg-shaped irregular samples with the ratio of the largest to the smallest dimension about 1.5 : 1 and a volume of about 100 cm³ (6.1 in³). After rounding off the samples with light hammer blows, 15 to 20 specimens, having a mass difference of $\pm 2\%$ are tested parallel to the longest axis and perpendicular to the plane of laminations. The compressive strength of these specimes, σ_{ci}, is given by

$$\sigma_{ci} = \frac{F}{A} \qquad (2.16)$$

where F = applied force at failure and
A = maximum area of cross-section of the specimen.

σ_{ci} and σ_c i.e. compressive strengths of regular specimens are related by the equation

$$\sigma_c = \frac{\sigma_{ci}}{0.19} \qquad (2.17)$$

HOBBS (1964a) conducted experiments on irregular specimens in the mass range of 30 to 128 g (0.066 to 0.280 lb). He crushed them parallel to their shortest dimensions without restricting them to any orientation of the laminations. He measured the area of contact of irregular specimens with the loading platens by placing a carbon paper and a graph paper between the specimen and each of the loading platens. The total area of these imprints at fracture was obtained by counting the blackened squares and the mean of the two total areas thus found was taken as the area of contact of the platens with the specimen. His results are given below:

1. There is a straight-line relationship between applied force at failure (F) and the mean specimen mass (m) when plotted on a log-log scale. The equation is

$$F \propto m^{0.56} \qquad (2.18)$$

If the mean mass of the irregular specimens is not 32 g (0.07 lb), the corrected value of the force at failure is given by $\dfrac{6.96\,F}{m^{0.56}}$.

2. There is a strong correlation between the compressive strength of irregular specimens (σ_{ci2}) defined as the average applied stress at failure and the volume of the specimens (V) of Donisthorpe siltstone I. The relationship is

$$\sigma_{ci2} \propto V^{0.071 \pm 0.003} \tag{2.19}$$

where σ_{ci2} = applied force at failure (F)/mean area of contact (A') and
V = volume of specimen.

This type of relationship, however, was not observed for Maesgwyn Cap mudstone and Pennant sandstone.

3. There is a close correlation between the compressive strength, σ_{ci2}, of irregular specimens, 32 g (0.07 lb) in mass, and compressive strength of cylinder of 2.54 cm (1 in) in length and 2.54 cm (1 in) in diameter (σ_{c1}) (see Fig. 2-50). The regression line equation is

$$\sigma_{c1} = 0.91\,\sigma_{ci2} - 3180 \tag{2.20}$$

where σ_{c1} and σ_{ci2} are in lbf/in^2.

The error in the regression estimate

$$= \pm 1260 \left[1 + \frac{(\sigma_{ci2} - 17\,660)^2}{1\,105 \times 10^5} \right]^{1/2} \tag{2.21}$$

EVANS and POMEROY (1966) carried out irregular specimen tests on Deep Duffryn and Barnsley Hard coals without adhering to any particular orientation of the bedding planes. For Deep Duffryn coal, they found no significant strength difference when the orientation of bedding planes was varied.

From their test results, they found the following relationships:

$$\sigma_{ci2} \propto V^{-0.09 \pm 0.03} \text{ for Deep Duffryn} \tag{2.22}$$

$$\sigma_{ci2} \propto V^{-0.04 \pm 0.02} \text{ for Barnsley Hards} \tag{2.23}$$

and

$$A' \propto V^{0.55 \pm 0.05} \text{ for Deep Duffryn} \tag{2.24}$$

$$A' \propto V^{0.51 \pm 0.06} \text{ for Barnsley Hards.} \tag{2.25}$$

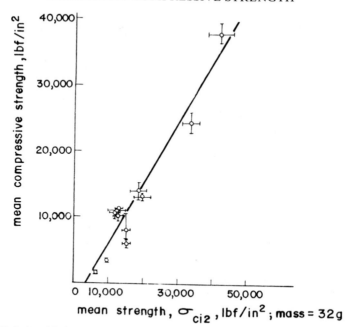

Fig. 2-50. Relationship between the average applied stress at fracture and the compressive strength (after HOBBS, 1964 a).

The results of their investigations are given in Table 10.

They also reported that strengths obtained from crushing of irregular specimens are about 1.7 to 2.0 times as large as those from testing of cubes of similar mass.

The study of the mode of failure of irregular specimens indicated that failure starts with the crumbling of areas in contact with the press platens, but final failure is a clear cut breakage which splits the specimen into two large pieces. The reason of this failure is the development of tensile stresses at right angles to the plane joining the points of contact of the specimen and the press platens.

From the myriad of equations and test specimen configurations used by different investigators, it would appear that the true compressive strength of a material must be known before any predictors of strength from tests on irregular specimens can be determined. This restricts the applicability of tests on irregular specimens to those situations where vast numbers of tests will be performed on material from one deposit for which many compressive strength values have already been determined by the usual techniques.

TABLE 10
Strengths of irregular lumps of Deep Duffryn coal and other related data
(after EVANS and POMEROY, 1966)

Mean mass (g)	Mean mass (lb)	Mass range (g)	Mass range (lb)	No. of specimens	Mean area of contact (cm²x10⁻³)	Mean area of contact (in²x10⁻³)	Mean crushing load (N)	Mean crushing load (lbf)	Mean compressive strengths MPa	Mean compressive strengths (lbf/in²)
Deep Duffryn										
4.5	(.01)	4-5	(.009-.011)	46	94.8±7.7	(14.7±1.2)	254±16	(57±3.5)	29.7±1.1	(4310±160)
19	(.04)	18-20	(.04-.044)	27	180±14.8	(27.9±2.3)	458±40	(103±9)	28.9±1.7	(4190±250)
75	(.17)	70-80	(.15-.18)	32	316.1±32.3	(49±5)	747±62	(168±14)	28.9±2.3	(4190±330)
130	(.29)	120-140	(.26-.31)	32	412.9±38.7	(64±6)	854±53	(192±12)	23.1±1.8	(3350±260)
500	(1.1)	450-550	(.99-1.21)	19	1019.4±129	(158±20)	1717±178	(386±40)	20.5±2.2	(2970±320)
Barnsley Hards										
1.2	(.003)	1.05-1.35	(.002-.003)	62	74.2±6.5	(11.5±1.0)	396±22	(89±5)	63.4±3.1	(9200±450)
6.5	(.014)	6-7	(.013-.015)	47	163.9±12.3	(25.4±1.9)	987±67	(222±15)	65.8±3.6	(9550±520)
11.0	(.024)	10-12	(.022-.026)	108	183.2±7.7	(28.4±1.2)	1094±44	(246±10)	69.0±1.8	(10000±260)
15.0	(.033)	15-17	(.033-.037)	46	241.3±20	(37.4±3.1)	1472±93	(331±21)	72.1±3.2	(10450±470)
22.0	(.05)	20-25	(.044-.055)	29	322.6±38.7	(50±6)	1699±111	(382±25)	63.6±4.5	(9220±650)
32.5	(.07)	30-35	(.066-.077)	35	432.3±38.7	(67±6)	2153±129	(484±29)	56.0±3.0	(8120±430)
65	(.14)	60-70	(.132-.154)	42	458.1±38.7	(71±6)	2326±214	(523±48)	51.6±2.7	(7480±390)
140	(.31)	130-150	(.29-.33)	22	729.1±96.8	(113±15)	4110±565	(924±127)	58.7±3.5	(8510±510)
320	(.71)	300-350	(.66-.77)	17	1290.4±129	(200±20)	6494±801	(1460±180)	51.2±3.1	(7430±450)
820	(1.81)	700-900	(1.54-1.98)	28	1806.6±167.8	(280±26)	9919±756	(2230±170)	59.2±3.6	(8580±520)

2.11.2. Protodyakonov Test

This is a very simple test meant to determine the resistance of rock to failure and can be applied to experiments on mass scale. This test is widely used in U.S.S.R. and other East European countries to determine the workability of coal seams. The test was devised by PROTODYAKONOV, SR. and has sometimes been called the pounding method (PROTODYAKONOV, 1962). Samples in the form of lumps 0.6 to 0.8 dm³ (36.6 to 48.8 in³) are taken from the rock bed, their number depending upon the coefficient of variation (V%) of rock hardness (Table 11). Each sample is broken up with a hammer and 5 test specimens, consisting of fragments of 20 to 40 mm (0.79 to 1.58 in) in size and of each 10 to 20 cm³ (0.61 to 1.22 in³) are picked. Each test specimen is placed in a cylinder of 76 mm (3 in) internal diameter and is pounded with a 2.4 kg (5.3 lb) drop mass falling through a distance of 0.6 m (23.6 in) (Fig. 2-51). The number of impacts, n, to which these test specimens are subjected is 5 to 15, depending upon the strength of the rock. After pounding all five specimens, the test material is sieved on a 0.5 mm (0.02 in) screen. Fines, which pass through the 0.5 mm (0.02 in) screen, are poured into the tube of a volumometer (Fig. 2-52) of 23 mm (0.91 in) diameter and the height of the column of dust, l, in mm in the volumometer is recorded. The strength coefficient, f, is given by the following equation:

$$f = \frac{20\,n}{l} \qquad (2.26)$$

This strength coefficient is related to the compressive strength by the equation

$$\sigma_c = \sqrt{1.06\,Ef} \qquad (2.27)$$

where σ_c = compressive strength, kgf/cm^2
   E = modulus of elasticity in compression, kgf/cm^2 and
   f = strength coefficient.

TABLE 11

Dependence of number of experiments on coefficient of variation

(after PROTODYAKONOV, 1962)

Coefficient of variation (V%)	No. of experiments (n)
30	9
25	6
20	4
15	3

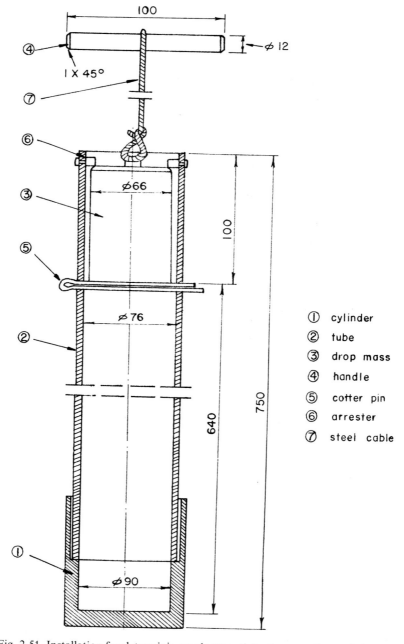

Fig. 2-51. Installation for determining rock strength by the pounding technique (after PROTODYAKONOV, 1962).

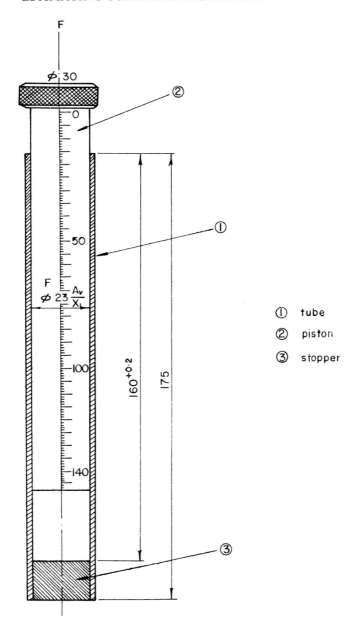

Fig. 2-52. Volumometer. The zero mark on the scale should be level with the edge of the tube when the piston is completely pushed in
(after PROTODYAKONOV, 1962).

PROTODYAKONOV further suggested that E can be determined empirically by the rebound of the hammer head, h, of the Shore scleroscope from a polished surface of rock specimen with the help of the following relationship:

$$E = 1.07 \times \frac{10^6 \, h}{154 - h} \, \text{kgf/cm} \qquad (2.28)$$

Therefore

$$\sigma_c \simeq 1050 \sqrt{\frac{f}{\dfrac{154}{h} - 1}} \, \text{kgf/cm}^2 \qquad (2.29)$$

SELIM and BRUCE (1970) modified the original method, in which the fines below 0.5 mm (0.02 in) are weighed and converted to a volume by dividing the specific gravity of the rock, thus avoiding the use of volumeter. The number of blows used is found, by trial and error, to give the minimum coefficient of rock strength, using 2 sets of specimens and 3 to 40 blows.

BROOK (1970) reported certain modifications to the test. After determining the number of blows required to produce a fines column of 50 mm (2 in), he used this value n in the standard formula, with l taken as 50 mm. He also mentioned that in finding a value for h, care must be taken to use a flat surface and the specimen must be about 50 mm (2 in) thick. An average of 100 readings was used to determine h for each rock. Table 12 gives his results for eight rocks.

TABLE 12

Protodyakonov test results for some rocks

(after BROOK, 1970)

Rock	f	h	σ_{c1}'* MPa	(lbf/in²)	σ_{c2}'** MPa	(lbf/in²)
1. Red sandstone	0.84	21.7	38.2	(5540)	36.0	(5221)
2. White sandstone	2.28	45.8	101.2	(14677)	93.2	(13517)
3. Blue sandstone	3.48	58.7	150.1	(21769)	137.8	(19985)
4. Limestone	4.68	59.0	174.6	(25323)	124.1	(17999)
5. Magnesian limestone	4.28	51.7	152.0	(22045)	150.6	(21842)
6. Metamorphosed limestone	7.50	77.0	275.7	(39985)	172.7	(25047)
7. Quartz-dolerite	10.64	77.5	336.5	(48803)	185.4	(26889)
8. Quartzite	4.50	95.0	276.6	(40116)	221.7	(32154)

* from Protodyakonov test
** from tests on regular specimens

These results show a good correlation between compressive strength values obtained from regular tests and Protodyakonov tests, except for the higher strength rocks. However, a more consistent correlation exists between Shore sclerescope rebound height, h, and compressive strength σ_{c2}, according to the formula

$$\sigma_{c2} = 2.55\,(h-6)\ \text{MPa} \qquad (2.30)$$

2.11.3. Impact Strength Test

EVANS and POMEROY (1966) used a procedure similar to Protodyakonov's one, and they called the measured property "Impact Strength Index, I.S.I."

The apparatus consists of a vertical steel cylinder of 4.45 cm (1.75 in) internal diameter, closed at the lower end by a screwed cap (Fig. 2-53). A steel plunger, 1.8 kg (4 lb) in mass and of 4.3 cm (1−11/16 in) in diameter at the bottom fits loosely inside the hollow cylinder. A steel cap, through which the plunger handle passes, is fitted to the cylinder. The cap has a dual purpose; it stops the coal dust from escaping and with the plunger raised to its full height, it controls the height through which the plunger falls. This height, measured from the bottom of the plunger to the inside surface of the base of the cylinder, is 30.5 cm (12 in).

Fig. 2-53. Impact strength index apparatus
(after EVANS and POMEROY, 1966).

The test consists of placing 100 g (0.22 lb) of coal, 0.95–0.32 cm (3/8–1/8 in) size range, in the cylinder and subjecting it to 20 blows of the plunger which is raised and dropped from the maximum height each time. The amount of coal remaining in the initial size range, after the test, is defined as the Impact Strength Index. The exact procedures used in the preparation of samples, and performance of test are given below:

Preparation of sample for test: A sample of coal is taken from the underground face or from the run-of-mine and is sieved through a 2.54 cm (1 in) sieve. The oversize coal is spread on a concrete floor and individual lumps of coal are broken by a 3.6 kg (8 lb) flatbased steel earth rammer to give maximum yield of fragments just under 2.54 cm (1 in) size. Breakage and sieving are repeated consecutively until all the coal passes through 2.54 cm (1 in) mesh sieve.

The 0.95–0.32 cm (3/8–1/8 in) fraction is then removed from the broken material by hand sieving and pieces trapped in the sieve meshes are rejected. Size fractions, each of about 125 g (0.28 lb), are removed from the 0.95–0.32 cm (3/8–1/8 in) sample by incremental sampling, successive increments being added to different fractions. Each fraction is then sieved on a 0.32 cm (1/8 in) B.S. sieve 20.30 cm (8 in) diameter for 3 minutes using a Russell sieving machine (or a sieving machine that has been standardized against a Russell machine). 100 ± 0.05 g (0.22 ± 0.0001 lb) is then carefully weighed from the sieved fraction, care being taken to avoid further degradation.

Test procedure: The 100 g (0.22 lb) sample is poured gently into the hollow cylinder of the I.S.I. apparatus which is then placed on a level floor. The surface of the coal is levelled carefully with a spatula without shaking the coal. The base of the apparatus is steadied with the feet and the top cap is fitted with the plunger raised. Keeping the base steady with the feet the operator raises the plunger to the full extent and drops it freely 20 times. The impacting rate is kept faster than once every two seconds. Finally, the cap and the plunger are removed and the coal resieved through the 0.32 cm (1/8 in) B.S. sieve, using the same sieving machine. It is sometimes necessary to tap the side of the I.S.I. apparatus slightly to eject the material. The mass of coal in grams remaining on the 0.32 cm (1/8 ln) sieve, including the material trapped in the sieve, is the Impact Strength Index of the coal.

Six samples are tested for each seam or subsection of each seam and the average value is taken as the I.S.I. I.S.I. values must differ by at least 3 units before a strength difference is taken as real. If the tests, however, are made in different laboratories this difference should be at least 4.5 units.

EVANS and POMEROY (1966) reported that I.S.I. has a relationship with compressive strength of cubes as shown in Fig. 2-54.

Hobbs (1964b) applied this method to rocks and found that compressive strength, σ_{c2}, in lbf/in², is related to I.S.I., f_1, as follows.

$$\sigma_{c2} = 769\, f_1 - 36360 \qquad (2.31)$$

The number obtained from Protodyakonov or Impact Strength Test is related to the energy required to fracture rock which is important in quantifying rock behaviour for many applications. For this purpose, these tests are being conducted in more and more laboratories. If these indices are available, compressive strength can be estimated although these tests are not specifically conducted to estimate compressive strength since it is much easier and more accurate to measure compressive strength directly.

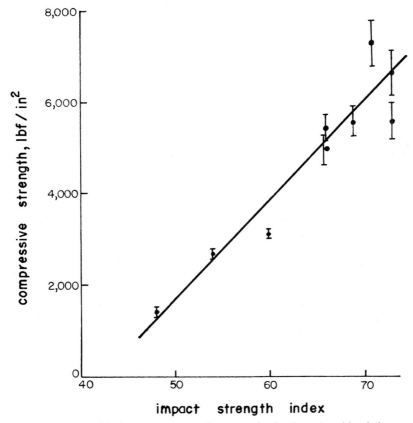

Fig. 2-54. Relationship between compressive strength of cubes of coal loaded perpendicular to bedding planes and impact strength index
(after Evans and Pomeroy, 1966).

2.12. Summary and Conclusions

Cylindrical specimens are most convenient and should be used. 2.2 to 6.6 cm (0.87 to 2.60 in) diameter specimens are suggested for the standard method of the compression test (HORIBE, 1970). I.S.R.M. Committee on Laboratory Tests (1972) suggested cylinders having a diameter preferably of not less than NX core size, 54 mm (2.13 in). The ratio of height-to-diameter should be about 2.5–3.0. If it is not practicable to prepare specimens with this height-to-diameter ratio, the test results are converted according to the relationship obtained from similar rocks.

The end faces of the cylinders have to be parallel to each other and perpendicular to the cylinder generatrix, and also be as flat as possible. Generators of the cylindrical surface should be straight and the diameter should be constant over the length of the specimen. The standards recommended by I.S.R.M. Committee on Laboratory Tests (1972) for the specimen preparation have been given in chapter 1 (Section 1.3.1.).

The testing machine should have at least one spherical head. It should be lightly lubricated with mineral oil. The platens must be ground. The specimen must be placed centrally between the platens.

Steel inserts of the same diameter as the specimen are recommended. The overall length of the platen should be at least equal to the diameter of the specimen (PENG, 1971).

Friction between platens and end surfaces of the specimen has a significant effect upon the test results and it is better to have the level of friction in tests approaching the value for the condition in practice.

The rate of loading has a variable effect on the compressive strength of rocks. OBERT, WINDES and DUVALL (1946) recommended 0.69 MPa/s (100 lbf/in^2/s) in their standardized procedures. PROTODYAKONOV (1969) recommended 1 MPa/s (140 lbf/in^2/s). In Japan, 0.1–1 MPa/s (14–140 lbf/in^2/s) is used as a standard (HORIBE, 1970). I.S.R.M. Committee on Laboratory Tests (1972) suggested the stress rate within the limits of 0.5 to 1.0 MPa/s (70 to 140 lbf/in^2/s).

The environment has also a significant effect on the compressive strength of rocks. It is best to test the rocks in the environment which is equivalent to the in situ conditions. As this is difficult and time consuming, I.S.R.M. Committee on Laboratory Tests (1972) suggested that the prepared specimens shall be stored prior to testing for 5 to 6 days in an environment of 20 ± 2 °C (68 ± 4 °F) and 50% humidity. For other conditions, extrapolation of the results in established relationships of similar rocks is recommended.

The failure of rock in compression is a progressive one and that rock maintains a certain strength even after the peak strength has been past and its deformation is further continued. There is a continuous decrease in the deformation modulus of the rock in the post-failure region (Fig. 2-43).

The post-failure curve for rocks can be obtained by using certain stiffening elements or using a servo-controlled machine with appropriate monotonously increasing feed back signals.*

The post-failure behaviour of the rocks in compression is a characteristic of the rock structure and the test-conditions. Rocks with extremely fine-grained homogeneous structure have post-failure behaviour belonging to class II while porous rocks have post-failure behaviour of class I (Fig. 2-45).

The class I and class II behaviours may change from one to the other depending upon the rate of loading, moisture content, specimen geometry, etc. Specimens of lower h/d ratio have a lower post-failure stiffness.

When the cores are not obtainable, irregularly shaped specimens can be used. There is a strong correlation between the compressive strengths of irregular specimens and regular specimens. If the relationships are found for all types of rocks, there is no reason why irregular specimen testing should not become popular.

The compressive strength values can also be estimated from the results of other tests such as the Protodyakonov test, Impact strength test, etc. Here again, correlations have to be found for various types of rocks.

In the report of the compressive strength test on cylindrical specimens, the following information is noted:

1. Location of the sampling place
2. Method of sampling
3. Kind of rock
4. Geological view
5. Storage environment
6. Preparation before testing
7. Size of specimen
8. Moisture content
9. Clearly recognisable external peculiarities
10. Direction of load when the rock has a stratification
11. Rate of loading

---

* See Appendix.

12. Identification, capacity and used range of the testing machine
13. Number of specimens
14. Mean, maximum and minimum values of the compressive strength
15. Standard deviation
16. Variance.

References

1. ALEKSEEV, A. D., ZHURAVLEV, V. I., YAROVAYA, L. I. and MOLCHANENKO, V. S.: Effect of the geometry and fracturing of rock specimens on their strength. Sov. Min. Sci., No. 3, May–June, 1970, pp. 281–285.

2. A.S.T.M.: Tentative method of test for compressive strength of natural building stone. A.S.T.M.: Designation: C170-41T, A.S.T.M. Standards – Part 2, 1942, pp. 1102–1104.

3. BALLA, A.: Stress conditions in triaxial compression. J. Soil Mech. Found. Div., Am. Soc. Civ. Eng., Vol. 86, No. SM6, Dec., 1960, pp. 57–84.

4. BECKMAN, R. T.: Compressive strength versus length-diameter ratios of potash specimens. U.S. Bureau of Mines Report of Investigations (U.S.B.M.R.I.) 6339, 1963, 15 p.

5. BIENIAWSKI, Z. T.: The compressive strength of hard rocks. Tydskrif vir Natuurwetenskappe, Vol. 8, Nos. 3–4, Sept.–Dec., 1968a, pp. 163–182.

6. BIENIAWSKI, Z. T.: The effect of specimen size on compressive strength of coal. Int. J. Rock Mech. Min. Sci., Vol. 5, No. 4, July, 1968b, pp. 325–335.

7. BIENIAWSKI, Z. T.: Deformational behaviour of fractured rock under multiaxial compression. Proc. Int. Conf. Struct., Solid Mech. Eng. Mater., Southampton, 1969, pp. 589–598.

8. BORDIA, S. K.: The effects of size and stress concentration on the dilatancy and fracture of rock. Int. J. Rock Mech. Min. Sci., Vol. 8, No. 6, Nov., 1971, pp. 629–640.

9. BORETTI-ONYSZKIEWICZ, W.: Joints in the flysch sandstones on the ground of strength examinations. Proc. 1st. Cong. Int. Soc. Rock Mech., Lisbon, 1966, Vol. 1, pp. 153–157.

10. BRACE, W. F.: Dependence of fracture strength of rocks on grain size. Proc. 4th Symp. Rock Mech., Univ. Park, Penn., 1961, pp. 99–103.

11. BRADY, B. T.: Effects of inserts on the elastic behaviour of cylindrical materials loaded between rough end-plates. Int. J. Rock Mech. Min. Sci., Vol. 8, No. 4, July, 1971, pp. 357–369.

12. BRADY, B. T., DUVALL, W. I. and HORINO, F. G.: A study of the post-failure characteristics of brittle rock. Proc. Symp. Rock Fracture, Nancy, 1971, Paper II–21.

13. BRIGHENTI, G.: Influence of cryogenic temperatures on the mechanical characteristics of rocks. Proc. 2nd Cong. Int. Soc. Rock Mech., Belgrade, 1970, Vol. 1, pp. 473–477.

14. BROOK, N.: A modified method of determining the PROTODYAKONOV number, and its correlation with compressive strength. Proc. 2nd Cong. Int. Soc. Rock Mech., Belgrade, 1970, Vol. 2, pp. 233–237.

15. BROWN, E. T. and HUDSON, J. A.: The influence of micro-structure on rock fracture on the laboratory scale. Proc. Symp. Rock Fracture, Nancy, 1971, Paper II–20.

16. BROWN, J. H. and POMEROY, C. D.: Friction between coal and metal surfaces. Proc. Conf. Mech. Prop. Non-metallic Brittle Materials, London, 1958, pp. 419–429.

17. BUNTING, D.: Chamber-pillars in deep anthracite-mines. Trans. A.I.M.E., Vol. 42, 1911, pp. 236–245.

18. BURSHTEIN, L. S.: Effect of moisture on the strength and deformability of sandstone. Sov. Min. Sci., No. 5, Sept.–Oct., 1969, pp. 573–576.

19. COLBACK, P. S. B. and WIID, B. L.: The influence of moisture content on the compressive strength of rocks. Proc. 3rd Can. Rock Mech. Symp., Toronto, 1965, pp. 65–83.

20. D'APPOLONIA, E. and NEWMARK, N. M.: A method for the solution of the restrained cylinder under compression. Proc. 1st U.S. Nat. Cong. Appl. Mech., Chicago, Illinois, 1951, pp. 217–226.

21. EVANS, I. and POMEROY, C. D.: The strength, fracture and workability of coal. London, Pergamon Press, 1966, 277 p.

22. FAIRHURST, C. and COOK, N. G. W.: The phenomenon of rock splitting parallel to the direction of maximum compression in the neighbourhood of a surface. Proc. 1st Cong. Int. Soc. Rock Mech., Lisbon, 1966, Vol. 1, pp. 687–692.

23. FEDA, J.: The influence of water content on the behaviour of subsoil, formed by highly weathered rocks. Proc. 1st Cong. Int. Soc. Rock Mech., Lisbon, 1966, Vol. 1, pp. 283–288.

24. FILON, L. N. G.: On the elastic equilibrium of circular cylinders under certain practical systems of load. Phil. Trans. Roy. Soc. London, Series A, Vol. 198, 1902, pp. 147–233.

25. GADDY, F. L.: A study of the ultimate strength of coal as related to the absolute size of the cubical specimens tested. Bull. Virginia Polytechnic Inst., Vol. 49, No. 10, Aug., 1956, 27 p.

26. GIRIJAVALLABHAN, C. V.: Stresses in restrained cylinder under axial compression. J. Soil Mech. Found. Div., Am. Soc. Civ. Eng., Vol. 96, No. SM 2, March, 1970, pp. 783–787.

27. GROSVENOR, N. E.: Specimen proportion – Key to better compressive strength tests. Min. Eng., Vol. 15, No. 1, Jan., 1963, pp. 31–33.

28. HAST, N.: Measuring stresses and deformation in solid materials. Stockholm, Centraltryckeriet, Esselte ab, 1943.

29. HAWKES, I. and MELLOR, M.: Uniaxial testing in rock mechanics laboratories. Eng. Geol., Vol. 4, 1970, pp. 177–285.

30. HOBBS, D. W.: A simple method for assessing the uniaxial compressive strength of rock. Int. J. Rock Mech. Min. Sci., Vol. 1, No. 1, Jan., 1964a, pp. 5–15.

31. HOBBS, D. W.: Rock compressive strength. Coll. Eng., Vol. 41, 1964b, pp. 287–292.

32. HODGSON, K. and COOK, N. G. W.: The effects of size and stress gradient on the strength of rock. Proc. 2nd Cong. Int. Soc. Rock Mech., Belgrade, 1970, Vol. 2, pp. 31–34.

33. HOLLAND, C. T.: The strength of coal in mine pillars. Proc. 6th Symp. Rock Mech., Rolla, Missouri, 1964, pp. 450–466.

34. HOLLAND, C. T. and OLSEN, D. A.: Interfacial friction, moisture and coal pillar strength. Trans. Soc. Min. Eng. A.I.M.E., Vol. 241, No. 3, Sept., 1968, pp. 323–328.

35. HORIBE, T.: The abstract of the report from "Committee concerning the method of the measurement of the strength of rock" in M.M.I.J. Rock Mech. in Japan, Vol. 1, 1970, pp. 29–31.

36. HOSKINS, J. R. and HORINO, F. G.: Influence of spherical head size and specimen diameters on the uniaxial compressive strength of rocks. U.S.B.M.R.I. 7234, 1969, 16 p.

37. HOUPERT, R.: The uniaxial compressive strength of rocks. Proc. 2nd Cong. Int. Soc. Rock Mech., Belgrade, 1970, Vol. 2, pp. 49–55.

38. HUDSON, J. A., BROWN, E. T. and FAIRHURST, C.: Shape of the complete stress-strain curve for rock. Proc. 13th Symp. Rock Mech., Urbana, Illinois, 1971, pp. 773–795.

39. HUDSON, J. A., CROUCH, S. L. and FAIRHURST, C.: Soft, stiff and servo-controlled testing machines: A review with reference to rock failure. Eng. Geol., Vol. 6, 1972, pp. 155–189.

40. ILIVITSKII, A. A. and NICKOLIN, V. I.: Determining the strength of rock strata on irregularly-shaped specimens. Ugol, Vol. 36, 1961, pp. 34–36.

41. International Bureau for Rock Mechanics: Group 3, Strength research, Appendix H, Prague, Mar. 21–25, 1961.

42. I.S.R.M. Committee on Laboratory Tests: Suggested methods for determining the uniaxial compressive strength of rock materials and the point load strength index. Document No. 1, Oct., 1972, 12 p.

43. JENKINS, J. D.: Discussion on paper – Stress-strain relations and breakage of rocks – by SELDENRATH, TH. R. and GRAMBERG, J. Proc. Conf. Mech. Prop. Non-metallic Brittle Materials, London, 1958, pp. 102–103.

44. KARTASHOV, YU. M., MAZUR-DZHURILOVSKII, YU. D. and GROKHOLSKII, A. A.: Determination of the uniaxial compressive strengths of rocks. Sov. Min. Sci., No. 3, May-June, 1970, pp. 339–341.

45. KJAERNSLI, B. and SANDE, A.: Compressibility of some coarse-grained materials. Proc. European Conf. Soil Mech. Found. Eng., Wiesbaden, 1963, Vol. 1, pp. 245–51.

46. KOBAYASHI, R.: On mechanical behaviours of rocks under various loading-rates. Rock Mech. in Japan, Vol. 1, 1970, pp. 56–58.

47. KOTTE, J. J., BERCZES, Z. G., GRAMBERG, J. and SELDENRATH, TH. R.: Stress-strain relations and breakage of cylindrical granitic rock specimens under uniaxial and triaxial loads. Int. J. Rock Mech. Min. Sci., Vol. 6, No. 6, Nov., 1969, pp. 581–595.

48. KOWALSKI, W. C.: The interdependence between the strength and voids ratio of limestones and marls in connection with their water saturating and anisotropy. Proc. 1st Cong. Int. Soc. Rock Mech., Lisbon, 1966, Vol. 1, pp. 143–144.

49. KROKOSKY, E. M. and HUSAK, A.: Strength characteristics of basalt rock in ultra-high vacuum. J. Geophys. Res., Vol. 73, No. 6, 15 March, 1968, pp. 2237–2247.

50. LAMA, R. D.: Elasticity and strength of coal seams in situ and an attempt to determine the energy in pressure bursting of roadsides. D. Sc. Tech. Thesis, Faculty of Mining, Academy of Min. & Metall., Cracow, Poland, 1966.

51. LUNDBORG, N.: The strength-size relation of granite. Int. J. Rock Mech. Min. Sci., Vol. 4, No. 3, July, 1967, pp. 269–272.

52. LUNDBORG, N.: Strength of rock-like materials. Int. J. Rock Mech. Min. Sci., Vol. 5, No. 5, Sept., 1968, pp. 427–454.

53. MEIKLE, P. G. and HOLLAND, C. T.: The effect of friction on the strength of model coal pillars. Trans. Soc. Min. Eng. A.I.M.E., Vol. 232, No. 4, Dec., 1965, pp. 322–327.

54. MELEKIDZE, I. G.: A study of the physico-mechanical properties of the rocks of some Georgian ore deposits. In Mechanical Properties of Rocks, Moscow, Ugletekhizdat, 1959.

55. MOGI, K.: The influence of the dimensions of specimens on the fracture strength of rocks. Bull. Earthquake Res. Inst., Tokyo Univ., Vol. 40, 1962, pp. 175–185.

56. MOGI, K.: Some precise measurements of fracture strength of rocks under uniform compressive stress. Rock Mech. Eng. Geol., Vol. 4, 1966, pp. 41–55.

57. OBERT, L., WINDES, S. L. and DUVALL, W. I.: Standardized tests for determining the physical properties of mine rock. U.S.B.M.R.I. 3891, 1946, 67 p.

58. PAUL, B. and GANGAL, M.: Initial and subsequent fracture curves for biaxial compression of brittle materials. Proc. 8th Symp. Rock Mech., Minneapolis, Minn., 1966, pp. 113–141.

59. PENG, S. D.: Stresses within elastic circular cylinders loaded uniaxially and triaxially. Int. J. Rock Mech. Min. Sci., Vol. 8, No. 5, Sept., 1971, pp. 399–432.

60. PERKINS, R. D., GREEN, S. J. and FRIEDMAN, M.: Uniaxial stress behaviour of porphyritic tonalite at strain rates to 10^3/second. Int. J. Rock Mech. Min. Sci., Vol. 7, No. 5, Sept., 1970, pp. 527–535.

61. PICKETT, G.: Application of the FOURIER method to the solution of certain boundary problems in the theory of elasticity. J. Appl. Mech., Vol. 11, 1944, pp. A 176–A 182.

62. PRICE, N. J.: The compressive strength of coal measure rocks. Coll. Eng., Vol. 37, 1960, pp. 283–292.

63. PROTODYAKONOV, M. M.: New methods of determining mechanical properties of rocks. Proc. 3rd Int. Conf. Strata Control, Paris, 1960, pp. 187–191.

64. PROTODYAKONOV, M. M.: Mechanical properties and drillability of rocks. Proc. 5th Symp. Rock Mech., Minneapolis, Minn., 1962, pp. 103–118.

65. PROTODYAKONOV, M. M.: Method of determining the strength of rocks under uniaxial compression. In Mechanical Properties of Rocks by M. M. PROTODYAKONOV, M. I. KOIFMAN, and others. Translated from Russian. Jerusalem, Israel Program for Scientific Translations, 1969, pp. 1–8.

66. PROTODYAKONOV, M. M. and VOBLIKOV, V. S.: Determining rock strength with specimens of irregular shape. Ugol, Vol. 32, 1957.

67. RINEHART, J. S.: Fracture of rocks. Int. J. Fracture Mech., Vol. 2, 1966, pp. 534–551.

68. ROBERTS, A.: Progress in the application of photoelastic techniques to rock mechanics. Proc. 6th Symp. Rock Mech., Rolla, Missouri, 1964, pp. 606–648.

69. RUIZ, M. D.: Some technological characteristics of twenty-six Brazilian rock types. Proc. 1st Cong. Int. Soc. Rock Mech., Lisbon, 1966, Vol. 1, pp. 115–119.

70. SALUSTOWICZ, A.: Zarys mechaniki gorotworu. Katowice, Wydawnictwo "Slask", 1965.

71. SELIM, A. A. and BRUCE, W. E.: Prediction of penetration rate for percussive drilling. U.S.B.M.R.I. 7396, 1970, 21 p.

72. SHOOK, W. B.: Critical survey of mechanical property test-methods for brittle materials. Ohio State University, Engineering Experiment Station, Columbus, Ohio, July, 1963, 136 p.

73. SIMPSON, D. R. and FERGUS, J. H.: The effect of water on the compressive strength of diabase. J. Geophys. Res., Vol. 73, No. 20, 15 Oct., 1968, pp. 6591–6594.

74. SKINNER, W. J.: Experiments on the compressive strength of anhydrite. The Engineer, Vol. 207, 1959, pp. 255–259; 288–292.

75. SMORODINOV, M. I., MOTOVILOV, E. A. and VOLKOV, V. A.: Determinations of correlation relationships between strength and some physical characteristics of rocks. Proc. 2nd Cong. Int. Soc. Rock Mech., Belgrade, 1970, Vol. 2, pp. 35–37.

76. SPAETH, W.: Einfluß der Federung der Zerreißmaschine auf das Spannungs-Dehnungs-Schaubild. Arch. Eisenhüttenwesen, Vol. 6, 1935, pp. 277–283.

77. STEART, F. A.: Strength and stability of pillars in coal mines. J. Chem. Metall. Min. Soc. S. Africa, Vol. 54, No. 8, Mar., 1954, pp. 309–325.

78. STREET, N and F.-D.-WANG: Surface potentials and rock strength. Proc. 1st Cong. Int. Soc. Rock Mech., Lisbon, 1966, Vol. 1, pp. 451–456.

79. TOKHTUYEV, G. V. and BORISENKO, V. G.: Some results of an investigation into the mechanical strength of rocks and ores of Krivoy Rog with irregular-shaped specimens. In Mechanical Properties of Rocks, Moscow, Ugletekhizdat, 1958.

80. TRUMBACHEV, V. F. and MELNIKOV, E. A.: Distribution of stresses in the intervening pillars at medium and steep dips. Proc. 4th Int. Conf. Strata Control and Rock Mech., New York, 1964, pp. 316–322.

81. WAWERSIK, W. R.: Detailed analysis of rock failure in laboratory compression tests. PH. D. THESIS, Univ. Minnesota, Minneapolis, Minn., 1968, 165 p.

82. WAWERSIK, W. R. and BRACE, W. F.: Post-failure behaviour of a granite and diabase. Rock Mech., Vol. 3, 1971, pp. 61–85.

83. ZARUBA, Q.: Geology of the Orlik dam site. Water Power, Vol. 17, 1965, pp. 273–279.

84. ZNANSKI, J.: Sklonnosi skal do tapania. Archiwum Gornictwa i Huntictwa, Tom 2, 1954.

85. ZNANSKI, J.: Polish research in the field of rockbursts. Proc. 7th Meeting Int. Bureau Rock Mech., Leipzig, 1965.

CHAPTER 3

Tensile Strength of Rock

3.1. Introduction

In section 2.3, it has been stated that the specimens tested for compressive strength often fail due to the development of tensile stresses. Tensile failure is also an important phenomenon in the mechanical winning of minerals, drilling and blasting of rocks, failure of roof and floor, etc., particularly because rocks are very much weaker in tension than in compression. It is imperative, then, that tensile strength of rocks should be studied in detail.

The greatest difficulty in the direct test for the determination of tensile strength of rocks is the gripping of specimens. To get uniform tensile stress distribution and for easy gripping, specially prepared specimens are required and they are difficult to make. As a result, a number of indirect methods have been developed for determining the tensile strength of rocks, but it is still doubtful whether we have an appropriate method, the results of which could be relied upon.

Various methods employed for determining the tensile strength of rocks are described here. Typical results of various workers are also included.

3.2. Direct Method

The method, in principle, is similar to that employed in the testing of metals. However, there are difficulties in gripping the specimens and applying a load parallel to the axis of the specimen. It is important that the specimen is mounted in tension grips without damaging the surface of the specimen. Besides, if the load cannot be applied parallel to the axis of the specimen within close limits, there will be a tendency to cause bending, producing abnormal stress concentrations. Several specimen shapes and methods of attaching specimens to the pulling system have been used by investigators engaged in the determination of tensile strength of rocks.

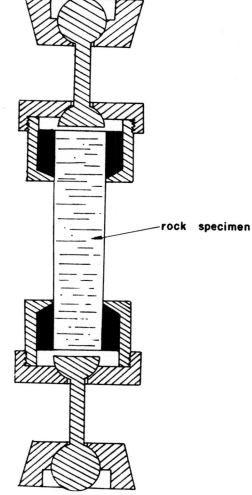

Fig. 3-1. Grips for tensile strength test
(after OBERT, WINDES and DUVALL, 1946).

OBERT, WINDES and DUVALL (1946) used a grip shown in Fig. 3-1 in which a cylindrical specimen is held in place with a Leadite compound cast around each end of the specimen forming a bearing surface. The grips are in contact with the Leadite cast and do not touch the specimen. A spherically seated joint in the grip cups is placed close to the end of the specimen and in line with the axis of the specimen. This permits self alignment. After testing a large number of specimens of marble, limestone, granite, sandstone, etc., they reported that Leadite compound is not suitable to hold specimens of tensile strength greater than 8.27 MPa (1200 lbf/in²). The method also gave large deviations.

WUERKER (1955) used briquette shaped specimens (Fig. 1-1) prepared from rock in different ways. Tensile strength values obtained by this method, however, do not represent true values because of the stress concentration caused at the curvature of the side of the specimen and the closeness of the grips. The ratio of the maximum to the average stress at the plane of failure is about 1.75. After applying correction, he found that the method gives quite satisfactory results. Standard deviation is about 4.7% for shale (7 specimens) and 10.7% for sandstone (9 specimens), which is quite within acceptable limits. The major difficulty with this method is in the preparation of specimens. He, however, claimed that such shaped specimens can be successfully prepared even from soft rocks by the method of coring and cutting described by him (Section 1.3) and briquettes can be tested in any arrangement of the bedding planes.

GROSVENOR (1961) used a procedure similar to that of OBERT, WINDES and DUVALL. He, however, used a sulphur conical plug instead of Leadite compound and found specimens breaking within the sulphur cast.

He also tested cylindrical specimens by gripping them in specially designed grips for a given size specimen. The grips are designed to distribute the stress around the core when tightened (Fig. 3-2). A universal joint or a flexible cable is used to prevent bending and twisting of the specimen. This system of gripping, however, did not give satisfactory results, since failure very often took place within the grips themselves due to the stress concentration set up by uneven tightening of grips.

To overcome the difficulties associated with gripping, and preparation of specimens of special shapes, FAIRHURST (1961) devised a typical method using cylindrical specimens and epoxy based cements (of approximately 20.69–27.58 MPa (3000–4000 lbf/in²) tensile strength). The specimen is glued to steel caps (Fig. 3-3) and loaded with the help of a flexible cable using a simple cantilever arrangement. For gluing, he used Minnesota Mining and Manufacturing Company adhesive EC 1838B/A. He made narrow lips, 0.008 cm (0.003 in) high, on to the cap ends to ensure that cement from the rock-steel interface is not extruded during curing.

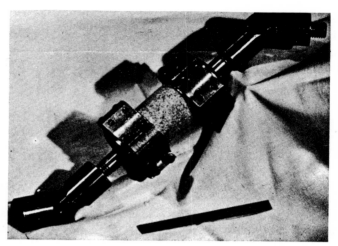

Fig. 3-2. Specimen in clamp type grips
(after GROSVENOR, 1961).

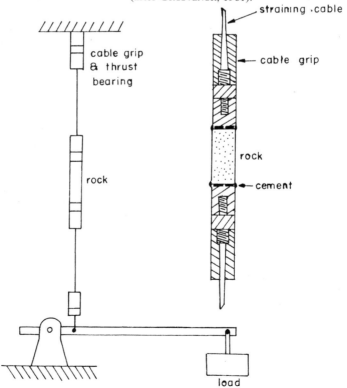

Fig. 3-3. Tensile test apparatus and gripping arrangement
(after FAIRHURST, 1961).

In this method, cylindrical, square or rectangular specimens can be used without any difficulty. It is essential that the specimen is accurately centred on the plate. To facilitate this, the cross-section of the end steel plate should be of the same size and shape as that of the specimen.

This method is dependable and gives relatively consistent results. It is satisfactory among the various tests developed for direct determination of tensile strength of many rocks. The preparation of specimens is also very simple. This method is sometimes referred to as the plate and glue method.

For very strong rocks, it may be difficult to develop sufficient bond strength. The end conditions become similar to those prevailing in the conventional compressive strength test with complete end restraint. Since most cables are made of twisted strands of steel, they may introduce torque into the test specimen.

YU (1963) also investigated this problem. When adopting a procedure similar to that of OBERT, WINDES and DUVALL, he used an epoxy resin cast (conical plug) in place of the Leadite cast and found failure occurring within the cast. He, however, suggested that this difficulty can be overcome by reducing the diameter of the central part of the specimen on a suitable curvature. He also investigated the plate and glue method using Devcon type A, plastic steel, and found that this adhesive could be useful for rocks of tensile strength below 6.9 MPa (1 000 lbf/in²). To improve adhesion, the ends of the specimen in contact with the plates were roughened.

The Rock Mechanics Division of the National Mechanical Engineering Research Institute of South Africa (HOEK, 1964) used specimens of a shape similar to that used in the testing of metals (Fig. 1-2). The specimen has a central straight test length (throat) of 4.32 cm (1.70 in) and diameter equal to 2.16 cm (0.85 in). The radius of curvature is 5.1 cm (2.0 in) and head is of 4.1 cm (1.6 in) diameter and 3.8 cm (1.5 in) long. HOEK reported that satisfactory results were obtained by using such specimens and testing them by gripping in the conventional wedge type grips.

BRACE (1963) also used such specimens except that the radius of curvature at the point of reduction of diameter is 10.20 cm (4.0 in) and the specimen has a straight test length (throat) of 2.54 cm (1.0 in) and diameter 1.27 cm (0.5 in), the head being 2.54 cm (1.0 in) in diameter. Heads of the specimen were impregnated with epoxy resins. He reported very successful results in the tension testing of such specimens.

HAWKES and MELLOR (1970) reported the use of aluminium collars designed to approximate the effect of rock fillets. A cylindrical specimen 2.54 cm

(1.00 in) diameter and 12.10 cm (4.75 in) long is cemented into chamfered aluminium collars (Fig. 3-4). The collars are machined to allow a clearance of approximately 0.008 cm (0.003 in) (total) between rock and aluminium, and they are slotted longitudinally to minimise hoop stress and provide some radial and circumferential strain freedom. In this method also, there is an unavoidable tendency for fracture to occur at the collar.

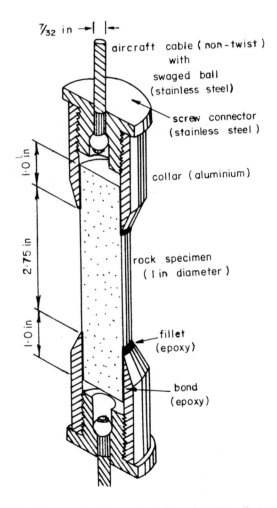

Fig. 3-4. Chamfered collar method for uniaxial tensile test
(after Hawkes and Mellor, 1970).

The U.S. Bureau of Mines previously used a fixture similar to Fairhurst's (except that chain linkage was substituted for the cables), and now they have developed a more reliable fixture (KRECH and CHAMBERLAIN, 1972; CHAMBERLAIN, 1974). The fixture essentially substitutes a spherical rod-end bearing for chain or cable attached via a suitable platen to each end of the specimen. The platens, which contain a 6.4 mm (0.25 in) lip, are attached to the specimen ends by applying a small amount of the newly marketed alphacyanimide adhesive which sets up upon application of light pressure and which bonds better than the epoxy resin systems.

MOKHNACHEV and GROMOVA (1970) prepared cylindrical specimens with a height (working base)-to-diameter ratio of 1.5 from blocks of limestone, sandstone, gabbro, diabase and mineralised siltstone. At the ends of the specimens, they attached spherical yokes with Wood's metal by means of which direct tension was applied. They conducted two series of tests. In the first series, loading rates varied from 0.001 to 0.01 kgf/cm^2/s (0.1 to 1 kPa/s) (0.0142 to 0.142 lbf/in^2/s). The time to fracture varied, according to material, from $80 \sim 600$ s to $10000 \sim 80000$ s. The second series of tests was done under loading rates of from 1 to 1 000 kgf/cm^2/s (0.1 to 98 MPa/s) (14.2 to 14 200 lbf/in^2/s). The loading duration for this series varied between 20 and 0.03 s.

For all the rocks, the tensile strength increased with the rate of loading (Fig. 3-5). The rate of its increase with the loading rate was different for each rock. The ratio of the tensile strength at maximum loading rate ~ 1000 kgf/cm^2/s (98 MPa/s) (14200 lbf/in^2/s) to the tensile strength at minimum loading rate ~ 0.001 kgf/cm^2/s (0.1 kPa/s) (0.0142 lbf/in^2/s) had the following values: for limestone, 2.6; for sandstone, 2.5; for gabbro, 2.0; for diabase, 1.7; for mineralised siltstone, 1.5. The weaker the rock and the lower the tensile strength, the greater was the relative increase of strength with increase of loading rate.

The curves of tensile strength, σ_t, versus loading rate, v_n, in Fig. 3-5 are different. For convenience in comparison, the values of σ_t found at any rate v_n and duration t_n were referred to the value of σ_t calculated at a loading rate of $v = 1$ kgf/cm^2/s (0.1 MPa/s) (14.2 lbf/in^2/s) and a loading duration of $t = 1$ s. According to the same principle, they processed and correlated the available quantitative data of other Soviet and foreign investigators, and this enabled them to extend the range of loading rates from 0.001 to 979 090 kgf/cm^2/s (0.1 kPa/s to 97.9 GPa/s) (0.0142 to 14.2×10^6 lbf/in^2/s).

Fig. 3-6 shows the resulting graph of tensile strength versus loading rate and Fig. 3-7 is a plot of tensile strength versus loading duration.

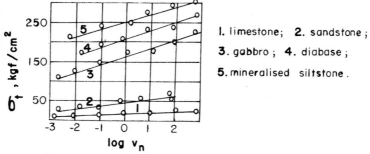

1. limestone;   2. sandstone;
3. gabbro ;   4. diabase ;
5. mineralised siltstone .

Fig. 3-5. Effect of rate of loading on tensile strength of rocks
(after MOKHNACHEV and GROMOVA, 1970).

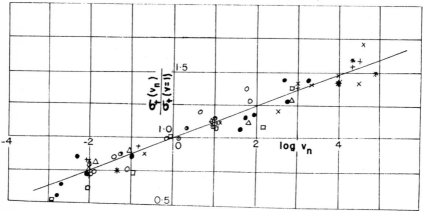

Fig. 3-6. Tensile strength versus loading rate
(after MOKHNACHEV and GROMOVA, 1970).

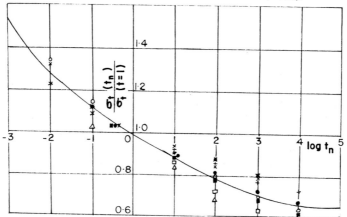

Fig. 3-7. Tensile strength versus loading duration
(after MOKHNACHEV and GROMOVA, 1970).

The following equations were obtained for the graphs in Figs. 3-6 and 3-7:

$$\frac{\sigma_t \,(v_n)}{\sigma_t \,(v=1)} = 0.12 \log v_n + 1 \tag{3.1}$$

$$\frac{\sigma_t \,(t_n)}{\sigma_t \,(t=1)} = 0.005 \,(\log t_n)^2 - 0.12 \log t_n + 1 \tag{3.2}$$

3.3. Indirect Methods

Several indirect methods have been developed to determine the tensile strength of rocks. These can, in general, be grouped as follows:

Bending tests:
1. Bending of prismatic and cylindrical specimens
2. Bending of discs

Hydraulic extension tests

Diametral compression of discs:
1. Brazilian test
2. Ring test

Miscellaneous methods:
1. Diametral compression of cylinders
2. Diametral compression of spheres
3. Compression of square plates along a diameter
4. Centrifugal tension

3.3.1. Bending Tests

1. Bending of prismatic and cylindrical specimens

When a beam is strained by bending, tensile, compressive and shear stresses are developed. In cases where a portion of the specimen is placed in pure bending, only tensile stresses are developed on the convex side of the beam and compressive stresses on the concave side of the beam. The maximum tensile stress at the extreme most fibre at failure can be taken as the tensile strength (it is also termed the modulus of rupture) and is given by the relationship

$$\sigma_t = -\frac{M c}{I} \tag{3.3}$$

where σ_t = tensile strength
    M = bending moment
    c = distance from neutral axis and
    I = moment of intertia of the cross-section of the beam about the
       neutral axis.

The basic assumptions in the derivation of this equation are:

1. Original transverse plane of the beam at the location of the moment calculations remains strictly a plane and normal to all longitudinal fibres after bending.

2. The material is homogeneous following Hooke's law so that stress distribution is linear across the bent beam and directly proportional to the distance from the neutral axis.

3. Bending occurs in the plane of symmetry of the beam.

4. The stress-strain behaviour is the same both in tension and compression and the neutral axis is located at the middle of the beam.

For rocks, the assumption 4 is not applicable and hence the results would be in error. To overcome this objection, the following modified equation was suggested by DUCKWORTH (1951) for rectangular beams taking into account the difference in Young's modulus values in tension and compression:

$$\sigma_t = -\frac{3 M (\varepsilon_1 + \varepsilon_2)}{b t^2 \varepsilon_1} \tag{3.4}$$

where σ_t = tensile strength
    M = bending moment
    ε_1 = tensile bending strain of the outer fibre
    ε_2 = compressive bending strain of the outer fibre
    b = width of the gauge section and
    t = thickness of the gauge section.

ADLER (1970) derived expressions and plotted curves to employ flexural test results on prismatic as well as cylindrical specimens in determining the tensile modulus of elasticity by using the 'transformed section' concept of mechanics of materials. From these curves, a correct modulus of rupture can be computed.

Rocks, however, are not completely elastic up to the point of fracture. The effect of creep in rocks tends to decrease the tensile stresses, resulting in higher calculated tensile strength.

Besides these properties of the rocks, there are several other practical limitations in the test such as wedging action beneath the concentrated loads, stress concentration at surface cracks and flaws, torsional stresses during the application of load, frictional forces between loading points and specimen surface, etc. although the use of load distributing bearings, etc. eliminates some of the problems with torsional stresses. The test is also surface sensitive and large errors can arise as a result of modification of the surface of the material during the preparation of specimens. Relatively long specimens are used in the tests and are often difficult to prepare.

TABLE 13
Effect of specimen diameter on the modulus of rupture
(after OBERT, WINDES and DUVALL, 1946)

Rock type	Diameter cm	(in)	Modulus of rupture MPa	(lbf/in^2)	No. of specimens tested	% standard deviation
Marble	2.2	(0.875)	19.1	(2770)	4	4
Marble	2.9	(1.125)	19.1	(2770)	4	6
Marble	4.1	(1.625)	18.4	(2670)	4	4
Marble	5.4	(2.125)	20.4	(2960)	4	4
Limestone	2.2	(0.875)	10.5	(1520)	4	4
Limestone	2.9	(1.125)	10.8	(1560)	10	9
Limestone	4.1	(1.625)	10.1	(1470)	4	11
Limestone	5.4	(2.125)	11.0	(1590)	5	8
Granite	2.2	(0.875)	18.4	(2670)	4	4
Granite	2.9	(1.125)	19.7	(2860)	4	1
Granite	4.1	(1.625)	21.0	(3050)	4	5
Granite	5.4	(2.125)	20.8	(3010)	4	1
Sandstone 1	2.2	(0.875)	2.4	(352)	1	–
Sandstone 1	2.9	(1.125)	2.9	(422)	4	5
Sandstone 1	4.1	(1.625)	3.4	(493)	4	7
Sandstone 1	5.4	(2.125)	3.8	(545)	4	6
Sandstone 2	2.2	(0.875)	2.0	(293)	4	42
Sandstone 2	2.9	(1.125)	3.0	(437)	4	10
Sandstone 2	4.1	(1.625)	3.4	(495)	4	1
Sandstone 2	5.4	(2.125)	3.4	(491)	4	8
Greenstone	2.2	(0.875)	48.1	(6970)	3	9
Greenstone	2.9	(1.125)	43.3	(6280)	3	17

OBERT, WINDES and DUVALL (1946) prepared 15.2 cm (6 in) long cylindrical
specimens of different diameters, from various rocks and tested them under
3-point loading. (The 3-point loading gives constant moment in central
third of the specimen.) Their results given in Table 13 show that the strength
is independent of the diameter of the specimen and that any diameter in
the range tested can be used for the test.

SHIH (1963) determined modulus of rupture on 2.2 cm (0.875 in) diameter
cores of different lengths. His results given in Fig. 3-8 show that strength
decreases with span.

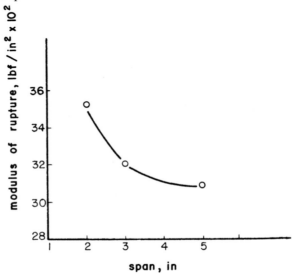

Fig. 3-8. Relationship between modulus of rupture and span in bending test
(after SHIH, 1963).

POMEROY and MORGANS (1956) prepared rectangular coal specimens of
sizes varying from 10.20 cm × 0.64 cm × 0.64 cm (4.00 in × 0.25 in × 0.25 in)
to 10.20 cm × 2.50 cm × 0.25 cm (4.0 in × 1.0 in × 0.1 in) and tested them
in a bending machine. The bending of beams is achieved by 4 equal line
loads symmetrically placed with respect to the centre.

Values obtained by this method are 2–3 times higher than those obtained by
direct test (EVANS, 1961), possibly due to the small area of the specimen
under tension. With the increase in the size of specimen or longer spans
under uniform moment, larger surface area and volume are brought under
tensile stresses and hence a decrease in strength takes place. SINHA and
SINGH (1968) reported that strength decreases with increase in the thickness

of the beam. For sandstone the strength of 2.5 cm (1 in) thick beam is about 75% of that of 5 mm (0.2 in) thick beam. Similarly, rectangular specimens show smaller strength compared to circular specimens if the area of cross-section is the same.

To overcome the distortion in the results because of concentration of stresses at the points of support and application of load, PROTODYAKONOV (1961) suggested some modifications in the test procedure. The specimen is placed in a vertical position (Fig. 3-9) and bent under the influence of two couples. The tensile strength is given by the equation

$$\sigma_t = -\frac{6\,Fl}{b\,t^2} \qquad\qquad (3.5)$$

where σ_t = tensile strength
      F = applied force
      l = length of the lever arm
      b = breadth and
      t = thickness.

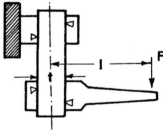

Fig. 3-9. Bending of prisms in vertical position by the application of couples (after PROTODYAKONOV, 1961).

BROWN and HUDSON (1971) and HUDSON, HARDY and FAIRHURST (1973) conducted bending tests with beams of Cold Spring Red granite (27.94 cm long, 7.62 cm or 5.08 cm deep and 2.54 cm wide) (11 in long, 3 in or 2 in deep and 1 in wide) with loaded span of 25.4 cm (10 in) for post-failure behaviour. The arrangement for feed back signal is given in Fig. 3-10 and the actual curves obtained are given in Fig. 3-11. This illustrates the reduction in the beam unloading modulus that occurs during the course of failure of the beam.

The load-lateral displacement curves obtained in the beam test for the Cold Spring Red granite (BROWN and HUDSON, 1971) for different specimens are given in Fig. 3-12. The curves for the two beams with the highest

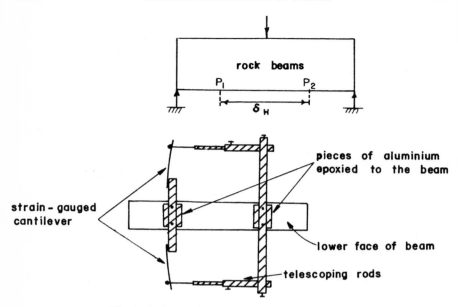

Fig. 3-10. Generation of feedback signal for beam test
(after HUDSON, HARDY and FAIRHURST, 1973).

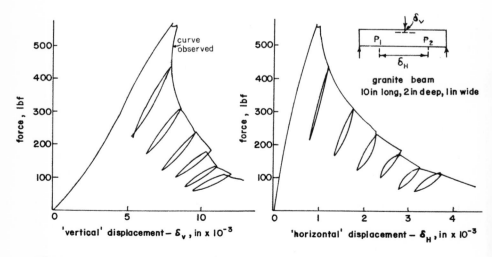

Fig. 3-11. Complete force-displacement curves illustrating the progressive reduction in
beam unloading modulus (after HUDSON, HARDY and FAIRHURST, 1973).

strength are linear to about 75% of the maximum load, but the curves for the two low strength beams are non-linear which is due to the presence of some severe cracks. All these curves converge to an end point indicating thereby that though initial state of the rock in the beams was different, the failure process seems to be the same.

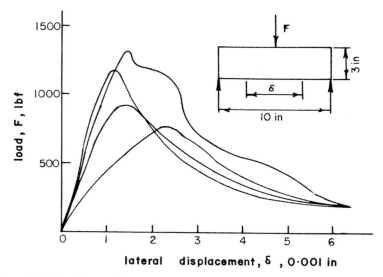

Fig. 3-12. Load-lateral displacement curves for Cold Spring Red granite beams (after BROWN and HUDSON, 1971).

In this tension test, the small volume of the specimen that is brought into play controls the post-failure behaviour dominated by the weakest part of the structure and so the results are not repetitive.

2. Bending of discs

When a plate with simply supported or clamped ends is loaded at the centre, tensile stresses are developed at the bottom surface. The simplest case is that of a circular plate simply supported at its edges and loaded at the centre (Fig. 3-13). The maximum tensile stress developed in the plate is (SEELY and SMITH, 1952)

$$\sigma_t = -\frac{3(1+v)F}{2\pi t^2}\left[\frac{1}{1+v}+\log_e\frac{r_d}{r_p}-\frac{1-v}{1+v}\cdot\frac{r_p^2}{4r_d^2}\right] \qquad (3.6)$$

where σ_t = maximum tensile stress
  v = Poisson's ratio of the material
  F = applied force
  t = thickness of the disc
  r_d = radius of the disc and
  r_p = radius of the area under uniform force.

This relationship is valid under the following conditions:

1. The deflection of the plate is relatively small ($\leq \frac{1}{2} t$). Otherwise, direct tensile stresses in addition to the bending stresses will contribute substantially to the failure of the plate.

2. The material is ideally elastic.

3. The plate remains flat, i.e., every straight line drawn through the plate normal to its middle surface before the plate is bent by the load remains straight and normal to the deflected middle surface after the plate is loaded.

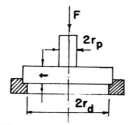

Fig. 3-13. Bending of a disc
(after Protodyakonov, 1961).

For rocks, the first condition usually holds good and the third condition can be fulfilled by carefully preparing the specimens. The second condition, however, is rarely true. As a result, yield may occur which causes readjustment of stresses.

Instead of supporting along the perimeter, the disc may be placed in a cylindrical guide with parallel end supports (Fig. 3-14) and a transverse load applied at the centre till the disc fails. The strength can be computed by assuming that rock fails after deformation proportional to the distance from the centre line (Mazanti and Sowers, 1965).

In the normal bending of discs failure usually occurs inside the ring ($2 r_p$) with the development of radial cracks. Jaeger (1967) reported that failures occur with the development of 3 cracks with the mean angle of 120° between the crack directions. In many cases discs fail into more than 3 pieces and there is more than one point of intersection of these cracks in the loading region. This method is very useful in determining the anisotropic strength properties of rocks.

In spite of the fact that the bending test usually gives higher values than the direct tensile test, the method is still used to determine the strength of rocks and is termed the modulus of rupture or flectural strength of rocks.

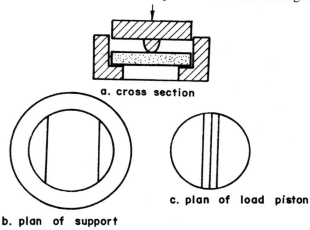

a. cross section

b. plan of support

c. plan of load piston

Fig. 3-14. Bending of a disc
(after MAZANTI and SOWERS, 1965).

3.3.2. Hydraulic Extension Tests

When a thick-walled ring or cylinder is subjected to an internal hydrostatic pressure, the stresses developed can be given by (SEELY and SMITH, 1952)

$$\sigma_\theta = -p_i \frac{r_i^2}{r_0^2 - r_i^2} \left[\frac{r_0^2}{r^2} + 1 \right] \tag{3.7}$$

$$\sigma_r = p_i \frac{r_i^2}{r_0^2 - r_i^2} \left[\frac{r_0^2}{r^2} - 1 \right] \tag{3.8}$$

where σ_θ = tangential tensile stress at a point
σ_r = radial compressive stress at a point
r_i = internal radius of the ring or cylinder
r_0 = external radius of the ring or cylinder
r = distance of the point from the centre and
p_i = internal hydrostatic pressure.

Failure of the ring or cylinder occurs due to tangential tensile stress. Its value is maximum at the inner surface and is given by ($r = r_i$)

$$\sigma_{\theta_i} = -p_i \frac{r_0^2 + r_i^2}{r_0^2 - r_i^2} \tag{3.9}$$

σ_{θ_i} at failure can be taken as the tensile strength of the material.

PROTODYAKONOV (1961) tested rings ($r_i/r_0 = 4.5/7.0$ and $t/r_i = 2$) by subjecting them to internal hydrostatic pressure of putty (consisting of resin 75% and paraffin 25%), placed in the central hole and compressed by coaxial punches (Fig. 3-15). The tensile strength is calculated from the relationship

$$\sigma_t = -\frac{F}{\pi r_i^2} \left[\frac{r_0^2 + r_i^2}{r_0^2 - r_i^2} \right] \tag{3.10}$$

where σ_t = tensile strength
       F = applied force at failure
       r_i = internal radius and
       r_0 = external radius.

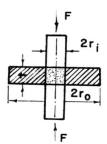

Fig. 3-15. Extension of a ring
(after PROTODYAKONOV, 1961).

Recently, HARDY and JAYARAMAN (1970) included this method in their investigations into methods for the determination of the tensile strength of rocks. They called this hoop-stress loading. The thickness of the specimens ranged from 6.35 to 10.16 cm (2.5 to 4.0 in). The internal and external diameters of the cylinders were 2.54 cm (1 in) and 5.10 cm (2 in) respectively.

The experiments were carried out with the aid of a loading jig designed to allow a thin-walled rubber tube to be hydraulically pressurised inside the hollow test specimen utilised in this test. A pressure transducer was incorporated in the associated hydraulic system to monitor the applied pressure.

3.3.3. Diametral Compression of Discs

1. Brazilian test

The Brazilian test, as the name suggests, originated from South America. The test makes use of a circular solid disc which is compressed to failure across a diameter. HONDROS (1959), assuming that the material is homogeneous, isotropic and linearly elastic, analysed the stress distribution in a thin disc loaded by uniform pressure radially applied over a short strip of the circumference at each end of the diameter (Fig. 3-16). Since the Brazilian test is only valid when primary fracture starts from the centre spreading along the loading diameter, the stress distribution along that diameter is of greatest interest. The stress component normal to the loading diameter, YY' (σ_θ) and the stress component along the loading diameter YY' (σ_r) are given by the expressions

$$\sigma_\theta = -\frac{F}{\pi r_0 t \alpha} \left\{ \frac{\left[1 - \left(\frac{r}{r_0}\right)^2\right] \sin 2\alpha}{1 - 2\left(\frac{r}{r_0}\right)^2 \cos 2\alpha + \left(\frac{r}{r_0}\right)^4} - \tan^{-1}\left[\frac{1 + \left(\frac{r}{r_0}\right)^2}{1 - \left(\frac{r}{r_0}\right)^2} \tan \alpha\right] \right\}$$

(3.11)

$$\sigma_r = +\frac{F}{\pi r_0 t \alpha} \left\{ \frac{\left[1 - \left(\frac{r}{r_0}\right)^2\right] \sin 2\alpha}{1 - 2\left(\frac{r}{r_0}\right)^2 \cos 2\alpha + \left(\frac{r}{r_0}\right)^4} + \tan^{-1}\left[\frac{1 + \left(\frac{r}{r_0}\right)^2}{1 - \left(\frac{r}{r_0}\right)^2} \tan \alpha\right] \right\}$$

(3.12)

where σ_θ = stress component normal to the loading diameter
σ_r = stress component along the loading diameter
F = applied force
r_0 = radius of the disc

t = thickness of the disc

2α = angular distance over which F is assumed to be distributed radially and

r = distance from the centre of the disc.

(Compressive stress is taken as positive.)

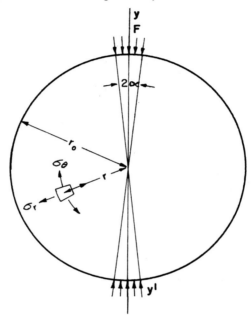

Fig. 3-16. The Brazilian test, showing notation used.

Values of σ_θ, σ_r and τ along the loaded diameter are given in Fig. 3-17a. When $\alpha = 0$, there is a change in stress values near the end points of the axis YY' as shown in Fig. 3-17b. σ_θ at the centre is

$$\sigma_\theta = -\frac{F}{\pi\, r_0\, t}\left[\frac{\sin 2\alpha}{\alpha} - 1\right] \tag{3.13}$$

$$\approx -\frac{F}{\pi\, r_0\, t}$$

This expression is used to calculate the tensile strength of the material. The stress value at the centre is independent of the loading configuration (line load or strip load). It is also assumed that the failure is independent of the compressive stresses present along $Y-Y'$ and the stresses developed along the Z-axis (normal to the disc face) and that the failure is essentially a tensile one.

If the disc is not thin other stresses are liable to occur, but if the specimen fractures diametrically this cannot be considered as tensile rupture.

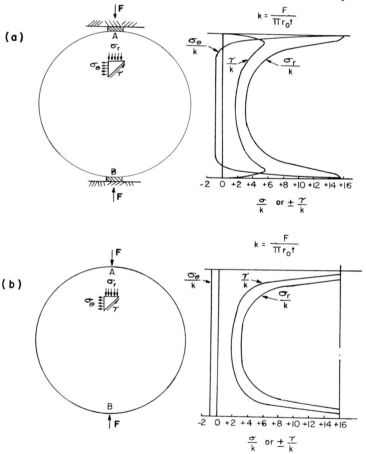

Fig. 3-17. Loading configuration and stress distribution across the loaded diameter for Brazilian test:
(a) Stress distribution across loaded diameter for a cylinder compressed between two flat plates;
(b) Stress distribution across loaded diameter for a cylinder compressed between two line loads
(after SHOOK, 1963).

In practice, however, the conditions are somewhat different. When it is a line contact, high shear stresses are developed which cause local crushing, thereby changing the loading conditions from line to strip. In the region of contact, appreciable tangential stresses are developed which modify the local stress distribution. Their effect is to create a horizontal compressive restraint which results in the formation of small incipient shear wedges.

For the Brazilian test to be valid, failure of the disc should take place with the development of a vertical crack, from the centre of the specimen, which proceeds upward and downward along the load axis YY'. ADDINALL and HACKETT (1965b) found experimentally that the origin of failure in a given disc, under given loading conditions is a function of the contact area. Generally it can be said that the origin of failure under practical loading conditions in the Brazilian test is not the centre of the disc. MELLOR and HAWKES (1971) proved quite conclusively that, in a properly conducted test, cracking does not start at the platen contacts since in many tests the diametral crack terminated about one-tenth of the diameter from the boundary. HUDSON, BROWN and RUMMEL (1972) studied the controlled failure of granite and marble discs in a servo-controlled machine using lateral displacement as a control signal in order to determine the location of failure initiation and the subsequent mode of specimen collapse. In all the tests, including the ones with distributed loads, failure initiated under the loading points. This was evidenced by cracks radiating out from a crushed zone below the loading points and the absence of any cracks in the centre of the disc. From these observations, they regarded the Brazilian test as an invalid one for the measurement of tensile strength. These observations are contrary to those of MELLOR and HAWKES.

The effect of the contact area and the nature of the platens on Brazilian test results was studied by ADDINALL and HACKETT (1964b and 1965a). To change the contact areas, they used different cushioning materials. The tensile strength values obtained for high-strength autoclaved plaster are given in Table 14. They observed two types of cracks in the failed specimens. Diametrical cracks were present in each case but in addition there were secondary cracks, less symmetrical and less complete when the modulus of the cushions was low. This was due to the platen bounce caused by sudden reduction in resistance to the applied load at failure. It was also reported that increase in the area of contact affected the point of origin of the fracture. The size of the wedges was found to be dependent upon the cushion material. Actual dimensions varied from 2.54 cm × 0.64 cm (1.00 in × 0.25 in) for steel platens alone, 2.54 cm × 1.00 cm (1.0 in × 0.4 in) for blotting paper and it increased to 2.54 cm × 2.54 cm (1 in × 1 in) for hard board cushions (ADDINALL and HACKETT, 1964b). When hard rubber cushions were used, the mode of fracture (Fig. 3-18) was entirely different. Discs failed with the development of cracks in their plane caused by the stress σ_z at right angle to disc diameter, the value of which is greater than the tensile stress σ_θ.

TAble 14

Effect of platen conditions on the tensile strength of autoclaved plaster

(after ADDINALL and HACKETT, 1964b)

Platen conditions	Mean tensile strength	
	MPa	(lbf/in^2)
No cushions	3.07	(445)
Araldite	3.12	(452)
Cardboard	3.88	(563)
Blotting paper	3.93	(570)
Hard board	4.60	(667)

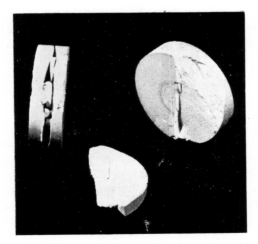

Fig. 3-18. Peculiar mode of fracture in plaster disc when using rubber platen material (after ADDINALL and HACKETT, 1964b).

FAIRHURST (1964) analysed the Brazilian test on the basis of GRIFFITH's criterion and showed that failure is in conformity with GRIFFITH's criterion. His conclusions are as follows:

1. Uniaxial tensile strength of material, when calculated by equation $\sigma_t = -\dfrac{F}{\pi\, r_0\, t}$, gives lower values for this test when loading is applied over small strip angles. For $\alpha = \tan^{-1} \frac{1}{12}$, material will fail when central tensile stress $\sigma_\theta = -0.7 \left(\dfrac{F}{\pi\, r_0\, t} \right)$.

Assuming that the uniaxial compressive strength is accurately known (8 times the tensile strength), then the indicated ratio of compression to tension would be 11.5 which means that the ratio of compressive to tensile strength not be fixed at 8 : 1 as the theory dictates.

2. The tensile strength, so determined, is dependent upon strip angle (in conformity with the findings of ADDINALL and HACKETT, 1964b). This dependence of tensile strength on strip angle decreases as the compression-tension ratio increases.

3. A greater region is critically stressed with larger strip angle ($\alpha = \tan^{-1} \frac{1}{6}$), and tensile strength value becomes more representative of the specimen as a whole rather than of a point in it.

COLBACK (1966) analysed the validity of the Brazilian test using the modified Griffith's criterion and concluded that failure must originate at the centre of the disc if the test is to be a valid tensile test. This condition can only be achieved by a distributed load with cardboard or wood. Soft plastics which are liable to extrude under load and thereby induce tangential tensile stresses should not be used. The load distribution can extend over as much as 1/10 of the diameter without affecting the stress distribution in the centre position of the disc. Under certain conditions fracture can initiate at the loading points and thereby invalidate the test.

Specimen geometry: BERENBAUM and BRODIE (1959b) as well as Yu (1963) found that if the ratio between the thickness of the disc and the diameter increases, the tensile strength decreases. DUBE and SINGH (1969) also reported similar results (Fig. 3-19). Results of MELLOR and HAWKES (1971) are given in Fig. 3-20.

PROTODYAKONOV (1961) used cylinders with a high (but unspecified) length-to-diameter ratio. The cylinders are subjected to compression by placing them in the press platens (line loading). Failure takes place due to the penetration of the prisms of the deformed rock at the places of contact. Tensile strength is calculated by the empirical relationship

$$\sigma_t = F \left(1 + \frac{10^{-4}\, F}{dl} \right) / dl \qquad (3.14)$$

where σ_t = tensile strength
  F = applied force
  l = length of the cylinder and
  d = diameter of the cylinder.

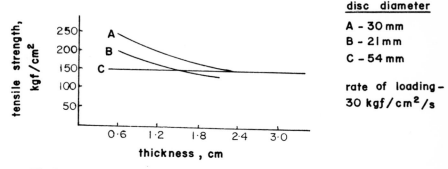

disc diameter

A – 30 mm
B – 21 mm
C – 54 mm

rate of loading –
30 kgf/cm²/s

Fig. 3-19. Effect of thickness on the tensile strength of sandstone (Brazilian test) (after DUBE and SINGH, 1969).

LUNDBORG (1967) investigated the dependence of tensile strength (by Brazilian test) on the volume of the material in the case of granite cylinders of the same length and diameter (2 cm, 3 cm, 4 cm and 6 cm) (0.79 in, 1.18 in, 1.57 in and 2.36 in). Fig. 3-21 shows his test results.

BERNAIX (1969) reported the results of HABIB and VOUILLE on the effect of diameter on the calculated tensile strength (Fig. 3-22).

MELLOR and HAWKES (1971) also investigated the influence of specimen diameter (over the practically feasible range of sizes, (2.54 to 7.62 cm) (1 to 3 in)) on Brazilian test results. The results (Fig. 3-23) show that the size effect for typical rocks is significant for diameters of 2.54 cm (1 in) and less, but they suggest that measured strength may tend to a steady value for diameters above about 7.62 cm (3 in).

Specimen geometry is usually chosen to suit the convenience of the individual experimenter, but to facilitate comparison of data it is desirable to standardize dimensions, and also to choose dimensions that will permit meaningful comparison of results with data from uniaxial tests.

Taking into account theoretical considerations, experimental findings, and practical limitations, MELLOR and HAWKES suggested that NX core size (5.4 cm) (2.125 in) diameter should be taken as the minimum acceptable size for Brazilian tests on typical rock materials. They also concluded that thickness equal to radius of the disc should be taken as the minimum acceptable thickness for Brazilian specimens.

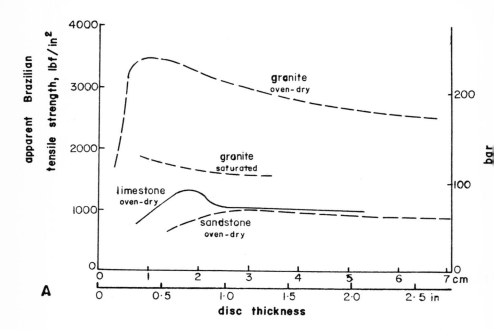

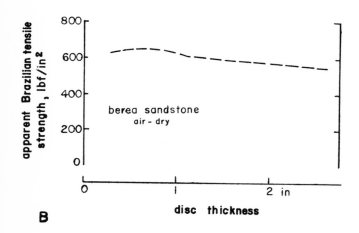

Fig. 3-20. Apparent Brazilian tensile strength as a function of disc thickness with
constant diameter:
A. Results of tests on random-thickness offcuts (high loading rate);
B. Results of tests on specially prepared specimens (low loading rate)
(after MELLOR and HAWKES, 1971).

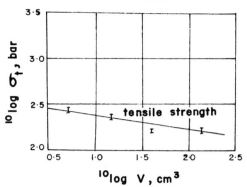

Fig. 3-21. Tensile strength of granite *vs* the volume of the test specimens
(after LUNDBORG, 1967).

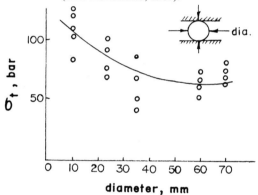

Fig. 3-22. Marquise limestone (scale effect). Tensile strength in a diametral compression
test as a function of the diameter of the specimen
(after BERNAIX, 1969).

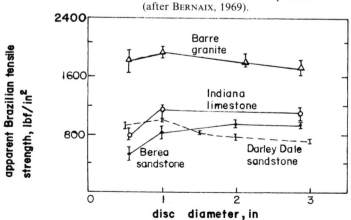

Fig. 3-23. Apparent Brazilian tensile strength as a function of disc diameter, with thickness equal to radius (after MELLOR and HAWKES, 1971).

Rate of loading: MELLOR and HAWKES (1971) made a small number of Brazilian tests on 5.4 cm (2.125 in) diameter discs of two rock types over a range of machine speeds from 0.01 to 7.1 cm/min (0.004 to 2.8 in/min) (approximate loading rates 0.001 to 1.8 MN/min (300 to 400 000 lbf/min)). In general (Fig. 3-24), the strength increased as the loading rate increased. For Berea sandstone, there is a drop in strength at the highest loading rate.

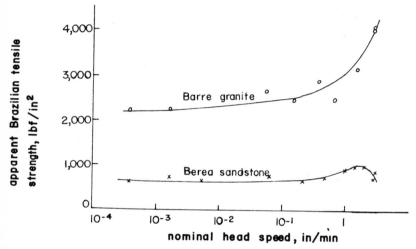

Fig. 3-24. Apparent Brazilian tensile strength as a function of loading rate for two rock types
(after MELLOR and HAWKES, 1971).

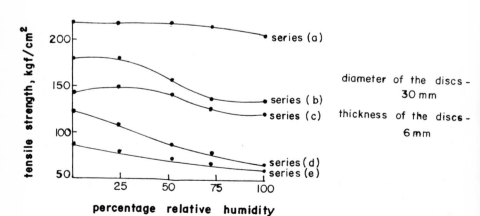

Fig. 3-25. Relation between strength and relative humidity
(after DUBE and SINGH, 1972).

Environment: DUBE and SINGH (1972) studied the effect of humidity on tensile strength of five different types of sandstones. Their results (Fig. 3-25) show a decrease in the strength ranging from 11 to 48% under fully saturated atmosphere.

VUTUKURI (1972) determined the effect of $AlCl_3$ solutions on the tensile strength of quartzite. He observed reduction in strength (compared to water) up to about 11% (Table 15).

TABLE 15

Effect of AlCl₃ solutions on tensile strength of quartzite

(after VUTUKURI, 1972)

Concentration of AlCl₃, %	Number of determinations	Mean tensile strength MPa (lbf/in²)	% standard deviation	% change in strength compared to water
0 (i.e., water)	20	13.8 (2006)	32	–
0.02	30	13.8 (2008)	30	–.1
0.04	30	14.0 (2027)	37	–1.1
0.06	20	12.3 (1783)	30	11.1
0.10	20	12.3 (1788)	34	10.9

Mineralogy and porosity: These are the intrinsic properties controlling rock strength.

MERRIAM, RIEKE III and KIM (1970) found the tensile strengths of a variety of granite rocks to be inversely proportional to quartz content. They attributed this relationship to textural differences as suggested by high-quartz rocks composed of equidimensional grains showing little crystal intergrowth, or interlocking, whereas low-quartz rocks consist of interlocking laths and prisms.

DUBE and SINGH (1972) observed increases in strength with increases in the percentage of matrix (matrix is essentially the cementing material) in sandstones.

DUBE and SINGH (1972) observed decreases in strength with increases in porosity in sandstones.

2. Ring test

The Brazilian test suffers from the disadvantage that not only tensile stresses are developed in the disc but also high shear stresses are set up close to the loading platens. Failure may take place not only with the development of tensile crack at the centre but also with the formation of small cones at the contact surfaces.

To limit the shearing stresses developed in the diametrically compressed disc in Brazilian test, the method of ring test has been developed where a disc with a central hole is subjected to diametral compression.

An approximate solution for the stress distribution around a circular hole in a disc loaded diametrically can be obtained by combining KIRSCH's solution for stress distribution around a circular hole in a stressed plate with the known solution for a solid disc with line loading. A more exact solution, obtained by HOBBS (1964), for the stress σ_θ at the intersection of the loading diameter with the hole is

$$\sigma_\theta = -\frac{F(6+38\,\varrho^2)}{\pi\,r_0\,t} \tag{3.15}$$

where σ_θ = stress component normal to the loading diameter at the inter-
    section of the loading diameter with the hole
F = applied force
ϱ = ratio between the internal radius (hole) r_i and external radius
    (disc) r_0, $\dfrac{r_i}{r_0}$
t = thickness and
r_0 = outside radius.

It will thus be seen that maximum σ_θ in a disc with the central hole is at least 6 times as great as the maximum σ_θ in the solid disc when subjected to the same diametral load. Thus, the ratio of maximum shear stress (at the point of contact) and maximum tensile stress in a disc with a small central hole is almost 1/6th of the similar ratio in the solid disc.

A new solution, using complex variable methods, was obtained by JAEGER and HOSKINS (1966) for the case in which the external load is distributed over a finite area of 15°. In Fig 3-26, their results on the distribution of tangential stress along the loading diameter for range of values of ϱ are given. The critical tensile stress at the intersection of the loading diameter with the hole, can be written as

$$\sigma_\theta = K\frac{F}{\pi\,r_0\,t} \tag{3.16}$$

where F = applied force
  K = a stress concentration factor (a function of ϱ)
  r_0 = outside radius of the ring and
  t = thickness of the ring.

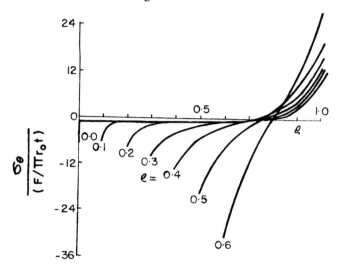

Fig. 3-26. Distribution of σ_θ along the loading diameter for rings. Compression positive
(after JAEGER and HOSKINS, 1966).

HIRAMATSU and OKA (1970) also analysed the stresses in a ring test piece
using the Fourier series under the assumption of a perfect elastic body and
of centripetal loading with a narrow loading angle. The values of K obtained
by them are given in Fig. 3-27. These results are in close agreement with
those of JAEGER and HOSKINS.

These analyses for the ring test yield a limiting value $K \rightarrow 6$ as $\varrho \rightarrow 0$. The direct
analysis for the solid disc (Brazilian test) leads to $K = 1$. The reason for the
discrepancy is fairly obvious. In the Brazilian test stress concentrations
produced by naturally occurring pores or cracks are ignored in determining
the stress field at failure. There is, then, a question as to whether results
of Brazilian tests should be interpreted with $K = 1$ or $K = 6$. $K = 1$ is, however,
used for the Brazilian test.

In a properly conducted ring test, primary fracture invariably occurs along
the loading diameter, and the crack initiates at or near the surface of the
hole. ADDINALL and HACKETT (1964a), however, stated that for discs

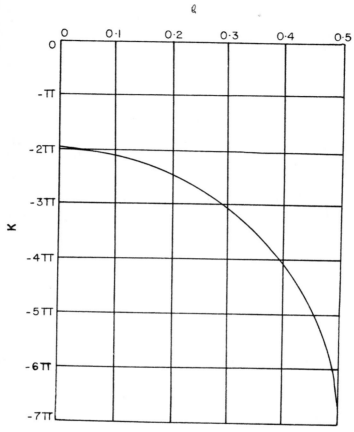

Fig. 3-27. The value of K for ring specimens vs ϱ
(after Hiramatsu and Oka, 1970).

with small diameter holes $(\varrho = 0.0156;\ 10.20\ \text{cm}\ (4\ \text{in})$ disc with 0.16 cm
(1/16 in) diameter hole), cracks bypassed the hole and left the hole in a
solid piece. They also reported that the fracture pattern for discs with a
small value of ϱ was similar to those found in solid discs, there being a
diametral crack and also well defined secondary cracks. As this ratio (ϱ)
increased, secondary cracks became less defined and with large ratios
$(\varrho = 0.5)$, they were often not present in the same positions. With larger
ratios, there was a tendency for secondary cracks to appear on a diameter
normal to the loaded diameter. Hobbs (1965) also reported similar observations. In rock discs with small diameter central holes, failure initiated along
the loaded diameter and subsidiary cracks differing in number from 0–4

formed in the two halves of the broken disc (Fig. 3-28). These subsidiary cracks started at, or close to the loaded edge and propagated to the surface of the central hole. The number of subsidiary cracks was dependent upon the tensile strength of the material; the higher the tensile strength, the larger was the number.

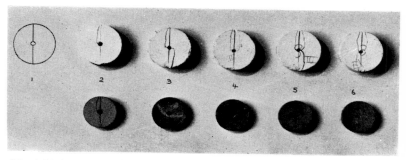

Fig. 3-28. Mode of fracture of plaster and rock discs with a small central hole (after HOBBS, 1965).

HUDSON, BROWN and RUMMEL (1972) studied controlled failure in ring tests in a servo-controlled machine using lateral displacement as a control signal for Charcoal Grey granite, Solenhofen limestone and Tennessee marble. For tests with $\varrho = 0.03$, failure did not initiate at the hole, but always initiated at the loading ends for point loading, but for distributed loading the failure initiated at the centre.

Specimen geometry: The results of ADDINALL and HACKETT (1964a) indicate that tensile strength decreases with the increase in the hole diameter and becomes independent of the hole size when $r_i = 3.8$ cm (1.5 in) (for plaster discs in the range of 10.2 cm, 15.2 cm and 20.3 cm (4 in, 6 in and 8 in)). HOBBS (1965) also reported decrease in tensile strength with increase in the diameter of the hole. Tensile strength calculated also decreases slightly with the increase in the thickness of the ring and increases with an increase in the diameter of the ring.

PRICE and KNILL (1966) also carried out tests to observe the variations in tensile strength relative to the geometry of the disc (Fig. 3-29). These tests showed a progressive increase in computed strength with the decreasing diameter of the central hole for the 11.6 cm (4.6 in) diameter discs.

HUDSON (1969) also conducted a series of tests on a gypsum plaster, with and without limestone chips to determine the effect of geometry on tensile strength values calculated (Fig. 3-30). To keep the effects of rate of loading to a minimum, tests were made at a deformation rate of 0.005 cm/min (0.002 in/

min) for the large hole sizes, and 0.013 cm/min (0.005 in/min) for the small hole sizes. For values of ϱ above 0.2, there is little variation. The tensile strength rises sharply below $\varrho=0.2$, until it reaches a constant value approximately double the large hole value. The point at which the tensile strength becomes constant represents the critical hole size below which the hole has no influence. According to HUDSON the tensile strength increase is caused by the gradual breakdown of elasticity theory.

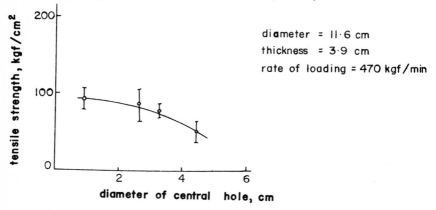

Fig. 3-29. Variation of tensile strength with geometry of limestone disc (after PRICE and KNILL, 1966).

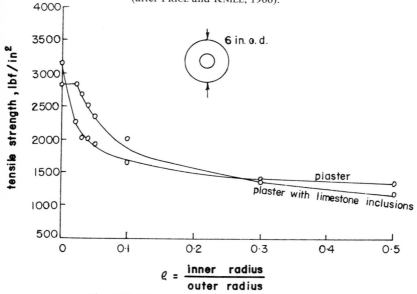

Fig. 3-30. Ring test results (after HUDSON, 1969).

Hobbs (1965) investigated the effect of eccentricity of the hole on strength. He found that eccentrically placed holes can either increase or decrease the fracture load. The fracture load increases with eccentricity when the hole centres lie on a diameter perpendicular to the line of the load and decreases with eccentricity when hole centres lie on the line of load. However, Hudson (1969) reported that the failure load does not decrease as a small hole is moved in position up the vertical diameter.

Rate of loading: Price and Knill (1966) studied the variation in tensile strength with rate of loading from ring tests on dolerite and metamorphosed limestone cores. The sizes of cores were 5.45 cm and 6.00 cm (2.1 in and 2.4 in) diameter. In the case of dolerite, the thickness of the discs were 2.54 cm (1 in) (5.45 cm and 6.00 cm (2.1 in and 2.4 in) diameter) and 3.9 cm (1.5 in) (6.0 cm (2.4 in) diameter). The diameter of the central hole was 0.9 cm (0.35 in) in all cases. The relationships are given in Figs. 3-31, 3-32 and 3-33. The tests on both materials showed that there was an increase in computed strength (highest 17% greater than lowest value in Fig. 3-31 and 44% in Fig. 3-33) with an increasing rate of loading. On the basis of the results they suggested that, relative to the nature of the rock and the geometry of the disc, there is an upper limit of rate of loading, above which tensile strength values computed from this test become unreliable.

Environment: Vutukuri (1965) used the ring test to evaluate the effect of fluids on the tensile strength of limestone. The discs were of 2.96 cm (1.167 in) diameter, 0.64 cm (0.25 in) thick with a central hole of 0.32 cm (0.125 in) diameter. The rings were saturated with different liquids and loaded diametrically. His results are given in Table 16. These clearly show that the tensile strength of limestone decreases with an increase in the dielectric constant of the saturating fluid.

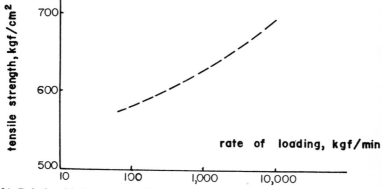

Fig. 3-31. Relationship between tensile strength and rate of loading for dolerite discs (after Price and Knill, 1966).

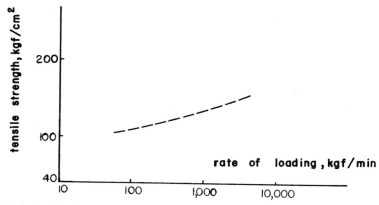

Fig. 3-32. Relationship between tensile strength and rate of loading for limestone discs, 2.54 cm thick (after PRICE and KNILL, 1966).

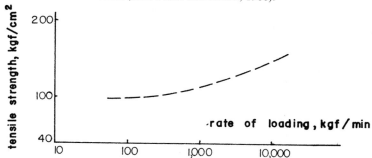

Fig. 3-33. Relationship between tensile strength and rate of loading for limestone discs, 3.9 cm thick (after PRICE and KNILL, 1966).

TABLE 16

Tensile strength of limestone values in different liquids from ring tests

(after VUTUKURI, 1965)

Liquid	Dielectric constant	Mean tensile strength MPa	(lbf/in²)
Water	80	28.2	(4090)
Glycerine	43	32.2	(4673)
Ethylene glycol	41	31.7	(4596)
Nitrobenzene	36	38.2	(5538)
Ethyl alcohol	27	37.1	(5374)
Benzaldehyde	18	33.3	(4831)
n-Butyl alcohol	8	37.9	(5498)

3.3.4. Miscellaneous Methods

1. Diametral compression of cylinders

JAEGER (1967) loaded 5.1 cm (2 in) diameter and 2.5 cm (1 in) long cylinders by four equal line loads (similar to the compression between V blocks or in the compression of a number of cylinders packed together in contact) (Fig. 3-34). He found that, for $\omega = 45°$, tensile strength is very nearly equal to the Brazilian tensile strength. For greater values of angle (ω), there exist still substantial tensile stresses at failure but are less than the Brazilian tensile strength (Table 17).

TABLE 17

Normal force F, N (lbf) and maximum tensile stress σ_{t_m}, MPa (lbf/in²)
at failure in 4 equal line loading of cylinders

(after JAEGER, 1967)

	Angle $\omega = 0$		45		60		90	
Carrara marble								
F	7117	(1600)	18149	(4080)	18371	(4130)	22953	(5160)
σ_{t_m}	6.9	(1000)	7.1	(1030)	3.2	(460)	1.4	(200)
Gosford sandstone								
F	3781	(850)	10453	(2350)	12900	(2900)	16192	(3640)
σ_{t_m}	3.7	(540)	4.1	(590)	2.3	(330)	1.0	(140)

Failure occurs invariably along almost straight lines joining the loading points. Failure cracks follow very closely the lines of maximum tensile stress (Fig. 3-34) even if not initiated on these lines. If $\omega = 90°$, circular cylinders are reduced to a square.

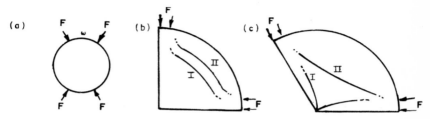

Fig. 3-34. (a) Cylinder compressed in two diametral planes inclined at ω;
(b) $\omega = 90°$. Curve I, limit of tensile field; Curve II, locus of maximum tensile stress;
(c) $\omega = 60°$. Curve I, limit of tensile field; Curve II, locus of maximum tensile stress
(after JAEGER, 1967).

He also loaded the cylinders along 3 lines (Fig. 3-35). The forces, at failure, for various values of ϕ are given in Table 18. The fracture load increases with increase in the value of angle ϕ. When the angle ϕ is zero, failure occurs as in the Brazilian test with the formation of crack along the compressed diameter. He observed that in Carrara marble crack always starts below the greatest load, extends along its diameter, and then swings towards one of the other two loads.

REICHMUTH (1962) compressed cylinders between two point contacts (Fig. 3-36). He suggested that for specimens of 1.27 cm (0.5 in) to 3.05 cm (1.2 in) diameter, satisfactory tensile strength values can be obtained by using the relationship

$$\sigma_t \simeq -\frac{0.96\ F}{d^2} \qquad (3.17)$$

where σ_t = tensile strength
F = applied force and
d = distance between the loading points.

TABLE 18

Normal force F, N (lbf) at failure in 3 line loading of cylinders

(after JAEGER, 1967)

Angle ϕ	0	22-1/2	30	45	60
Carrara	14234	15124	15569	23576	25800
marble	(3200)	(3400)	(3500)	(5300)	(5800)
Gosford	7562	10676	11121	14902	15346
sandstone	(1700)	(2400)	(2500)	(3350)	(3450)

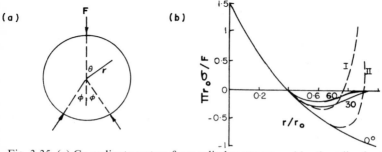

Fig. 3-35. (a) Co-ordinate system for a cylinder compressed by three line loads;

(b) Variation of stress with radius: Solid lines are for concentrated loads at the values $0°, 30°, 60°$ of θ. Broken lines are for $\theta = 0$ and loads distributed over angles of $15°$ (Curve I) or $5°$ (Curve II) (after JAEGER, 1967).

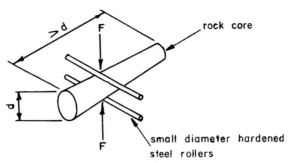

Fig. 3-36. Point loading method for cylinders
(after REICHMUTH, 1962).

2. Diametral compression of spheres

By analogy with the cylindrical case, the subjection of a sphere with concentrated loads at opposite ends shows an extension failure in a plane or
planes passing through the loaded diameter. Stress distribution in a sphere
compressed diametrally was determined by HIRAMATSU and OKA (1966).
The tensile strength is determined from the following equation:

$$\sigma_t = -\frac{0.225 \times F}{r^2} \tag{3.18}$$

where σ_t = tensile strength
      F = applied force at failure and
      r = radius of sphere.

Failure of spheres occurs by an extension fracture. JAEGER (1967) observed
shattering and division of the spheres into two parts. In trachyte, he observed division of the sphere into three lunes of angles approximately 120°.

3. Compression of square plates along a diameter

When a square plate is compressed on opposite ends between a pair of
symmetrically placed flattened indenters, tensile stresses develop in its
central region. BERENBAUM and BRODIE (1959a) determined the stress distributions along the two central axes from photoelastic analysis. SUNDARA
RAJA IYENGAR and CHANDRASHEKHARA (1962) obtained a theoretical solution assuming the pressure distribution under the indenters as uniform,
parabolic and one resulting from 'constant displacement' on a semi-infinite
boundary, for different ratios of indenter-width to side of square.

If the width of the plate is 2 a and the width of indenter is 2 c, under a force
of F, (Fig. 3-37) the maximum value of tensile stress at the centre for diffe-

rent ratios of indenter-width to side of square for uniform, parabolic loading and for 'constant displacement' condition is given in Fig. 3-38. The
results of BERENBAUM and BRODIE are also plotted on this figure.

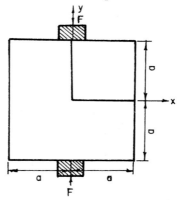

Fig. 3-37. Compression of square plate along a diameter
(after SUNDARA RAJA IYENGAR and CHANDRASHEKHARA, 1962).

In the case of $c/a=0.25$, the results of photoelastic analysis agree fairly
well with those of the theoretical solution in the case of uniform pressure
distribution under the indenters. For the other ratios, 0.125 and 0.5, the
experimental results do not agree well with the theoretical solutions when
the pressure distribution under the indenter is uniform or parabolic. On
the other hand, there is a fair agreement for $c/a=0.25$, 0.375 and 0.5 between the experimental results and those of the theoretical solution in the
case of 'constant displacement' condition. In the case of $c/a=0.125$, the
value of maximum σ_x stress from the photoelastic analysis is 0.74 $F/2a$.
The maximum value from theoretical analysis is 0.629 $F/2a$. They suggested
there might have been some error while evaluating the individual principal
stresses from the photoelastic results.

From Fig. 3-38 it may be seen that the magnitude of maximum tensile stress
at the centre of the square is practically independent of the type of pressure
distribution under the indenter up to $c/a=0.25$. Hence it may be recommended that for the determination of tensile strength of brittle materials, the
width of the indenters may be restricted to 0.25 times the side of the square
specimen. Further with these dimensions of the indenters it is possible to
avoid shear failure.

They also extended the solution to orthotropic materials.

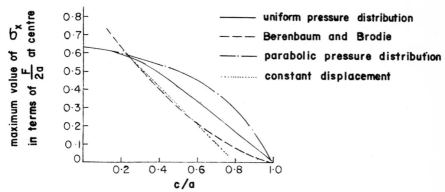

Fig. 3-38. Maximum value of σ_x in terms of $F/2a$ at centre for different c/a ratios for uniform and parabolic pressure distributions and for 'constant displacement' condition (after SUNDARA RAJA IYENGAR and CHANDRASHEKHARA, 1962).

BERENBAUM and BRODIE (1959b) studied the strength of two coals by using square plates measuring 2.54 cm × 2.54 cm × 1.27 cm (1 in × 1 in × ½ in). The indenters varied from $c/a = \frac{1}{8}$ to $c/a = \frac{3}{4}$. About fifteen specimens of each coal were used at each indenter size and Table 19 shows the tensile strengths deduced. It is seen that the strengths are independent of indenter size (within the experimental uncertainty).

TABLE 19

Tensile strengths determined by the indentation method

(after BERENBAUM and BRODIE, 1959b)

Coal	Tensile strength in MPa (lbf/in²) at indicated ratio of indenter size to specimen side					Brazilian test
	1/8	1/4	3/8	1/2	3/4	
Barnsley Hard	4.9 ± 0.18 (423 ± 26)	2.8 ± 0.15 (399 ± 22)	2.8 ± 0.11 (413 ± 17)	2.6 ± 0.14 (375 ± 20)	3.2 ± 0.11 (470 ± 16)	2.6 ± 0.21 (380 ± 30)
Oakdale	0.9 ± 0.06 (134 ± 8)	0.8 ± 0.10 (109 ± 14)	0.9 ± 0.17 (125 ± 25)	1.1 ± 0.14 (154 ± 21)	1.1 ± 0.12 (158 ± 18)	0.8 ± 0.12 (119 ± 17)

DAVIES and STAGG (1970) used two test arrangements using square shaped specimens (Fig. 3-39). The loading was done through steel or timber packings on the top face and supported on the bottom face either on similar packings (type A specimen) or directly on the lower platen of the testing machine (type B specimens). The stress distribution was determined from a linear elastic finite element analysis and Fig. 3-40 shows the horizontal stresses across the vertical plane. For type A the tensile stress at the centre is $\dfrac{0.98 \times 2F}{\pi dt}$. Two distributions are shown for type B: the full line when the bottom is free to slide and the dotted line when sliding is prevented. The tensile stresses at the centre are about $\dfrac{F}{\pi dt}$.

The maximum tensile stresses occur at a point about $0.2\ d$ below the loading point and the ratio of these stresses for type A/type B is 1.48.

Sandstone specimens of $d = 150$ mm (6 in) and $t = 100$ mm (4 in) were tested. Two types of packings were used (12.5 mm (0.5 in) wide) steel bars and timber strips.

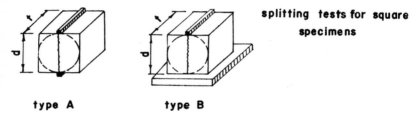

splitting tests for square specimens

type A   type B

Fig. 3-39. Test arrangement for type A and type B square section specimens
(after DAVIES and STAGG, 1970).

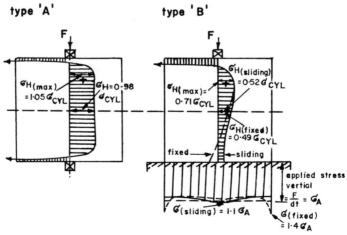

Fig. 3-40. Finite element analysis. Distribution of horizontal stresses across vertical centre line of specimens and vertical reactive stresses on platen plate for type B
(after DAVIES and STAGG, 1970).

Sudden brittle failure always occurred and was initiated under the upper loading point. Thus the tests cannot be regarded as a true indication of the intrinsic tensile strength of the rock specimens. On average, the type B specimens carried 1.46 times the load of the type A specimens. This compares favourably with the maximum tensile stress ratio of 1.48 obtained from the finite element analysis.

The type of packing only affected the post failure crack patterns.

HIRAMATSU and OKA (1970) also investigated the stresses in a rectangular plate by the method involving the FOURIER series. The values of k in the equation $\sigma_t = k \dfrac{F}{hw}$ are given in Fig. 3-41 (h = height of plate; w = thickness of plate).

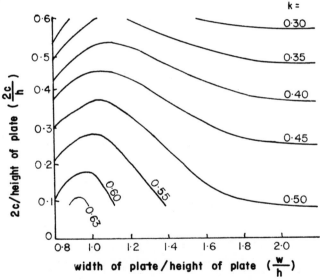

Fig. 3-41. The value of k for rectangular plate specimens vs w/h and $2c/h$ (after HIRAMATSU and OKA, 1970).

The strengths by the rectangular plate tests, $\sigma_{t_{re}}$, are shown in Fig. 3-42. When compared to the results of Brazilian tests, $\sigma_{t_{re}}$ is small when $\dfrac{2c}{h}$ is smaller than 0.15, and under the conditions of $\dfrac{2c}{h} = 0.15 \sim 0.4$ and $\dfrac{w}{h} = 1.5 \sim 2.0$, $\sigma_{t_{re}}$ is slightly larger and is not much affected by $\dfrac{2c}{h}$.

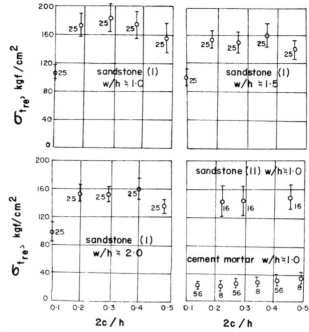

Fig. 3-42. The value of $\sigma_{t_{re}}$ obtained by rectangular plate tests; the numeral by each segment shows the number of tests
(after HIRAMATSU and OKA, 1970).

Fig. 3-43. Centrifugal tensile test rig
(after BERNAIX, 1969).

4. Centrifugal tension

Tensile strength can also be determined from centrifugal tension by means of an apparatus given in Fig. 3-43 (BERNAIX, 1969). The maximum rotational speed of this machine (12 000 rpm) is such that tensile stresses of 10 MPa (1 450 lbf/in²) can be achieved.

3.4. Testing of Specimens of Irregular Shape

Determining the strength using irregular shaped specimens reduces by many times the labour involved in the preparation of specimens, but the results are more inconsistent. The use of such specimens calls, therefore, for testing a greater number of specimens to obtain the same degree of reliability as obtained in the case of testing of specimens of a regular shape. But even then, the total labour consumed in testing is considerably reduced.

3.4.1. Direct Test

A specimen of irregular shape is embedded in cement between two metal dies, leaving a narrow transverse slit between the dies (Fig. 3-44). The dies are pulled in a universal testing machine until the specimen fails. Carbon and white paper are pressed against the specimen to obtain the rupture surface outline. The area of the rupture surface is then measured with a planimeter. The average tensile strength equals

$$\sigma_{t_a} = \frac{F_t}{A}$$
(3.19)

where F_t = the tensile force and
A = the rupture surface area.

This method has some disadvantages: Possibly, there exists a bending moment owing to non-centred (eccentric) loads on the specimen which consequently lower the strength. It is limited to rocks whose strength is less than that of cement. It also involves a time delay due to the period required for setting of the cement.

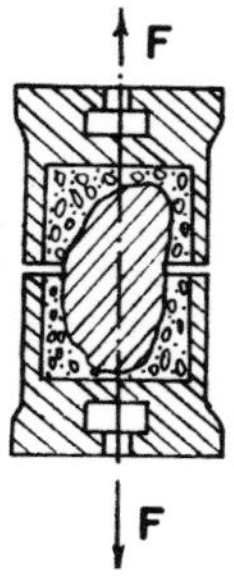

Fig. 3-44. Direct tensile test on irregularly shaped specimen
(after PROTODYAKONOV, 1961).

3.4.2. Hydraulic Extension of Irregular Ring

The specimen is prepared by drilling a central hole through an irregular piece of rock. A perforated tube within a rubber casing is inserted in the hole (Fig. 3-45). Oil is injected into the tube and uniform pressure (p) inside the specimen is produced. After the specimen has been broken, its inner radius, r_i, and outer radius, r_0, are measured. The tensile failure stress is computed assuming that a crack first appears on the inner radius of the specimen and gradually develops until it reaches the centre of the thickness of the specimen, at which time instantaneous failure takes place. The equation so derived, is obtained from LAME's theory for thick-walled cylinders, taking into account the appearance of the first crack, giving (PROTODYAKONOV, 1961)

$$\sigma_t \simeq -2.69 \, r_0 p_0 / r_i \qquad (3.20)$$

where σ_t =tensile strength
$\quad\quad p_0$ =oil pressure
$\quad\quad r_0$ =outer radius and
$\quad\quad r_i$ =inner radius.

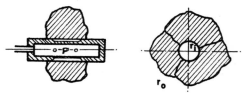

Fig. 3-45. Hydraulic extension of irregular ring
(after PROTODYAKONOV, 1961).

3.4.3. Compression of Irregular Specimen

Pieces of rock are chosen whose volumes do not differ by more than a factor of two. After blunting their sharp edges, they are placed between platens of a compressive testing machine and crushed (Fig. 3-46). The specimens normally rupture along a plane connecting the points of loading. The failure is assumed to be due to uniform tension applied across this surface.

PROTODYAKONOV (1961) gave the following formula for the calculation of tensile strength:

$$\sigma_t \simeq -F/v^{2/3} \qquad (3.21)$$

where σ_t = tensile strength
$\quad F$ = the compressive force at failure and
$\quad v$ = volume of the specimen.

HIRAMATSU and OKA (1966) analysed the stresses in the specimen, mathematically and photoelastically. They came to the conclusion that the tensile strength may be calculated by the equation

$$\sigma_t = -0.9 \, F/d^2 \tag{3.22}$$

where σ_t = tensile strength
$\quad F$ = force and
$\quad d$ = distance between the points of loading.

They also concluded that this tensile strength is nearly the same as that found from the Brazilian test.

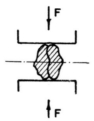

Fig. 3-46. Compression of irregular specimen
(after PROTODYAKONOV, 1961).

3.5. Comparison of Results Obtained by Different Methods

A number of methods have been described for the determination of the tensile strength of rocks. Various investigators have used more than one method in their tests. The results obtained by them are given here for comparison and for assessing the validity of each testing method (Table 20).

Careful measurement of uniaxial tensile strength and diametral compression tests on discs and rings were made for 3 rocks – Berea sandstone, Indiana limestone, Barre granite by MELLOR and HAWKES (1971). All tests were conducted in a 1.5 MN (336000 lbf) press, which had relatively "stiff" characteristics for the small loads required.

In Fig. 3-47 tensile strength calculated from the foregoing test results is plotted against ϱ for the three rocks, and the measured uniaxial strength is given for two of the rocks. Ring tensile strength is calculated from equa-

TABLE 20

Comparison of results obtained by different methods

Rock type	Method used for testing [MPa (lbf/in²)]								Reference
	Direct	Bending of prisms	Bending of cylinders	Bending of discs	Hydraulic extension test	Brazilian test	Ring test	Compression of square plates along a diameter	
Barre granite	9.4 (1358)				10.6 (1534)	11.5 (1663)	18.5 (2690)		HARDY & JAYARAMAN (1970)
Indiana limestone	3.5 (511)				5.8 (841)	5.2 (758)	9.8 (1428)		HARDY & JAYARAMAN (1970)
Leuders limestone	5.5 (792)				7.8 (1127)	5.9 (850)	8.7 (1264)		HARDY & JAYARAMAN (1970)
Berea sandstone	2.1 (310)				3.9 (571)	3.1 (446)	5.4 (780)		HARDY & JAYARAMAN (1970)
Crab Orchard sandstone	6.9 (1005)				11.9 (1723)	11.6 (1676)	14.6 (2118)		HARDY & JAYARAMAN (1970)
Izumi sandstone						11.6 (1676)	26.1 (3791) (ρ = 0.51) 29.5 (4274) (ρ = 0.274)		HIRAMATSU & OKA (1970)
Bowral trachyte	13.7 (1990)		25.2 (3650)	25.1 (3640)		12.0 (1740) (α = 7-1/2°)	24.1 (3500) (ρ = 0.5)	7.5 (1090)	JAEGER, 1967 & JAEGER & HOSKINS, 1966
Gosford sandstone	3.6 (520)		7.9 (1140)	7.9 (1140)		3.7 (540) (α = 7-1/2°)	8.3 (1200) (ρ = 0.5)	3.1 (450)	JAEGER, 1967 & JAEGER & HOSKINS, 1966
Carrara marble	6.9 (1000)		11.8 (1710)	17.9 (2600)		8.7 (1265) (α = 7-1/2°)	17.2 (2500) (ρ = 0.5)	4.6 (670)	JAEGER, 1967 & JAEGER & HOSKINS, 1966
Plaster		6.2 (896)				3.0 (442)	10.8 (1566)	3.6 (527)	HOBBS, 1965
Porphyry	12.4 (1800)			39.6 (5740)		15.8 (2290)			YU, 1963
Barnsley Hard coal		4.3 (620)						2.4 (345)	BERENBAUM & BRODIE, 1959b
Concrete	1.9 (275)	4.2 (605)				2.8 (405)			WRIGHT 1955

tion $\sigma_\theta = K \dfrac{F}{\pi r_0 t}$, using values of K given by the analysis of JAEGER and HOSKINS. As a direct measure of uniaxial tensile strength the ring tensile values are patently absurd, but the disc results appear to give a reasonable value for tensile strength.

It is seen from the survey that results vary within wide limits. Strength values determined by direct pull test are the lowest in most cases, because the volume of material under the tensile stresses is the highest. In all other methods, not only is the volume under maximum tensile stress too small, but threre is a combination of stresses also and the combined effect of these stresses has not been evaluated as yet. Obviously, the results obtained from these methods are questionable.

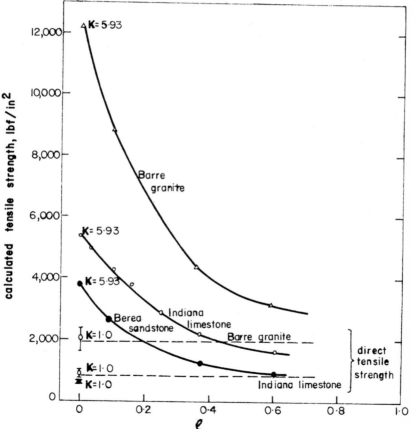

Fig. 3-47. Calculated tensile strength as a function of ϱ for three rock types
(after MELLOR and HAWKES, 1971).

The best method seems to be the direct pull test used by FAIRHURST (Fig. 3-3). The U.S. Bureau of Mines fixture described by KRECH and CHAMBERLAIN appears to be more reliable. Strength values obtained by other methods may be useful where failure takes place not due to uniaxial tensile stresses but to a combination of stresses. Applicability of results will hence differ from case to case.

3.6. Summary and Conclusions

If the tensile strength is required for some engineering or experimental purpose, the authors recommend that it should be measured with the same specimen geometry and loading conditions for which it is required. The value of the maximum stress may not be relevant because it may not be the direct cause of failure. The value may have been miscalculated because of a disparity between failure initiation and total structural collapse or because linear elasticity theory was used. The value indicates, however, in terms of the apparent maximum tensile stress when failure will occur again in the same situation. Since the test specimen must be on a reduced scale, all dimensions should be equally reduced and an estimate of the volume effect obtained.

In the following paragraphs, however, recommendations on some tests are given:

Direct test: The specimen shape, a cylinder with central section of reduced diameter, appears to eliminate many of the undesirable effects of direct test. About the throat, the ratio of the length to the diameter (d) is recommended to be from 1.5 to 2, and the diameter of both ends to be $(1.4-1.5)$ d, and the radius of curvature of the shoulder parts to be $(1-2)$ d. The diameter of the parallel parts of the specimen is from 22 to 66 mm (0.87 to 2.60 in) (HORIBE, 1970).

Since it is very difficult to form such specimens, methods used by FAIRHURST (1961), HAWKES and MELLOR (1970) and U.S. Bureau of Mines (KRECH and CHAMBERLAIN, 1972) can be recommended for routine testing.

The load has to be applied exactly in the axial direction and a rate of loading of $0.01-0.1$ MPa/s ($1.42-14.2$ lbf/in^2/s) is recommended until failure is obtained (HORIBE, 1970).

Bending tests: Bending tests on prismatic and cylindrical specimens are simple. Cylindrical specimens are usually used because drill cores obtained in the field can be adopted easily. The diameters can be from 2.2 to 5.4 cm (0.875 to 2.125 in). The length of the specimen is to be 15.2 cm (6 in).

The results are particularly useful when they are to be used in the design of spans for room and pillar workings in bedded deposits.

Bending tests on discs are very simple and require minimum amount of rock cores. They are particularly useful in determining the anisotropic strength properties of rocks.

Diametral compression of discs: Diametral compression of discs has strong practical appeal. The Brazilian test, made on solid discs, is particularly appealing for its simplicity in specimen preparation, but it produces failure in a biaxial, rather than a uniaxial stress field. The failure may initiate at the platens rather than at the centre, invalidating the test.

To make sure that failure originates at the centre of the disc, COLBACK (1966) recommended distributed loading with cardboard or wood of 0.64 mm (0.025 in) thick. MELLOR and HAWKES (1971) suggested that the thickness of cardboard platen cushions should be about 0.01 times the specimen diameter.

MELLOR and HAWKES (1971) recommended the application of load through a curved-jaw jig with a spherical seat. The loading jaws should be designed to give an angle of contact of $\approx 1/6$, and in addition the specimens should be wrapped with a single layer of double-weight masking tape.

Regarding the diameter of the specimens, NX core size (5.4 cm) (2.125 in) should be taken as the minimum acceptable size (MELLOR and HAWKES, 1971). The ratio of the length to the diameter is recommended to be from 0.5 to 1 (HORIBE, 1970).

Loading rate must be determined to some extent by the properties of the material and the proposed application of the data. For typical rocks a deformation rate of approximately 0.64 cm/min (0.25 in/min) will probably be satisfactory for many practical purposes (MELLOR and HAWKES, 1971).

The ring test causes failure to initiate in a uniaxial stress field, but the crack must propagate through steep stress gradients, and only a small volume of material is critically stressed.

As observed by various research workers, a very small hole has no significant effect as a stress raiser. A very large hole (relative to outside diameter) may produce an effect comparable to that predicted by theory.

From the available literature, it appears that ring tests cannot provide a useful measure of the uniaxial tensile strength of rocks. Results of ring tests give tensile strengths which are, in general, far higher than the uniaxial values. Calculated ring tensile strength is a strong function of ϱ for a given external specimen size, although it might be more accurate to say that calculated strength is a function of absolute hole size for a given rock type. The calculated tensile strength tends to a limiting asymptotic value for high values of ϱ ($\varrho > 0.5$).

Indentation test: For the determination of tensile strength of rocks, the width of the indenters may be restricted to 0.25 times the side of the square specimen (SUNDARA RAJA IYENGAR and CHANDRASHEKHARA, 1962). If shear failure occurs under loading points, the test results cannot be regarded as a true indication of the intrinsic tensile strength of the rock specimens.

In the report of the tests, the items to be described are the same as in the case of the compression test.

References

1. ADDINALL, E. and HACKETT, P.: Tensile failure in rock-like materials. Proc. 6th Symp. Rock Mech., Rolla, Missouri, 1964a, pp. 515–538.
2. ADDINALL, E. and HACKETT, P.: The effect of platen conditions on the tensile strengths of rock-like materials. Civ. Eng. Public Works Rev., Vol. 59, 1964b, pp. 1250–1253.
3. ADDINALL, E. and HACKETT, P.: Rock in tension – A problem in strata control – The Brazilian test. Coll. Guard., Vol. 210, 1965a, pp. 53–56.
4. ADDINALL, E. and HACKETT, P.: Study with particular reference to testing of brittle materials of the Brazilian test and ring test. Civ. Eng. Public Works Rev., Vol. 60, 1965b, pp. 1056–1058.
5. ADLER, L.: Evaluating double elasticity in drill cores under flexure. Int. J. Rock Mech. Min. Sci., Vol. 7, No. 4, July, 1970, pp. 357–370.
6. BERENBAUM, R. and BRODIE, I.: Measurement of the tensile strength of brittle materials. Brit. J. Appl. Phys., Vol. 10, 1959a, pp. 281–287.
7. BERENBAUM, R. and BRODIE, I.: The tensile strength of coal. J. Inst. Fuel, Vol. 32, 1959b, pp. 320–327.
8. BERNAIX, J.: New laboratory methods of studying the mechanical properties of rocks. Int. J. Rock Mech. Min. Sci., Vol. 6, No. 1, Jan., 1969, pp. 43–90.
9. BRACE, W.F.: Brittle fracture of rocks. Proc. Int. Conf. State of Stress in the Earth's Crust, Santa Monica, California, 1963, pp. 110–174.
10. BROWN, E.T. and HUDSON, J.A.: The influence of micro-structure on rock fracture on the laboratory scale. Proc. Symp. Rock Fracture, Nancy, 1971, Paper II-20.
11. CHAMBERLAIN, P.G.: Personal communication. 1974.
12. COLBACK, P.S.B.: An analysis of brittle fracture initiation and propagation in the Brazilian test. Proc. 1st Cong. Int. Soc. Rock Mech., Lisbon, 1966, Vol. 1, pp. 385–391.
13. DAVIES, J.D. and STAGG, K.G.: Splitting tests on rock specimens. Proc. 2nd Cong. Int. Soc. Rock Mech., Belgrade, 1970, Vol. 2, pp. 343–349.
14. DUBE, A.K. and SINGH, B.: Determination of tensile strength of rocks by disc test method. J. Mines, Metals and Fuels, Vol. 17, No. 9, Sept., 1969, pp. 305–307.

15. DUBE, A. K. and SINGH, B.: Effect of humidity on tensile strength of sandstone. J. Mines, Metals and Fuels, Vol. 20, No. 1, Jan., 1972, pp. 8–10.

16. DUCKWORTH, W. H.: Precise tensile properties of ceramic bodies. J. Am. Cer. Soc., Vol. 34, No. 1, Jan. 1, 1951, pp. 1–9.

17. EVANS, I.: The tensile strength of coal. Coll. Eng., Vol. 38, 1961, pp. 428–434.

18. FAIRHURST, C.: Laboratory measurement of some physical properties of rock. Proc. 4th Symp. Rock Mech., Univ. Park, Penn., 1961, pp. 105–118.

19. FAIRHURST, C.: On the validity of the 'Brazilian' test for brittle materials. Int. J. Rock Mech. Min. Sci., Vol. 1, No. 4, Oct., 1964, pp. 535–546.

20. GROSVENOR, N. E.: New method for determining the tensile strength of a rock. Trans. A.I.M.E., Vol. 220, 1961, pp. 447–449.

21. HARDY, H. R. and JAYARAMAN, N. I.: An investigation of methods for the determination of the tensile strength of rock. Proc. 2nd Cong. Int. Soc. Rock Mech., Belgrade, 1970, Vol. 3, pp. 85–92.

22. HAWKES, I. and MELLOR, M.: Uniaxial testing in rock mechanics laboratories. Eng. Geol., Vol. 4, 1970, pp. 177–285.

23. HIRAMATSU, Y. and OKA, Y.: Determination of the tensile strength of rock by a compression test of an irregular test piece. Int. J. Rock Mech. Min. Sci., Vol. 3, No. 2, May, 1966, pp. 89–99.

24. HIRAMATSU, Y. and OKA, Y.: Disc test, ring test, rectangular plate test and irregular specimen test for determining the tensile strength of rocks. Proc. 2nd Cong. Int. Soc. Rock Mech., Belgrade, 1970, Vol. 2, pp. 199–206.

25. HOBBS, D. W.: The tensile strength of rocks. Int. J. Rock Mech. Min. Sci., Vol. 1, No. 3, May, 1964, pp. 385–396.

26. HOBBS, D. W.: An assessment of a technique for determining the tensile strength of rock. Brit. J. Appl. Phys., Vol. 16, 1965, pp. 259–268.

27. HOEK, E.: Fracture of anisotropic rock. J. S. African Inst. Min. Metal., Vol. 64. No. 10, May, 1964, pp. 501–518.

28. HONDROS, G.: The evaluation of Poisson's ratio and the modulus of materials of a low tensile resistance by the Brazilian (indirect tensile) test with particular reference to concrete. Aust. J. App. Sci., Vol. 10, 1959, pp. 243–268.

29. HORIBE, T.: The abstract of the report from "Committee concerning the method of the measurement of the strength of rock" in M.M.I.J. Rock Mech. in Japan, Vol. 1, 1970, pp. 29–31.

30. HUDSON, J. A.: Tensile strength and the ring test. Int. J. Rock Mech. Min. Sci., Vol. 6, No. 1, Jan., 1969, pp. 91–97.

31. HUDSON, J. A., BROWN, E. T. and RUMMEL, F.: The controlled failure of rock discs and rings loaded in diametral compression. Int. J. Rock Mech. Min. Sci., Vol. 9, No. 2, March, 1972, pp. 241–248.

32. HUDSON, J. A., HARDY, M. P. and FAIRHURST, C.: The failure of rock beams Part 2 – Experimental studies. Int. J. Rock Mech. Min. Sci., Vol. 10, No. 1, Jan., 1973, pp. 69–82.

33. JAEGER, J. C.: Failure of rocks under tensile conditions. Int. J. Rock Mech. Min. Sci., Vol. 4, No. 2, April, 1967, pp. 219–227.

34. JAEGER, J. C. and HOSKINS, E. R.: Stresses and failure in rings of rock loaded in diametral tension or compression. Brit. J. Appl. Phys., Vol. 17, 1966, pp. 685–692.

35. KRECH, W. W. and CHAMBERLAIN, P. G.: New techniques for rock fracture energy measurements. Paper No. S.P.E. 4060, Society of Petroleum Engineers of A.I.M.E., 1972.

36. LUNDBORG, N.: The strength-size relation of granite. Int. J. Rock Mech. Min. Sci., Vol. 4, No. 3, July, 1967, pp. 269–272.

37. MAZANTI, B. B. and SOWERS, G. F.: Laboratory testing of rock strength. Proc. Symp. Testing Techniques for Rock Mech., Seattle, Wash., 1965, pp. 207–227.

38. MELLOR, M. and HAWKES, I.: Measurement of tensile strength by diametral compression of discs and annuli. Eng. Geol., Vol. 5, 1971, pp. 173–225.

39. MERRIAM, R., RIEKE III, H. H. and KIM, Y. C.: Tensile strength related to mineralogy and texture of some granitic rocks. Eng. Geol., Vol. 4, 1970, pp. 155–160.

40. MOKHNACHEV, M. P. and GROMOVA, N. V.: Laws of variation of tensile strength indices and deformation properties of rocks with rate and duration of loading. Sov. Min. Sci., No. 6, Nov.–Dec., 1970, pp. 609–612.

41. OBERT, L., WINDES, S. L. and DUVALL, W. I.: Standardized tests for determining the physical properties of mine rock. U.S.B.M.R.I. 3891, 1946, 67 p.

42. POMEROY, C. D. and MORGANS, W. T. A.: The tensile strength of coal. Brit. J. Appl. Phys., Vol. 7, No. 7, July, 1956, pp. 243–246.

43. PRICE, D. G. and KNILL, J. L.: A study of the tensile strength of isotropic rocks. Proc. 1st Cong. Int. Soc. Rock Mech., Lisbon, 1966, Vol. 1, pp. 439–442.

44. PROTODYAKONOV, M. M.: Methods of studying the strength of rocks, used in the U.S.S.R. Proc. Int. Symp. Min. Res., Rolla, Missouri, 1961, Vol. 2, pp. 649–668.

45. REICHMUTH, D. R.: Correlation of force-displacement data with physical properties of rock for percussive drilling systems. Proc. 5th Symp. Rock Mech., Minneapolis, Minn., 1962, pp. 33–59.

46. SEELY, F. B. and SMITH, J. O.: Advanced mechanics of materials. New York, Wiley, 1952, 680 p.

47. SHIH, T.-S.: Investigation of the physical properties of a Gaspe Skarn. Proc. 2nd Can. Rock Mech. Symp., Kingston, Ontario, 1963, pp. 75–79.

48. SHOOK, W. B.: Critical survey of mechanical property test – methods for brittle materials. Ohio State University, Engineering Experiment Station, Columbus, Ohio, July, 1963, 136 p.

49. SINHA, K. N. and SINGH, B.: Research and development in coal mining. Proc. Tech. Conf. Min., Dhanbad, Bihar, 1968.

50. SUNDARA RAJA IYENGAR, K. T. and CHANDRASHEKHARA, K.: On the theory of the indentation test for the measurement of tensile strength of brittle materials. Brit. J. Appl. Phys., Vol. 13, 1962, pp. 501–507.

51. VUTUKURI, V. S.: An evaluation of the ring test in determining surface energy. M. S. Thesis, Univ. Wisconsin, Madison, Wisconsin, 1965, 62 p.

52. VUTUKURI, V. S.: Effect of aluminium chloride solutions on the tensile strength of quartzite. Trans. A.I.M.E., Vol. 252, 1972, pp. 407–409.

53. WRIGHT, P. J. F.: Comments on an indirect tensile test on concrete cylinders. Mag. Conc. Res., Vol. 7, No. 20, July, 1955, pp. 87–96.

54. WUERKER, R. G.: Measuring the tensile strength of rocks. Min. Eng., Vol. 7, No. 2, Feb., 1955, p. 157.

55. YU, Y. S.: Investigation of the physical properties of a Sigma mine porphyry. Proc. 2nd Can. Rock Mech. Symp., Kingston, Ontario, 1963, pp. 80–83.

CHAPTER 4

Shear Strength of Rock

4.1. Introduction

The term 'shear strength' has not yet been well defined and is used to cover several different concepts such as

(a) Strength against pure shear.

(b) Shear stress required for failure when the stress normal to the plane of failure is zero.

(c) The shear diagram in solid mechanics which depends upon the pressure applied.

(d) Mohr's'stress envelope.

According to Everling (1964), shear strength can be defined as the breaking shearing stress applied to an imposed plane with normal force lacking. This can be given by

$$\tau_t = \frac{T}{A} \qquad (4.1)$$

where τ_t = shear strength
$\quad\quad T$ = shearing force necessary to cause failure along a plane and
$\quad\quad A$ = cross-sectional area along which failure occurs.

The practical manifestation of the theoretical concept is always an approximation. Each of the innumerable tests devised for testing rocks has certain limitations, and over the years attempts have been made to devise the test which most closely approaches the theoretical ideal.

In this chapter, different methods devised for measuring shear strength of rock are given. Typical results are also included.

4.2. Method of Determining Shear Strength by Torsion

A typical cylindrical specimen for torsion testing is shown in Fig. 4-1. The ends are made square for easier gripping.

When a specimen is subjected to torsion by holding its ends in chucks of a torsion machine, maximum shear stress develops at the outermost fibre and can be given by

$$\tau_{max} = \frac{16\ T}{\pi\ d^3} \tag{4.2}$$

where τ_{max} = maximum shear stress
    T = twisting moment and
    d = diameter of the specimen.

Fig. 4-1. Cylindrical specimen for torsion testing
(after Protodyakonov, 1969).

Stress distribution on the surface of a cylindrical specimen in the torsion test can be described as pure shear which is equivalent to the biaxial stress state of pure compression in one direction and pure tension of an equivalent magnitude in the transverse direction. The directions of shear stresses at the surface of a twisted cylinder are parallel and transverse to the axis of the cylinder, or very nearly so, whereas the torsional compressive and tensile stresses are at an angle of 45° to the axis of the cylinder.

For an isotropic material which is weaker in shear than in tension, cracks will form both in the axial and transverse directions. In the case of rocks, which are usually weaker in tension and comparatively stronger in shear, the cracking will be helical. Hence, rock fracture in a torsion test is not in fact due to shear but a tensile one and this must be borne in mind.

In torsion test it is very important to see that no bending moment is applied to the specimen. To eliminate this, specimens should be truly straight. This is particularly so for the specimens with larger diameter. Any bending transmitted through the specimen will result in additional stresses which can be calculated by the bending formula and added by superposition to those resulting from torsion. If fracture in torsion test of brittle material occurs in tension, the modified equation for maximum tensile stress is given below.

$$\sigma_{t_{max}} = -16 (M + \sqrt{M^2+T^2})/\pi\, d^3 \qquad (4.3)$$

where $\sigma_{t_{max}}$ = maximum tensile stress at the surface from the combined effects of bending and torsion
M = bending moment
T = twisting moment and
d = diameter of specimen.

The direction along which the above maximum tensile stress will act depends upon the relative magnitudes of bending and twisting moments, and will result in the plane of fracture being between 45° and 90° from the axial direction.

From this point of view, it is desirable to work with specimens of minimum length, but it is equally important to provide sufficient distance between points of application of load (gauge length) so as to ensure true stress distribution. Since maximum stress is at the surface, and hence only a small volume of the material is under high stress therefore strength values are higher than determined by direct tension test and lower than those determined by bending test.

Another point that must be kept in view is that in this test maximum stress occurs on the surface and hence the condition of the surface with respect to cracks and other flaws is of primary importance. The process of preparation of the specimens affecting the surface property of the rock, will affect the strength values.

To overcome the problem of fracture due to tension rather than shear in torsion test for brittle materials, specimens of shape shown in Fig. 4-2 may be thought of (PROTODYAKONOV, 1969). The specimen is a square cross-section prism with a thin cut turned in its central part. It is assumed that, in spite of the low tensile strength of rock, fracture will occur from shearing stresses, since the screw-shaped surface of tensile fracture would be much larger than the cross-section of the thin round neck under torsion.

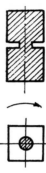

Fig. 4-2. Specimen with neck for torsion testing
(after PROTODYAKONOV, 1969).

VOROPINOV (1967) determined the shear strength by torsion method. To eliminate the occurrence of bending moments, he prepared the cylindrical specimens in a special way. First, an uncut piece of rock was placed into a die (steel or plastic tubes) and a jacket of synthetic resin was poured around it. When the resin had become sufficiently hard the die and the rock specimen were cut by a lathe into a core of circular cross-section; this ensured coaxial alignment of the die and the rock core. To prevent the occurrence of a normal component of stress during torsion, he reduced the testing length of the specimen to a minimum by forming a slot of 0.8 mm (0.031 in) length by means of a diamond saw.

The influence of the normal component is practically insignificant when the cut is 0.8 mm (0.031 in) wide. When for some reason or other it proves impossible to cut a slot so that the width of the cut is larger, it is necessary to make a correction to the test by measuring the vertical area of the failure and establishing the normal component of stress according to the theory of plastic failure in torsion. The influence of the clamping effect is eliminated by embedding the rock specimen in the die.

The torsion apparatus used by him is given in Fig. 4-3. Pouring of a liquid into a large suspended container has been adopted as the simplest and most readily controllable method of loading.

The prepared specimen is inserted between the jaws and tightened into place. Following release of the brake and zero setting of the recording devices the load is allowed to flow through an adjustable orifice plate which can be set to provide the rate of loading required. The strain can be computed from the measured angular displacement from a consideration of the geometry of the test specimen.

He conducted tests at various different sets of loading rates 19.6 to 97.9, 979, 4895–9791, 48955–97909 kPa/s (2.84 to 14.2, 142, 710–1420, 7100–14200 lbf/in²/s) (0.2 to 1.0, 10, 50–100, 500–1000 kp/cm²/s) and the results of some of the tests are given in Fig. 4-4.

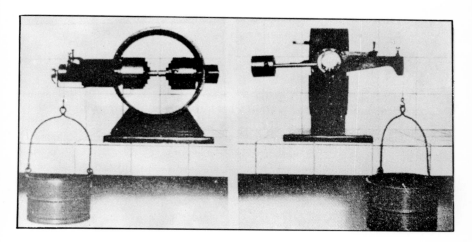

Fig. 4-3. Torsion apparatus used by VOROPINOV (a) side view, (b) front view (after VOROPINOV, 1967).

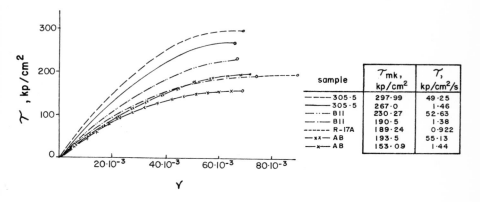

sample	τ_{mk}, kp/cm²	τ, kp/cm²/s
-----305·5	297·99	49·25
———305·5	267·0	1·46
—···— BII	230·27	52·63
—·—BII	190·5	1·38
------R-17A	189·24	0·922
—xx—AB	193·5	55·13
—x—AB	153·09	1·44

Fig. 4-4. Deformation diagrams for the torsion test at different rates of loading (after VOROPINOV, 1967).

4.3. Methods in which the Normal Stress on the Shearing Plane is Zero

The following methods are discussed here in detail:

(1) Single shear test.
(2) Double shear test.
(3) Punch test.

4.3.1. Single Shear Test

The loading arrangement (PROTODYAKONOV, 1969) is given in Fig. 4-5. A square prismatic specimen is rigidly held in a special fixture with one end protruding; through a slot in the fixture a shearing cutter with a straight cutting edge can be moved. An advantage of this method is that it permits several repetitions of tests with the same specimen. A disadvantage is the occurrence of bending stresses that cannot be measured; another disadvantage lies in stress concentrations caused by the cutting edge.

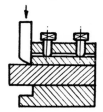

Fig. 4-5. Single shear test (after PROTODYAKONOV, 1969).

4.3.2. Double Shear Test

The set up for double shear test of prismatic specimens is given in Fig. 4-6. Both ends of a specimen are held in a fixture, each end on a support. Shearing in two planes is caused by a flat-end cutter occupying the entire space between the supports. This reduces tensile stresses caused by bending but stress concentrations at the cutting edges, and the tensile stresses cannot be entirely eliminated, so that failure does not occur along the theoretical shearing planes but at an angle to them. There is little prospect for repeated tests on the same specimen.

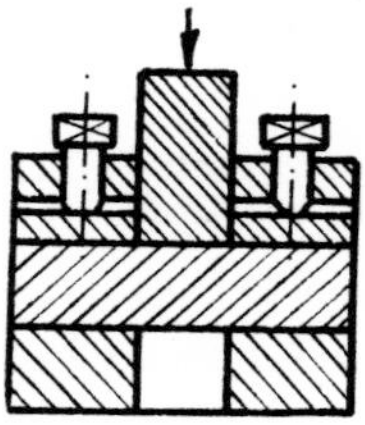

Fig. 4-6. Double shear test (after PROTODYAKONOV, 1969).

The cylindrical cores can also be used for tests. In that case, the loading equipment consists of a single block through which a round hole is drilled horizontally to accommodate the specimen. The block is then cut into three portions and the central portion is loaded, shearing off the portion of the specimen along two planes.

4.3.3. Punch Test

A flat disc is held in a fixture on a ring-shaped support (Fig. 4-7). Shearing is achieved by a cylindrical plunger whose diameter equals the inside diameter of the support. In this case tensile stresses caused by bending arise to a somewhat lesser extent. A specimen can only be tested once.

MAZANTI and SOWERS (1965) used discs cut from a diamond drill core of thickness $^1/_4$ or $^1/_5$th of diameter. Their test arrangement is given in Fig. 4-8.

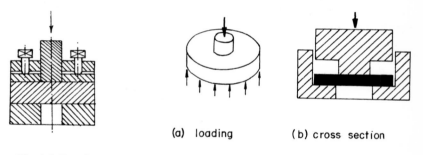

(a) loading   (b) cross section

Fig. 4-7. Punch test
(after PROTODYAKONOV, 1969).

Fig. 4-8. Punch test
(after MAZANTI and SOWERS, 1965).

4.3.4. Discussion

Tensile stresses are present; they are caused by bending and stress concentrations near the cutting edge. High shear stresses occur at the loading edges and hence stress is not uniform on the fracture plane. Hence, breaking force will be lower than that when stress distribution is uniform and fracture is developed freely. Photoelastic fringe pattern of the double shear test showing points of stress concentration at the ends of imposed planes of fracture is given in Fig. 4-9 (EVERLING, 1964). Similarly, the force required to punch will not be proportional to the area of the shearing surfaces. Another point that must be kept in view is that in the tests maximum stress concentrations occur near the loading points on the surface and hence the condition of the surface with respect to cracks and other flaws is of primary importance. The process of preparation of the specimens affecting the surface property of the rock will affect the strength values.

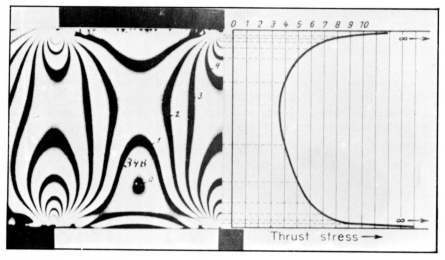

Fig. 4-9. Photoelastic fringe pattern of double shear test showing points of stress concentration at the ends of imposed planes of fracture
(after EVERLING, 1964).

4.4. Methods of Determining Shear Strength with Compression

To eliminate unknown tensile stresses, which lead to results indicating a lower shear strength than that possessed by the tested rock, methods of determining shear strength with compression were developed. With such methods compression stresses can be calculated in the shearing plane, and this eliminates unknown tensile stresses.

4.4.1. Single Shear with Compression of Cylindrical Specimen (Fig. 4–10)

A cylindrical specimen is placed between a fixed and a movable piece, each having a cylindrical recess enclosing half of the specimen. The normal force is caused by a weight. The shearing force is applied horizontally. After rupture the shear force can continue to be applied in order to obtain the residual strength values resulting from face-to-face friction (Fig. 4-11).

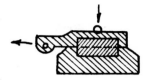

Fig. 4-10. Single shear with compression of cylindrical specimen
(after PROTODYAKONOV, 1969).

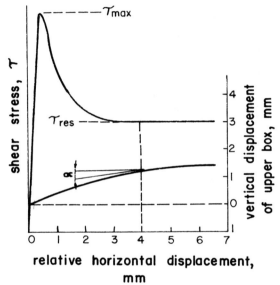

Fig. 4-11. Shear test. General appearance of stress-deformation curves
(after BERNAIX, 1969).

It is commonly considered that the strength of the rock will become constant
if sufficient relative movement is developed. However in a practical test the
experimental equipment may not be capable of exerting the required
displacement so that there are real difficulties involved in the measurement
of this "residual strength". Experimental data suggests that the displacement
necessary to develop the residual state increases with strength (KRSMANOVIC,
1967). With less hard rocks (sandstone and conglomerate), the residual
strengths were obtained at shear deformations of about 45 mm (1.77 in).
With hard limestones, the required deformations range from about 50–100 mm
(1.97 to 3.94 in). Values of ϕ (residual) for the sandstone were 31–33° and
this is the order anticipated by comparison with sands or gravels. The
residual ϕ for the conglomerate was 35°. The shear strength of the limestone
was considerably greater and if the shear strength was measured by a "ϕ"
the value at a displacement of 30 mm (1.18 in) was 56°.

Various rocks behave differently with regard to relations of the peak and the residual strengths. In Fig. 4-12, the relationships between the ratio τ_t/τ_r (peak shear strength/residual shear strength) and the normal stresses, σ, are given for various rocks. The greatest diminutions of strength are obtained for rocks with the greatest compressive strength (limestones), and the smallest – in case of rocks with small strength (sandstones) (KRSMANOVIC, TUFO and LANGOF, 1966).

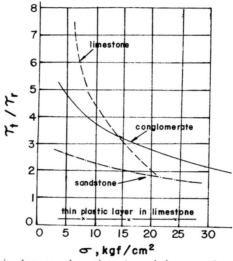

Fig. 4-12. Relationships between the ratio, τ_t/τ_r, and the normal stresses σ for various rocks (after KRSMANOVIC, TUFO and LANGOF, 1966).

BERNAIX (1969) used the apparatus shown in Fig. 4-13 where the tangential force is measured by means of a very rigid dynamometer functioning on the vibrating-wire principle. As the instantaneous relative displacement of the two boxes at the moment of rupture is therefore very slight, the investigation of friction after rupture suffers no disturbance.

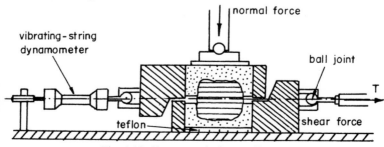

Fig. 4-13. Shear test rig for small samples
(after BERNAIX, 1969).

The typical results of tests on Malpasset gneiss are given in Fig. 4-14.

TAMADA (1970) obtained relationships between shear strength of sedimentary rocks and time elapsed in static water (Fig. 4-15). The specimens are 2.0 cm (0.79 in) in thickness and about 5.5 cm (2.17 in) in diameter. The variation of shear strength with time may be expressed as follows:

$$\tau_t = \tau_{t_0} \exp\left(-\beta\left(1 - e^{-rt}\right)\right) \qquad (4.4)$$

where τ_t = shear strength
          t = time elapsed and
     τ_{t_0}, β and r = constants.

The constant value is attained after a few days.

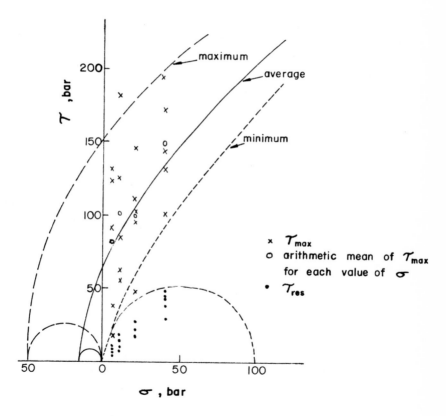

Fig. 4-14. Shear test results on Malpasset gneiss
(after BERNAIX, 1969).

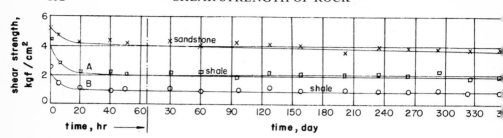

Fig. 4-15. Variation of shear strength with time
(after Tamada, 1970).

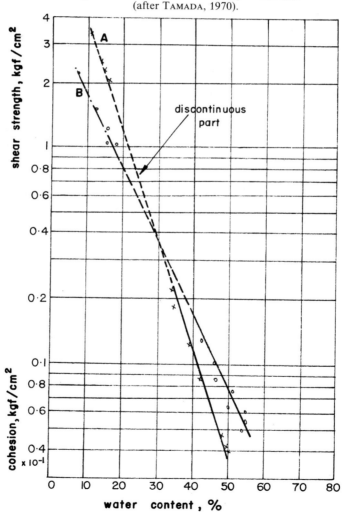

Fig. 4-16. Relation between shear strength, cohesion and water content
(after Tamada, 1970).

The relationship between shear strength of sedimentary rock and water content; the relationship between cohesion of landslide clay which is weathered into from the sedimentary rock above-mentioned and water content are given in Fig. 4-16. The mathematical formulae are

$$\tau_t = \tau_{t_0} \exp\left(-n_{\tau_t} w\right) \tag{4.5}$$

$$c = c_0 \exp\left(-n_c w\right) \tag{4.6}$$

$$n_c = n_{\tau_t} \tag{4.7}$$

In these expressions τ_{t_0}, c_0, n_{τ_t}, n_c are constants and c is cohesion and w is water content.

KENTY (1970) suggested another method of test for direct shear strength of rock core specimens up to 15.2 cm (6 in) in diameter. The principle of rock core direct shearing is illustrated schematically in Fig. 4-17.

Test specimens are placed in an aluminium box made in two parts (blocks), each part having a recess to receive specimens. The two blocks assembled with the specimen are placed within a framework consisting of two aluminium plates connected by four aluminium tie rods each with a nut on each end. One block is fitted with a pair of hardened stainless steel races for ball bearings for minimising friction of the moving block. The baseplate is fitted with companion races. A coil spring is inserted between the other block and its companion cover plate to hold the normal load on the specimen.

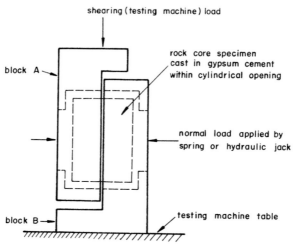

Fig. 4-17. Direct shear of rock core – Schematic (after KENTY, 1970).

4.4.2. Single Shear with Compression of a Cube-shaped Specimen (Fig. 4–18)

The loading is done by two hydraulic jacks, one of them applied vertically for the normal load, the other horizontally for the shearing force. The set up actually represents a hydraulic press acting in two directions and is very bulky.

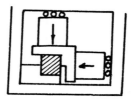

Fig. 4-18. Single shear of cube-shaped specimen (after PROTODYAKONOV, 1969).

4.4.3. Double Shear with Compression of a Prismatic Specimen (Fig. 4–19)

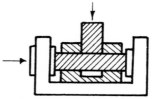

Fig. 4-19. Double shear with compression of a prismatic specimen (after PROTODYAKONOV, 1969).

A prismatic specimen is placed horizontally in a fixture providing two supports. Normal pressure along the longer axis of the specimen is provided from one side by a hydraulic jack. Double shear is achieved by a square plunger occupying the entire space between the supports (principle similar to Fig. 4-6). The fixture with the specimen is placed between the platens of a testing machine, which provides the shearing force to the plunger. This method is somewhat simpler than the preceding one.

ZAHARY (1963) used a similar apparatus and found an increase in the shear strength from 54.4 to 140 MPa (7890 to 20300 lbf/in^2) with an increase in axial stress from 0 to 75.8 MPa (0 to 11000 lbf/in^2) in andesite.

MAURER (1965) also used a similar apparatus to determine the shear strength of rocks. He found that shear strength increased from about 20.7 to 53.8 MPa (3000 to 7800 lbf/in^2) when axial stress was increased from 0 to 27.6 MPa

(0 to 4000 lbf/in²). A typical curve showing the effect of normal stress σ on shear strength is given in Fig. 4-20.

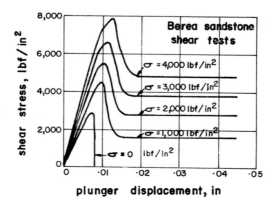

Fig. 4-20. The effect of normal stress σ on shear strength
(after MAURER, 1965).

The results of tests on specimens with thicknesses varying from 3.2 to 12.7 mm (⅛ to ½ in) showed that the shear strength is independent of specimen thickness (MAURER, 1966).

In the shear test, the axial pressure is limited to a maximum value of uniaxial compressive strength. In order to study the shear strength for high normal stresses, a hydrostatic fluid pressure is applied to the shear machine and test specimen (MAURER, 1966). The rock specimens are coated with plastic to prevent the fluid from entering the pore spaces. This coating is effective in sealing the rocks. The vertical load was measured using strain gauges located above the plunger. A deflectometer was used to obtain force-displacement curve.

The shear strength of the rocks increased rapidly as the axial pressure (normal stress) is increased (Fig. 4-21). The normal stress in these tests was limited to the compressive strength of the rock.

To determine the shear strengths at high normal stresses, additional tests were made with hydrostatic fluid pressure on the rock. Surprisingly, it was found that the hydrostatic pressure produced smaller increases in shear strength than axial pressure. The dashed lines on Fig. 4-21 show the comparison between the axial and hydrostatic pressure tests. The reason for this difference is not known, but it is suggested that the intermediate stress has an important effect on the failure mechanism.

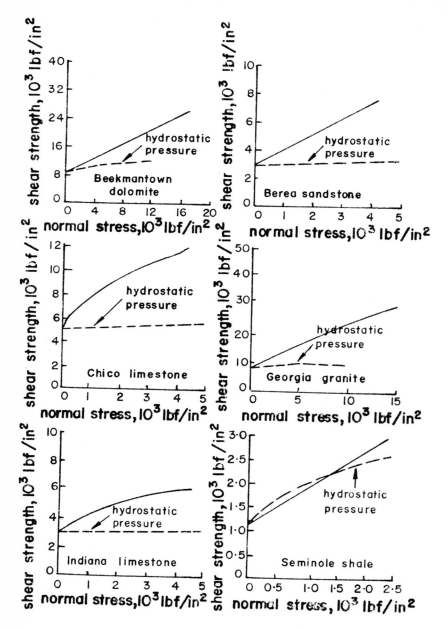

Fig. 4-21. Shear strength *vs* axial and hydrostatic pressures
(after MAURER, 1966).

LUNDBORG (1966) also used a similar apparatus to determine the shear strength of ten rocks and four ores. The specimens were cylinders 15 mm (0.59 in) in diameter and 45 mm (1.77 in) in length. The relationship between shear strength and axial pressure was found to be nonlinear and he expressed by a simple two-parameter expression

$$\tau_n = c + \frac{\mu p_n}{1 + \mu p_n / (\tau_i - c)} \qquad (4.8)$$

where τ_n = shear strength at normal pressure p_n
$\quad c$ = cohesion (shear strength at normal pressure = 0)
$\quad \mu$ = coefficient of friction
$\quad p_n$ = normal pressure and
$\quad \tau_i$ = upper limit of shear strength when p_n becomes infinity.

The constants μ, c and τ_i for different rocks and ores are given in Table 21.

In Fig. 4-22, the effect of normal stress, σ, on shear strength is shown. The shear line represents the average shearing stress leading to fracture with the normal stress σ imposed on the plane of fracture. Its course alters with the size of the test specimen and with the test installation. If the normal force N is increased to approach the uniaxial compressive strength of the specimen, then the shearing force $2T$ required to cause fracture increases no further and instead decreases. If N itself leads to failure, then $2T = 0$. The shear line runs approximately linear only with small forces (N), then increases more slowly and decreases again and strikes the axis of the abscissa when the normal stress is equal to the uniaxial compressive strength.

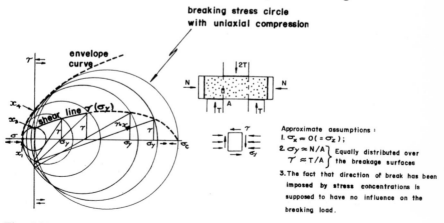

Fig. 4-22. Relationship between MOHR's envelope and the shear line derived from double shear tests with the normal force N increased up to uniaxial compressive strength σ_c (after EVERLING, 1964).

TABLE 21

The constants μ, c and τ_i for different rocks and ores

(after LUNDBORG, 1966)

Material	Locality	μ	c, MPa (lbf/in^2)	τ_i, MPa (lbf/in^2)
Granite I	Bohuslan	2.0	60 (8700)	970 (140650)
Pegmatite-gneiss	Valdemarsvik	2.5	50 (7250)	1170 (169650)
Granite II	Bredseleforsen	2.0	40 (5800)	1020 (147900)
Gneiss-granite	Valdemarsvik	2.5	60 (8700)	680 (98600)
Quartzite	Gautojaure	2.0	60 (8700)	610 (88450)
Grey slate	Granboforsen	1.8	30 (4350)	570 (82650)
Skarnbreccia	Malmberget	1.5	40 (5800)	2040 (295800)
Micagneiss	Vindelforsen	1.2	50 (7250)	760 (110200)
Limestone	Granboforsen	1.2	30 (4350)	870 (126150)
Black slate	Gautojaure	1.0	60 (8700)	480 (69600)
Lead ore	Laisvall	2.5	60 (8700)	810 (117450)
Magnetite	Grangesberg	1.8	30 (4350)	830 (120350)
Leptite	Grangesberg	2.4	30 (4350)	630 (91350)
Iron byrites	Rutjebacken	1.7	20 (2900)	550 (79750)

It may, however, be pointed out that pairs of values of τ and σ so obtained cannot be interpreted as co-ordinates of the points of MOHR's envelope.

4.4.4. Single Shear with Compression between Bevelled Dies (Fig. 4–23)

A cube –, prism – or cylinder – shaped specimen is placed between two bevelled dies set up in a testing machine and sheared along a predetermined plane. So as to obviate a resistance to a horizontal displacement of the top die, a number of rollers are placed between the top die and the platen of the testing machine, with the roller axes set parallel (but not equidistant) to the shearing plane. The vertical force of the testing machine is automatically split into a component normal to the shearing plane and a shearing component along this plane. The inclination of the shearing plane is given by the setting of the dies. In order to obtain various ratios between the normal and tangential components of forces and stresses, there is a set of wedges permitting an adjustment of the die – and specimen – setting angles. For using cylindrical specimens instead of square ones, special cylindrically grooved insets are provided; the cylinder axis is set inclined at the same angle as the shearing plane. This method is particularly simple and has been often used lately by Soviet researchers.

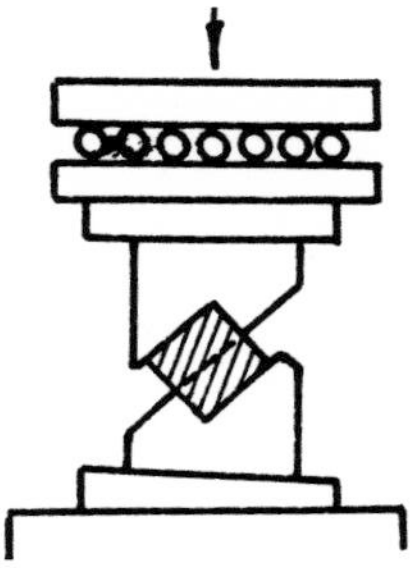

Fig. 4-23. Single shear between bevelled dies (after PROTODYAKONOV, 1969).

Details

The following equations give the two components of compressing force F, i.e., the normal component N and the shearing (tangential) component T:

$$N = F \sin \alpha \qquad (4.9)$$

$$T = F \cos \alpha \qquad (4.10)$$

The respective stresses are

$$\sigma = \frac{F \sin \alpha}{bl} \qquad (4.11)$$

$$\tau = \frac{F \cos \alpha}{bl} \qquad (4.12)$$

where $\sigma =$ the normal stress acting on the shearing plane
       $\tau =$ shearing stress in the shearing plane

F = vertical force of the press
α = angle which the vertical force makes with the plane of failure
b = width of the plane of failure and
l = length of the plane of failure.

The ratio of the compression force F to the shear area bl is designated by q.

The method of plotting the MOHR-diagram representing the state of stress in the shear area is shown in Fig. 4-24a. The points can be found either by plotting the values of σ and τ on the co-ordinate axis, or by q along a line passing through 0 at an angle α to the ordinate axis.

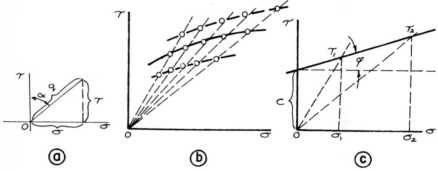

Fig. 4-24. Plotting of (MOHR) envelopes:
(a) co-ordinate system;
(b) plotting a curved envelope;
(c) plotting a rectilinear envelope
(after PROTODYAKONOV, 1969).

Plotting the MOHR-diagram points for various shearing-plane-inclination angles (Fig. 4-24b) permits the construction of the Mohr envelope. The figure also shows the scattering of experimental points.

The curvature of the envelope is sometimes disregarded, and the envelope is considered a straight line. In such a case two points are sufficient for two values of α (Fig. 4-24c). By drawing a straight line through the two points and extending it to intersect the ordinate axis the so-called cohesion c and the internal-friction angle ϕ can be found.

$$c = \frac{q_1 q_2 \sin (\alpha_2 - \alpha_1)}{q_2 \sin \alpha_2 - q_1 \sin \alpha_1} \tag{4.13}$$

$$\tan \phi = \frac{q_2 \cos \alpha_2 - q_1 \cos \alpha_1}{q_2 \sin \alpha_2 - q_1 \sin \alpha_1} \tag{4.14}$$

Satisfactory results are obtained with α ranging from 30 to 50°. If it is too small, tensile stresses may develop and the dies may be upset. If it is too large, shearing may occur along another than the desired plane, accompanied by an over-compression of the specimen.

Cylindrical specimens are easier to make and they may be sheared either "over the generatrix" (Fig. 4-25 a) or "across the face" (Fig. 4-25 b). In the first case shearing has been found not to occur over a plane, and setting is less convenient; the second alternative has therefore gained preference.

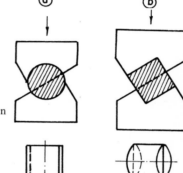

Fig. 4-25. Testing a cylindrical specimen with bevelled dies:
    (a) shear "over generatrix";
    (b) shear "across face"
(after PROTODYAKONOV, 1969).

The specimens must fit the dies, since inaccuracies and resulting clearances will lead to unequal stress distribution. If the diameter tolerance is greater than -0.1 mm (-0.004 in), copper-foil compensation insets must be used for the cylindrically hollowed bevelled dies.

Each bevelled die (half) is made of 2 parts, i.e., a body and a working inset. This will permit the use of the same bodies and different insets for specimens of different size or shape.

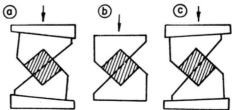

Fig. 4-26. Setting of wedges for altering the shearing angle:
    (a) α = 50°;   (b) α = 45°;   (c) α = 40°
(after PROTODYAKONOV, 1969).

For altering the angle α, the combination of different dies and wedges is most effective. PROTODYAKONOV (1969) recommended 3 sets of dies for angles of 30°, 45°, and 60°, and one pair of wedges, each for 5°. By reversing the wedges (Fig. 4-26a and c), or not using any (Fig. 4-26b), the following angles can be obtained.

Dies	Wedges	Resulting angle
30°	− 5°	25°
30°	0°	30°
30°	+ 5°	35°
45°	− 5°	40°
45°	0°	45°
45°	+ 5°	50°
60°	− 5°	55°
60°	0°	60°
60°	+ 5°	65°

A set of rollers must be used to obviate a resistance of the top die to lateral displacement. These rollers should be set in a flat frame for easier handling. The roller diameter should be 12 to 15 mm (0.45 to 0.59 in).

PROTODYAKONOV (1969) recommended the following:

Shape and size of specimens: The specimens should be cylindrical. Specimen diameter = 42 mm (1.65 in). Specimen length = 42 mm (1.65 in). Tolerances: The following tolerances, in mm (in) are acceptable:

Specimen diameter	—	− 0.1 (− 0.004)
Specimen length	—	± 2.5 (± 0.1)
Conicity, cross-section ovality, and barrel-shaped distortion	—	± 0.05 (± 0.002)
Warping and convexity of faces and their nonperpendicularity to the generatrix	—	± 0.05 (± 0.002)

Rate of loading: The rate of loading should be kept within 490 to 979 kPa/s (71 to 142 lbf/in^2/s) seen as the ratio of the vertical compressing force to the shear area.

Effect of specimen size

ILNITSKAYA (1969) investigated the influence of specimen size on shear strength of gabbro and marble. The cores had diameters of 10 mm, 22 mm, 40 mm, 50 mm and 70 mm (0.39 in, 0.87 in, 1.57 in, 1.97 in and 2.76 in);

the heights were $2\sqrt{A}$ cm (in) where A is the face area in cm² (in²). All specimens were tested for shear at two different angles of the shearing plane to the horizontal, viz., 50° and 70°.

His results are given in Fig. 4-27. With an increase of the cross-section by a factor exceeding 110, the cohesion (shear resistance) is reduced by factors of approximately 1.3 to 1.4.

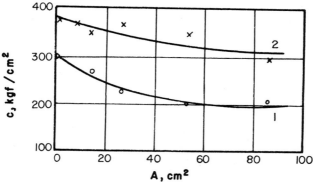

Fig. 4-27. Cohesion of marble (1) and gabbro (2) as a function of size
(after ILNITSKAYA, 1969).

Testing of irregularly shaped specimens

The method can also be used for testing specimens of irregular shape where the specimen is embedded in a concrete or cement cast leaving a narrow slit in the cast. After the concrete has hardened the dies are compressed in a compression machine (Fig. 4-28a). At least two angles of inclination of the slit should be used. Most frequently used angles are 40° and 60°.

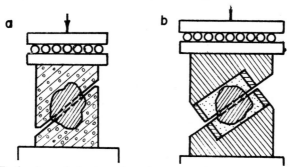

Fig. 4-28. Testing irregularly shaped specimens for shear under compression:
(a) with mold casings removed;
(b) with mold casings
(after PROTODYAKONOV, 1969).

The alternative method, with steel casings (Fig. 4-28 b), is more convenient. Such casings enclosing the specimen are set between bevelled dies, as in Fig. 4-23. Thus the same dies may be used for both regularly and irregularly shaped specimens.

The surface area of the plane of failure is measured by pressing it against a carbon paper placed on a graph paper and counting the squares in the outline or by planimetering the outline.

4.4.5. Method of Constricted Oblique Shear

This method is modification of single shear with compression between bevelled dies (BROUL and HOFRICHTER, 1967). A number of rectangular cuts of set width and depth are made in the upper flat surface of the cylindrical test specimen. On the edge of one of the cuts, a vertical force is applied through a small hard cylindrical bit until failure occurs (see Fig. 4-29). With a microscope, the lateral shift of bit, Δr_r, its vertical, or axial, displacement h, and the length of the chord of the lower base, a, are measured to calculate the area and inclination of the failure plane. The stresses on the failure plane are calculated using these values with the failure load.

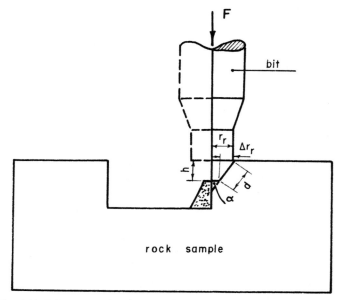

Fig. 4-29. Diagrammatic representation of the method of oblique shear (after BROUL and HOFRICHTER, 1967).

Angle of inclination of the shear plane

$$\tan \alpha = \frac{\Delta r_r}{h} \qquad (4.15)$$

Inclined displacement of the bit

$$d = \frac{h}{\cos \alpha} = \frac{\Delta r_r}{\sin \alpha} \qquad (4.16)$$

The length of the lower base of the oblique cylinder jacket $\overgroup{r_r \cdot \beta}$

$$\sin \frac{\beta}{2} = \frac{a}{2 r_r} \qquad (4.17)$$

By combining the equations (4.15) and (4.17) the following expression is deduced for the area of the failure plane:

$$A = \pi r_r \frac{h}{\cos \alpha} - \frac{h}{2} (\pi r_r - \overgroup{r_r \cdot \beta}) \qquad (4.18)$$

The normal and shear stresses on the failure plane are as follows:

$$\sigma = \frac{F}{A} \sin \alpha = \frac{F \sin \alpha}{\pi r_r \dfrac{h}{\cos \alpha} - \dfrac{h}{2} (\pi r_r - \overgroup{r_r \cdot \beta})} \qquad (4.19)$$

$$\tau = \frac{F}{A} \cos \alpha = \frac{F \cos \alpha}{\pi r_r \dfrac{h}{\cos \alpha} - \dfrac{h}{2} (\pi r_r - \overgroup{r_r \cdot \beta})} \qquad (4.20)$$

4.4.6. Triaxial Test

It is possible to produce truly uniform and known stress condition in the whole interior of the specimen only in triaxial test and MOHR's envelope can best be drawn from the data obtained from triaxial testing of rocks. In this method, shear stresses are not produced by means of tangential forces as in other tests. Their magnitudes depend upon principal compressive stresses and in fact the largest shear stress always appears in one direction which is inclined at 45° to the direction of the principal compressive stress. (The technique of testing, equipment used and results are discussed in detail in Chapter 5). The method is based upon the determination of the axial stress σ_1 at failure for different confining pressures σ_3. The data, σ_1 and σ_3, for a number of specimens can be represented on τ and σ axes to give a family of MOHR circles (Fig. 4-30), the tangent to which gives the MOHR envelope. The point at which this envelope cuts the τ-axis gives the shear strength of the rock.

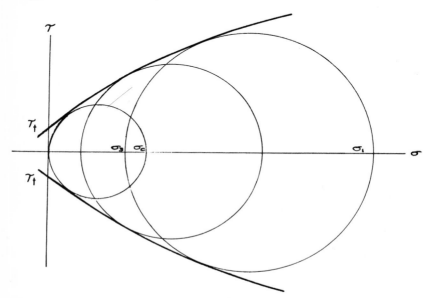

Fig. 4-30. MOHR's envelope determined from the failure stresses in a group of triaxial specimens.

Although the triaxial tests seem to be the best method of obtaining shear strength of rocks, it requires expensive equipment and tests are time-consuming. Besides, it is very difficult to vary independently the shear stress τ and normal stress σ on a predetermined plane of failure for the normal stress developed on any plane is a function of both the axial force and the confining pressure.

4.5. Estimation of Shear Strength Employing MOHR's Representation of Uniaxial Tensile and Compressive Strengths

WUERKER (1959) obtained shear strengths of rocks from consideration of MOHR's representation of uniaxial tensile and compressive strengths

(Fig. 4-31). These, of course, cannot be relied upon because the tangent curve may not be a straight line and tensile strength values may be unreliable.

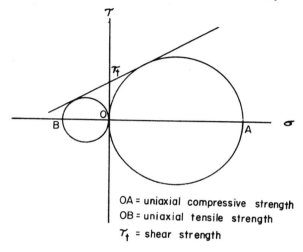

OA = uniaxial compressive strength
OB = uniaxial tensile strength
τ_t = shear strength

Fig. 4-31. MOHR's representation of tensile, compressive, and shear strengths.

HORIBE (1970) suggested the following method for the calculation of the shear strength: The value of the compressive strength of rocks is usually greater than three times that of the tensile strength. Then considering GRIFFITH's hypothesis, draw the circle which has the diameter of $4\sigma_t$ passing the point of $-\sigma_t$ and $+3\sigma_t$ on the σ-axis. The shear strength is suggested from the intercept of the common tangent of that circle and the circle of the compressive strength with τ-axis, and is given by the following equation:

$$\tau_t = \sigma_c \cdot \sigma_t / 2 \sqrt{\sigma_t \left(\sigma_c - 3\,\sigma_t \right)} \qquad (4.21)$$

4.6. Comparison of Results Obtained by Different Methods

BROUL and HOFRICHTER (1967) determined the shear strength of an extremely homogeneous fine-grained carboniferous sandstone (the Godula sandstone) by different methods. Their results are given in Table 22. The rate of loading was kept below 1 MPa/s (142 lbf/in²/s), maintaining the temperature and humidity constant throughout the test.

The following are some of the remarks made by them on these methods and the results:

Torsion method: Because of the uniformity of the state of stress induced in the specimen, of all the methods this one yields the most reproducible value.

TABLE 22

Comparison of values of shear strength

(after BROUL and HOFRICHTER, 1967)

Method used	τ_t, MPa (lbf/in²)	Deviation from the value from triaxial tests, %	Coefficient of variation, %	Necessary number of tests
1. Torsion	15 (2173)	2	5-10	3-5
2. Punch test	24 to 8.8 (3465 to 1278)	41-59	15-40	5-7
3. Single shear with compression between bevelled dies	16.6 (2414)	11	15-30	3-9
4. Constricted oblique shear	47.7 (σ=20.3) (6915) (2939)	32	4-30	5-7

Punch test: Although this test requires only small quantities of rock core it suffers from the disadvantage that an anisotropic state of stress exists along the walls of the perforation while the punch is forced through the specimen, due to the ability of the rock to compress laterally. The effect of this phenomenon greatly depends on the ratio between the thickness of the specimen and the diameter of the punch. If the specimen is very thin in comparison to the diameter of the punch the shear stress will be fairly evenly distributed. Two different ranges of thickness/punch diameter ratio, t/d_r, namely

$$0.5\,d_r \geq t \geq 0.13\,d_r \quad \text{and} \quad t \leq 0.13\,d_r$$

were used and because of the large dispersion in the strength values they consider the test to be only of use for purposes of orientation.

Single shear with compression between bevelled dies: With this test, it is possible to determine τ as a function of σ, but it is laborious and expensive, and a great quantity of rock is required. The greater the angle of shear plane in relation to the axial force, the less is the reliability of the result.

Constricted oblique shear test: In addition to the advantages of simplicity, the possibility of taking a large number of observations and ease of specimen preparation, the test allows the rock to fail along any failure surface and not one predetermined by the test itself. On the other hand, it has the disadvantage that no account can possibly be taken of the influence that the rock surrounding the bit has on the failure, the so-called gripping effect.

This method is convenient in cases where the supply of rock is scarce.

From the point of view of specimen preparation, the method of constricted oblique shear is the most time-consuming and that of single shear with compression between bevelled dies is the least time-consuming, the remaining two methods being more or less equally laborious.

Torsion method yielded values in closest agreement with the triaxial value, while the method of simple shear by punches exhibited the greatest deviation in shear strength. The remaining two methods produced results of equal reliability. Torsion method was found to be the most suitable for determining shear strength of rock both as regards the exactness of the results and the testing costs.

LUNDBORG (1968) compared the values of shear strength obtained by double shear with compression and triaxial tests (Fig. 4-32). The values according to the double shear test with compression are somewhat higher throughout than those according to the triaxial tests. This is not surprising as the rupture in the triaxial test has greater liberty in choosing a rupture surface whereas this is predetermined in the double shear test with compression. His results from double shear tests with compression on 14 kinds of Swedish rocks and 4 ores are given in Fig. 4-33.

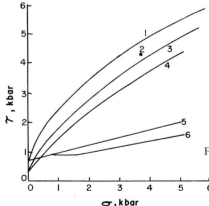

1. granite from double shear test with compression
2. granite in brass envelope from triaxial test
3. granite in plastic envelope from triaxial test
4. granite without envelope in oil from triaxial test
5. plexiglass from double shear test with compression
6. plexiglass without envelope in oil from triaxial test

Fig. 4-32. Shear strength of granite and plexiglass (after LUNDBORG, 1968).

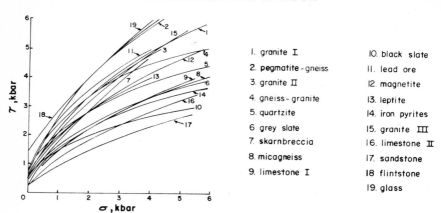

1. granite I	10. black slate
2. pegmatite - gneiss	11. lead ore
3. granite II	12. magnetite
4. gneiss - granite	13. leptite
5. quartzite	14. iron pyrites
6. grey slate	15. granite III
7. skarnbreccia	16. limestone II
8. micagneiss	17. sandstone
9. limestone I	18. flintstone
	19. glass

Fig. 4-33. Shear strength of some Swedish rocks and ores
(after LUNDBORG, 1968).

4.7. Summary and Conclusions

Torsion tests: In the case of rocks, which are usually weaker in tension and comparatively stronger in shear, the fracture in a torsion test is not in fact due to shear but a tensile one. To overcome the problem of fracture due to tension rather than shear in torsion test for rocks, a specimen of shape shown in Fig. 4-2 is recommended. BROUL and HOFRICHTER (1967), after determining the shear strength of an extremely homogeneous fine-grained carboniferous sandstone by different methods, came to the conclusion that the torsion method yields the most representative value in closest agreement with the triaxial value because of the uniformity of the state of stress induced in the specimen. This test is surface sensitive.

Methods in which the normal stress on the shearing plane is zero: In these tests, tensile stresses, which cannot be measured, occur due to bending and stress concentrations caused by the cutting edges. High shear stresses occur at the loading edges and hence stress is not uniform on the fracture plane. The test results are also surface sensitive.

When only relative values are required, these tests may be recommended. The data obtained in such tests should be regarded as characterising, in an arbitrary manner, a resistance to combined shearing and tensile stresses. The order of preference would be punch test, single shear test and double shear test. For the punch test, the thickness of discs may be $\frac{1}{4}$ or $\frac{1}{5}$th of diameter. Single shear test permits several tests on a single specimen.

Methods of determining shear strength with compression: To eliminate unknown tensile stresses, which lead to results indicating a lower shear strength than possessed by the tested rock, methods of determining shear strength with compression were developed. With these methods compression stresses can be calculated in the shearing plane, and this eliminates unknown tensile stresses.

The method shown in Fig. 4-10 is the more widely known and used shear test. Double shear with compression of specimen is coming into more use and is somewhat simpler than the preceding one. The results of tests on specimens with thicknesses varying from 3.2 to 12.7 mm ($\frac{1}{8}$ to $\frac{1}{2}$ in) showed that the shear strength is independent of specimen thickness (MAURER, 1966). The method given in Fig. 4-23 is strongly advocated by the Russian group. The recommendations of PROTODYAKONOV (1969) have been given in the text. This method can also be used for testing specimens of irregular shape.

In all the tests where the fracture of the specimens is brought along a predetermined plane, the shear strength values so determined will not be a true representative of the specimen as a whole. These values may be smaller or greater depending upon the nature of the plane along which fracture is caused.

The method of constricted oblique shear is simple; there is a possibility of taking a large number of observations and the test allows the rock to fail along any failure surface and not one predetermined by the test itself. On the other hand, it has the disadvantage that no account can possibly be taken of the influence that the rock surrounding the bit has on the failure, the so-called gripping effect.

The triaxial test seems to be the best method of obtaining shear strength of rocks, but it requires expensive equipment and the test is time-consuming. Besides, it is very difficult to vary independently the shear stress and normal stress on a predetermined plane of failure.

Estimation of shear strength employing MOHR's representation of uniaxial tensile and compressive strengths: This method can be used if strength values are not available from actual tests.

There are many factors that affect the test results significantly. ILNITSKAYA (1969) studied the effect of specimen size on shear strength by the method – Single shear with compression between bevelled dies. VOROPINOV (1967) determined the shear strength by torsion method at different loading rates. TAMADA (1970) obtained relationships between shear strength of sedimentary rocks and time elapsed in the static water. He also obtained relationships between (a) shear strength of sedimentary rock and water content and (b) cohesion of landslide clay which is weathered into from the sedimentary rock above mentioned and water content. The method used was – single shear with compression of cylindrical specimen.

Here the authors recommend that the shear strength should be measured with the same specimen geometry and loading conditions for which it is required. Since the test specimen must be on a reduced scale, all dimensions should be equally reduced and an estimate of the volume effect obtained.

In the report of the tests, the items to be described are the same as in the case of the compression test.

References

1. BERNAIX, J.: New laboratory methods of studying the mechanical properties of rocks. Int. J. Rock Mech. Min. Sci., Vol. 6, No. 1, Jan., 1969, pp. 43–90.

2. BROUL, J. and HOFRICHTER, P.: A comparison of four different methods of determining the shear strength of rock. Proc. Geotechnical Conf. Shear Strength Properties of Natural Soils and Rocks, Oslo, 1967, Vol. 1, pp. 259–264.

3. EVERLING, G.: Comments upon the definition of shear strength. Int. J. Rock Mech. Min. Sci., Vol. 1, No. 2, March, 1964, pp. 145–154.

4. HORIBE, T.: The abstract of the report from "Committee concerning the method of the measurement of the strength of rock" in M.M.I.J. Rock Mech. in Japan, Vol. 1, 1970, pp. 29–31.

5. ILNITSKAYA, E.I.: Effect of rock-specimen size on mechanical properties in shear tests. In Mechanical Properties of Rocks by M.M. Protodyakonov, M.I. Koifman, and others. Translated from Russian. Jerusalem, Israel Program for Scientific Translations, 1969, pp. 28–33.

6. KENTY, J.D.: Suggested method of test for direct shear strength of rock core specimens. In Special Procedures for Testing Soil and Rock for Engineering Purposes. A.S.T.M. Special Technical Publication No. 479, 1970, pp. 613–617.

7. KRSMANOVIC, D.: Initial and residual shear strength of hard rocks. Geotechnique, Vol. 17, 1967, pp. 145–160.

8. KRSMANOVIC, D., TUFO, M. and LANGOF, Z.: Shear strength of rock masses and possibilities of its reproduction on models. Proc. 1st Cong. Int. Soc. Rock Mech., Lisbon, 1966, Vol. 1, pp. 537–542.

9. LUNDBORG, N.: Triaxial shear strength of some Swedish rocks and ores. Proc. 1st Cong. Int. Soc. Rock Mech., Lisbon, 1966, Vol. 1, pp. 251–255.

10. LUNDBORG, N.: Strength of rock-like materials. Int. J. Rock Mech. Min. Sci., Vol. 5, No. 5, Sept., 1968, pp. 427–454.

11. MAURER, W. C.: Shear failure of rock under compression. Soc. Pet. Eng. J., Vol. 5, No. 2, June, 1965, pp. 167–176.

12. MAURER, W. C.: Shear failure of rock under axial and hydrostatic pressure. Proc. 1st Cong. Int. Soc. Rock Mech., Lisbon, 1966, Vol. 1, pp. 337–341.

13. MAZANTI, B. B. and SOWERS, G. F.: Laboratory testing of rock strength. Proc. Symp. Testing Techniques for Rock Mech., Seattle, Wash., 1965, pp. 207–227.

14. PROTODYAKONOV, M. M.: Methods of determining the shearing strength of rocks. In Mechanical Properties of Rocks by M. M. Protodyakonov, M. I. Koifman, and others. Translated from Russian. Jerusalem, Israel Program for Scientific Translations, 1969, pp. 15–27.

15. TAMADA, B.: Studies on the collapse phenomenon of sedimentary rock by absorption of water at landslide area. Rock Mech. in Japan, Vol. 1, 1970, pp. 68–70.

16. VOROPINOV, J.: Rheological research on rocks in shear. Proc. Geotechnical Conf. Shear Strength Properties of Natural Soils and Rocks, Oslo, 1967, Vol. 1, pp. 305–309.

17. WUERKER, R. G.: The shear strength of rocks. Min. Eng., Vol. 11, No. 10, Oct., 1959, pp. 1022–1026.

18. ZAHARY, G.: A study of strength characteristics of an andesite. Can. Min. Metall. Bull., Vol. 56, No. 620, Dec., 1963, pp. 874–876.

CHAPTER 5

Strength of Rock under Triaxial and Biaxial Stresses

5.1. Introduction

It is known that natural rock formations are in a triaxially stressed state and the strength of rock under such state is important in calculating the bearing capacity of foundation rocks and size of pillars, in the design of dams, in the study of the mechanism of folding and faulting and in deep drilling. Although, in laboratories, rock properties are mostly studied under stresses of a specific nature, such as compression, tensile, bending or shear stresses, a number of laboratory experiments on rock have been made under high confining pressure.

In this chapter, the strength of rock under triaxial stress will be considered in detail.

At the face, one of the principal stresses is zero and the rock is under bi-axial stress. Hence the strength of rock under biaxial stress is important and is included in a separate section in this chapter.

In this chapter a section on failure criteria is also included.

5.2. Testing Techniques

Properties of rocks under a triaxial stress have been studied by various methods. Since the pioneering work of VON KARMAN (1911), many accurate experiments have been made on jacketed cylindrical specimens subject to an axial force and lateral fluid-confining pressure. Although this kind of experiment has been called the triaxial test (Fig. 5-1a), the stress state in this experiment is limited to a special case in which two of the principal stresses are equal. In this book, this test is called the conventional triaxial test.

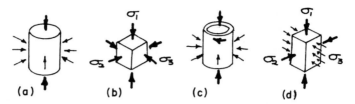

Fig. 5-1. Various methods for triaxial compression. Thick arrow indicates compression or torsion through solid end pieces; thin arrows indicate compression by fluid pressure: (a) axial compression or tension under fluid-confining pressure (conventional triaxial test); (b) triaxial compression by three solid pistons; (c) compression and torsion of a hollow cylinder under fluid-confining pressure; (d) triaxial compression by biaxial solid pistons and fluid-confining pressure (after MOGI, 1971 a).

To achieve more general stress states, various experiments have been made. These tests have included torsion of solid cylinders under compression, punching under confining pressure, Brazilian tests under confining pressure, and hollow cylinders under compression.

In principle, triaxial homogeneous stresses, $\sigma_1 > \sigma_2 > \sigma_3$, seem to be obtained by loading a rectangular parallelopiped across its three pairs of mutually perpendicular surfaces (Fig. 5-1b).

To obtain a homogeneous combined stress state, very thin hollow cylinders can also be subjected to combined compression and torsion under confining pressure (Fig. 5-1c). MOGI (1971a) used an arrangement shown in Fig. 5-1d.

5.3. Conventional Triaxial Test

The most commonly used arrangements are given in Fig. 5-2. These are

1. Longitudinal compression and confining pressure.
2. Longitudinal compression with confining pressure and interstitial pore pressure.
3. Longitudinal extension and confining pressure.

In all these cases, specimens are cylindrical in shape, but in extension tests, very often, specially prepared specimens similar to those used by the Rock Mechanics Division of the National Mechanical Engineering Research Institute of South Africa (Fig. 1-2) have been used (BRACE, 1963).

The rock specimens and the steel end discs are protected from coming in contact with the fluid by enclosing them in copper or brass sleeves (0.10–

0.15 mm (0.004–0.006 in) thick for compression tests and 0.15–0.25 mm
(0.006–0.010 in) thick for extension tests). These are sealed against the
conical surfaces of the upper and lower pistons using steel sealing rings.
Very often certain types of plastic, polythene or rubber sleeves are used in
place of copper or brass sleeves. When testing the specimens with confining
pressure and interstitial pressure, the piston ends are provided with several
openings (3–5) of 0.76 mm (0.03 in) diameter. In extension tests, bushings
are provided to centre the specimens in the high pressure cells.

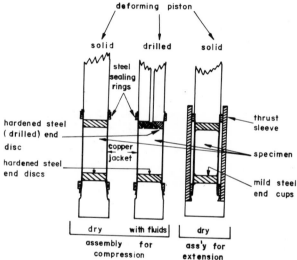

Fig. 5-2. Specimen mounting assembly for dry compression, compression with interstitial
fluids, and extension
(after HEARD, 1960).

5.3.1. Stress Distribution in Specimens under Triaxial Compression

KOTTE, BERCZES, GRAMBERG and SELDENRATH (1969) obtained stress
distribution for a cylinder with height-diameter ratio of 2 under triaxial
loading with a radial hydraulic supporting load of about 5% of the axial
load assuming FILON's boundary conditions. The values for σ_z, σ_r and σ_θ,
expressed in the unit σ_1 (average stress on the end planes) are given in Fig. 5-3.

Fig. 5-3 (a) shows that σ_z does not differ much from the picture of Fig. 2-3
(a) in Chapter 2 (uniaxial loading). Fig. 5-3 (b) and Fig. 5-3 (c) show that
the lines of equal stresses are positive (compression considered positive)
for every value of z and r, which signifies that in any point within the cylinder
only compressive stresses are induced while loading.

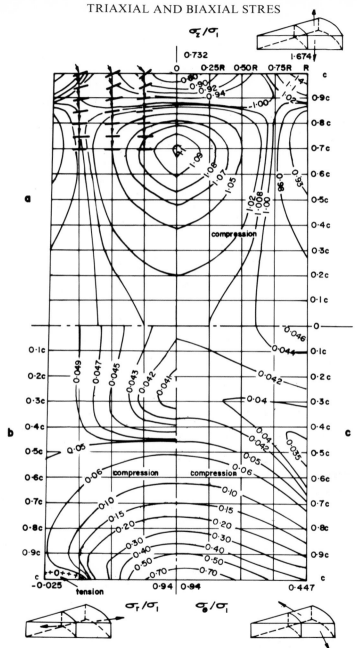

Fig. 5-3. Lines of equal principal stress under triaxial loading
(after KOTTE et al., 1969).

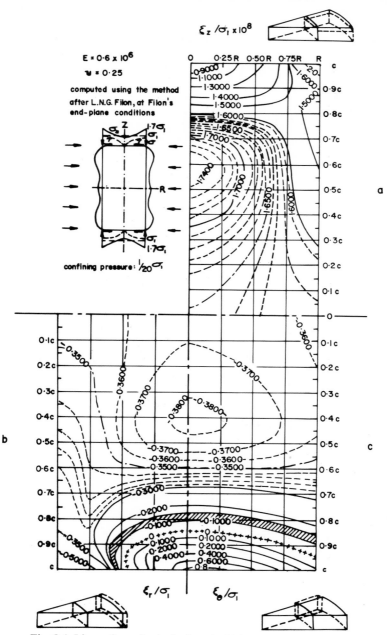

Fig. 5-4. Lines of equal principal strain under triaxial loading $\sigma_1 \times 10^6$ (after KOTTE et al., 1969).

In Fig. 5-4, lines of equal principal strain under triaxial loading are given. ε_z is compressive in every point within the cylinder. ε_r and ε_θ are tensile in some areas. That means, even though stresses are compressive in all parts of the specimen, corresponding strains can be tensile.

BRADY (1971) reported the results of a three-dimensional axisymmetric finite element investigation of the effect of confining pressure on the stress distribution within an elastic cylindrical specimen loaded axially between rough end plates of the same diameter as the specimen. The results indicate that end-effects arising from an elastic mismatch between the specimen and end-plate decrease gradually with an increase of confining pressure for values of σ_3/σ_1 (σ_3 is the confining pressure, σ_1 is the applied axial stress) less than 0.3. For values of σ_3/σ_1 equal to 0.1, end effects are negligible for height, h, to diameter, d, ratios of the specimen greater than 1.00. The effect of radial end-constraint on measurements of Young's modulus and Poisson's ratio is insignificant for a h/d value of the specimen of at least two provided these measurements are made in the central portions of the specimen.

5.3.2. Measurement of Strain

Measurement of strain is usually done with electrical resistance strain gauges. For accurate determination, it is essential to measure the strain in the central portion of the specimen with h/d value of at least two.

In one case, specimen ends were embedded in cup shaped loading pistons (Fig. 5-5) and the annular space was filled with an epoxy cement or with high temperature organosilicon cement. The specimen surface was covered with thin layers of epoxy cement or it was enclosed in a thin copper (0.10 mm (0.004 in) thick), rubber or polythene tube. The length of the free part of the specimen was $2d$ while the total length of the specimen was $2.5d$ ($d=$ diameter of the specimen). Strain gauges were mounted in the central portion of the specimen with the gauge length not more than $0.8d$ (BAIDYUK, 1967).

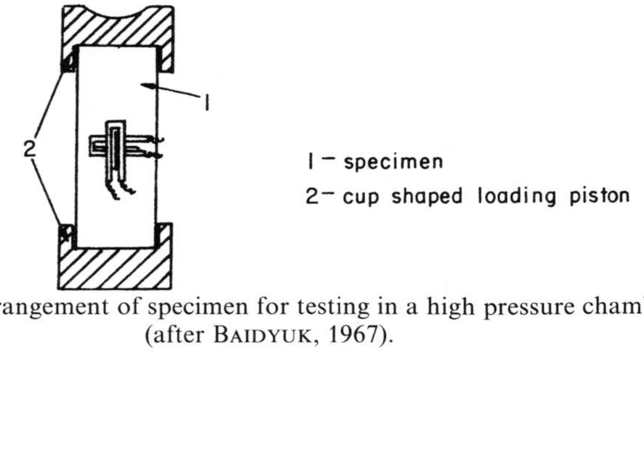

1 − specimen
2 − cup shaped loading piston

Fig. 5-5. Arrangement of specimen for testing in a high pressure chamber (after BAIDYUK, 1967).

Attempts have also been made to decrease the length of the test specimen by reducing the friction at the specimen ends. One arrangement is given in Fig. 5-6 (BAIDYUK, 1967). Here the loading surface consists of two 0.15 mm (0.006 in) thick copper discs soldered together at the edges with 0.20–0.30 mm (0.008–0.012 in) thick fluoroethylene packing placed in between them. The end plates are soldered to the copper sleeve meant to protect the specimen from the hydraulic fluid. The arrangement is reported to produce minimum barrel shaped bulging while the necessary length can be reduced to $1.2d$ with a gauge length of $0.8d$.

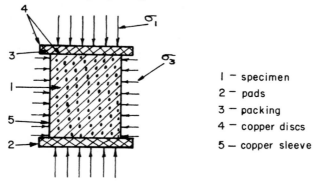

1 – specimen
2 – pads
3 – packing
4 – copper discs
5 – copper sleeve

Fig. 5-6. Arrangement of specimen for testing in a high pressure chamber with reduced friction on the ends
(after BAIDYUK, 1967).

5.3.3. Testing Equipment

The testing equipment for the study of rock properties under confining pressure consists of the following units:

1. A high pressure cell to house the specimen provided with connections for introducing high pressure fluid, with arrangements for loading the specimen and with appropriate connections for switching in pressure and strain measuring devices.

2. A loading machine for axial loading and a high pressure pump for introducing oil for lateral loading of the specimens.

3. Load and strain measuring and recording apparatus.

Conventional triaxial tests have been conducted on many rocks by various workers. VON KARMAN (1911) was the pioneer of the triaxial testing of rocks as we know it today. His apparatus was no different in principle from that used in the present conventional triaxial tests. His specimens were covered with a thin brass jacket to prevent the confining fluid from entering the pores in the rocks. In these experiments the axial compressive stress was greater than the confining pressure. BOKER (1915) adapted VON KARMAN's apparatus so that he could carry out 'extension' tests, in which the axial compressive stress was less than the confining pressure, and also torsion tests with a separate confining pressure and axial load.

Much of the present day work on rock deformation is associated with GRIGGS and his co-workers (GRIGGS and MILLER, 1951; GRIGGS, TURNER and HEARD, 1960; HANDIN, 1953; HANDIN and HAGER, 1957). They have been able to develop apparatus similar to VON KARMAN's operating at pressures up to about 1 GPa (145 000 lbf/in^2) and temperatures up to 800 °C (1 472 °F) (at temperatures above 300–400 °C (572–752 °F) a gas must be used to apply the confining pressure). For geological and geophysical applications, triaxial testing under high temperatures is required and this type of a apparatus is warranted for such work.

In 1958, MURRELL described the National Coal Board apparatus. PRICE (1958) used basically the same apparatus except that he used electrical resistance strain gauges for measurement of strain instead of dial gauges for measurement of deformation.

In 1959, a further experimental advance was made when ROBINSON studied the effect of pore pressures on the fracture of sedimentary rocks. In order to do this the ram in his apparatus had a hole drilled axially so that water could be forced under pressure into the rock.

SERDENGECTI and BOOZER (1961) designed one of the sophisticated pieces of apparatus which permits a study of the effect of confinement, temperature, pore pressure and rate of loading. They also described means of measuring the axial load and the axial deformation directly inside the pressure chamber which enables one to avoid the necessity of making corrections for the frictional forces exerted on the ram. Such equipment is warranted for research purposes.

In 1961, STAVROGIN (BAIDYUK, 1967) designed a novel apparatus in which the axial and radial pressures are applied simultaneously through the same fluid with the help of appropriately designed intensifiers. The stress state induced by this technique of loading is characteristic of the state of stress in the earth caused by the gravity field. Since, in all rock mechanics laboratories, compression testing machines are available for uniaxial testing, equipment for applying lateral pressures only is purchased.

In 1963, OBERT designed a simple and inexpensive apparatus for triaxial testing of rocks at room temperature. In 1964, SCHWARTZ described an apparatus with a facility to study the effect of pore pressures on the fracture of rocks. NEFF (1965) also described a triaxial compression chamber with pore pressure measuring capability. HOEK and FRANKLIN (1968) also developed a simple and inexpensive cell.

LOGAN and HANDIN (1970) developed an apparatus employing a gas loading cylinder which allows axial strain rates up to 10^2/s on a specimen 2 cm (0.79 in) in diameter and 4 cm (1.57 in) long.

In recent years, equipment for dynamic testing (SAUCIER, 1966; EHRGOTT, 1970) and for high stiffness testing (BIENIAWSKI et al., 1969) has also been developed. Such equipment would be useful for determining dynamic triaxial strength and strength of fractured rock respectively.

Depending upon the requirements of the experimenter, the testing equipment will be selected. For normal engineering applications, equipment similar to U.S.B.M. apparatus (Figs. 5-7, 5-8 and 5-9) or HOEK and FRANKLIN apparatus (Fig. 5-10) can be recommended. The American Society for Testing and Materials (A.S.T.M.) issued a standard in 1968 under designation D 2664-67. In summary, the standard is as follows:

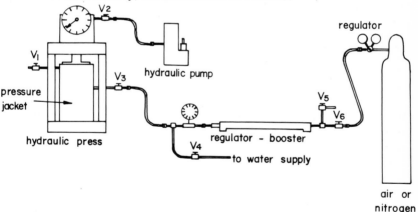

Fig. 5-7. Schematic diagram of hydraulic system in U.S.B.M. apparatus (after OBERT, 1963).

Loading device: A suitable device for applying axial load to the specimen. It shall be of sufficient capacity to apply load at a rate conforming to the requirements set forth under 'Procedure'.

Pressure maintaining device: A hydraulic pump, pressure intensifier (a pressure intensifier as described by OBERT (1963) has been found to fulfil the requirements) or other system of sufficient capacity to maintain constant the desired lateral pressure, σ_3.

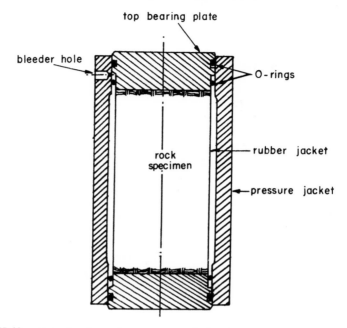

Fig. 5-8. Half section of rock specimen, pressure jacket, and bearing plate assembly (after OBERT, 1963).

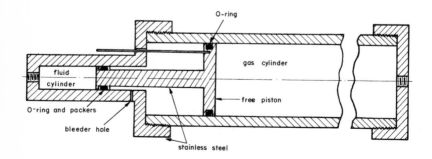

Fig. 5-9. Half section of the regulator-booster for the hydraulic system (after OBERT, 1963).

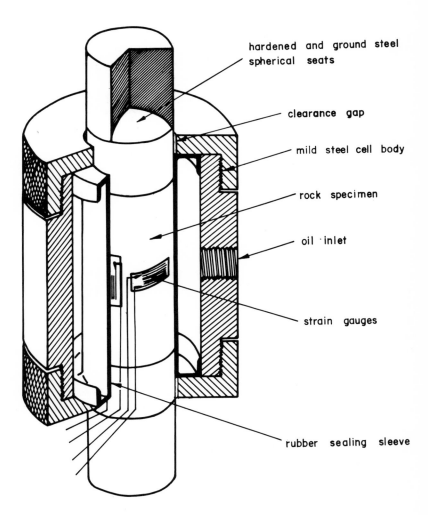

hardened and ground steel
spherical seats

clearance gap

mild steel cell body

rock specimen

oil inlet

strain gauges

rubber sealing sleeve

Fig. 5-10. Cutaway view of triaxial cell
(after HOEK and FRANKLIN, 1968).

Triaxial compression chamber: An apparatus in which the test specimen may be enclosed in an impermeable flexible membrane; placed between two hardened platens, one of which shall be spherically seated; subjected to a constant lateral fluid pressure; and then loaded axially to failure. The platens shall be made of tool steel hardened to a minimum of Rockwell C 58, the bearing faces of which shall not depart from plane surfaces by more than 0.0127 mm (0.0005 in) when the platens are new and which shall be maintained within a permissible variation of 0.0254 mm (0.001 in). In addition to the platens and membrane, the apparatus shall consist of a high-pressure cylinder with overflow valve, a base, suitable entry ports for filling the cylinder with hydraulic fluid and applying the lateral pressure, and hoses, gauges, and valves as needed.

Deformation measuring device: High-grade dial micrometers or other measuring devices graduated to read in 0.002 mm (0.0001 in) units, and accurate within 0.002 mm (0.0001 in) in any 0.02 mm (0.001 in) range, and within 0.005 mm (0.0002 in) in any 0.2 mm (0.01 in) range shall be provided for measuring axial deformation due to loading. These may consist of micrometer screws, dial micrometers, or linear variable differential transformers securely attached to the high pressure cylinder.

Electrical resistance strain gauges applied directly to the rock specimen in the axial direction may also be used. In addition, the use of circumferentially applied strain gauges will permit the observation of data necessary in the calculation of Poisson's ratio. In this case three axial (vertical) gauges should be equally spaced around the specimen at mid-height and three circumferential (horizontal) gauges similarly located around the circumference.

Flexible membrane: A flexible membrane of suitable material to exclude the confining fluid from the specimen, and which shall not significantly extrude into abrupt surface pores. It should be sufficiently long to extend well onto the platens and when slightly stretched be of the same diameter as the rock specimen. (Neoprene rubber tubing of 1.6 mm (1/16 in) wall thickness and of 40 to 60 Durometer hardness, Shore Type A, has been found generally suitable for this purpose.)

Test specimens: Test specimens shall be right circular cylinders within the tolerances herein specified. The sides of the specimen shall be generally smooth and free of abrupt irregularities with all elements straight to within 0.1 mm (0.005 in) over the full length of the specimen. The ends of the specimen shall be cut parallel to each other and at right angles to the longitudinal axis. They shall be ground and lapped until flat to 0.02 mm (0.001 in). The ends shall not depart from perpendicularity to the axis of the specimen by more than 0.25 deg. The specimen shall have a height-to-diameter ratio (h/d) of 2.0 to 2.5 and a diameter of not less than NX core size, approximately 54 mm (2–1/8 in).

(It is desirable that the diameter of specimens be at least 10 times greater than the diameter of the largest mineral grain. It is considered that the specified minimum specimen diameter of approximately 54 mm (2-1/8 in) will satisfy this criterion in the majority of cases. Since specimens larger than the specified minimum may require excessively large loading devices to cause failure, it may be necessary in some instances to test specimens that do not comply with this criterion. In this case, or when cores of diameter smaller than the specified minimum must be tested because of the unavailability of larger size specimens, suitable notation of these facts shall be made in the test report.)

The diameter of the test specimen shall be determined to the nearest 0.2 mm (0.01 in) by averaging two diameters measured at right angles to each other at about mid-height of the specimen. The height of the test specimen shall be determined by averaging five equally distributed measurements of the height of the specimen, taken by means of a dial comparator.

Moisture condition of the specimen at time of test can have a significant effect upon the indicated strength of the rock. Good practice generally dictates that laboratory tests be made upon specimens representative of field conditions. Thus it follows that the field moisture condition of the specimen should be preserved until time of test. On the other hand, there may be reasons for testing specimens at other moisture contents including zero. In any case the moisture content of the test specimen should be tailored to the problem at hand. In report, moisture content and degree of saturation at time of test should be included.

Procedure: Place the lower platen on the base. Wipe clean the bearing faces of the upper and lower platens and of the test specimen, and place the test specimen on the lower platen. Place the upper platen on the specimen and properly align. Fit the flexible membrane over the specimen and platens and instal rubber or neoprene O-rings to seal the specimen from the confining fluid. Place the cylinder over the specimen, ensuring proper seal with the base, and connect hydraulic pressure lines. Position the deformation measuring device and fill the chamber with hydraulic fluid. Apply a slight axial load, approximately 110 N (25 lbf), to the triaxial compression chamber by means of the loading device in order to properly seat the bearing parts of the apparatus. Take an initial reading on the deformation device. Slowly raise the lateral fluid pressure to the pre-determined test level and at the same time apply sufficient axial load to prevent the deformation measuring device from deviating from the initial reading. When the pre-determined test level of fluid pressure is reached, note and record the axial load registered by the loading device. Consider this load to be the zero or starting load for the test.

Apply axial load continuously and without shock until the load becomes constant, or reduces, or a pre-determined amount of strain is achieved. Apply the load in such a manner as to produce a strain rate as constant as feasible throughout the test. Do not permit the strain rate at any given time to deviate by more than 10 per cent from that selected. The strain rate selected should be that which will produce failure of a similar test specimen in unconfined compression, in a test time of between 2 and 15 min. The selected strain rate for a given rock type shall be adhered to for all tests in a given series or investigation. Maintain constant the pre-determined confining pressure throughout the test and observe and record readings of deformation as required.

Calculations: Since total deformation is recorded during the test, suitable calibration for apparatus deformation must be made. This may be accomplished by inserting into the apparatus a steel cylinder having proven elastic properties and observing differences in deformation between the assembly and steel cylinder throughout the loading range. The apparatus deformation is then subtracted from the total deformation at each increment of load in order to arrive at specimen deformation from which the axial strain of the specimen is computed.

Because of the heterogeneous nature of rock and the scatter in results often encountered, it is considered good practice to make at least three tests of essentially identical specimens at each confining pressure investigated.

Where the role of pore pressure is important, it is better to test saturated specimens with controlled pore pressure. For such tests, provision has to be made in the apparatus for introducing interstitial fluid into the specimen independently and at any desired pressure. HECK (1970) suggested one method to A.S.T.M. as a possible standard. The relevant portions are given here.

Pore pressure – maintaining equipment: A water supply tank with a capacity of 7 200 cm^3 (2 gal) to store rust-inhibited water. It shall be strong enough to withstand about 1.4 MPa (200 lbf/in^2) air pressure. A pressure intensifier (OBERT's one has been found to be satisfactory), pressure regulator, nitrogen gas pressure bottle, pressure transducers that operate in the range of 0 to 70 MPa (0 to 10 000 lbf/in^2), strain indicators or x–y recorder, valves, hoses and fittings of sufficient capacity to apply and regulate the desired pore pressure shall be provided. Low pressure gauges (0 to 10 MPa) (0 to 1 500 lbf/

in²) graduated to read in units of not more than 50 kPa (10 lbf/in²) may be used in place of the transducers when the induced pore pressure is not expected to be greater than 10 MPa (1 500 lbf/in²). Calibration of the transducers with a dead load tester shall be performed before they are to be used.

A pore fluid pressure is applied to the specimen from both ends through five radially drilled holes in the platens. As the test specimen is axially loaded, with the pore pressure system closed, the induced pore pressure is measured by means of suitable pressure transducers or gauges.

The test specimen shall be tested in a saturated condition. This is accomplished by simple immersion in water at atmospheric pressure, under vacuum, or pressure, or a combination of these depending upon the porosity and permeability of the rock.

Before the test is begun the specimen shall be back-pressured in the assembled triaxial apparatus to drive any remaining air bubbles into solution in order to obtain complete saturation. This is accomplished by observing the incremental rise in pore pressure that occurs as a result of a corresponding increase in chamber pressure. When both are equal, the rock specimen is fully saturated.

5.3.4. Results

Effect of confining pressure on strength of rock

VON KARMAN (1911) conducted experiments on specimens of Carrara marble in copper jackets at room temperature. The results of these experiments typify of the salient features of rock behaviour in triaxial tests, Fig. 5-11. As the confining pressure increases, the compressive strength increases.

MURRELL (1958) found a large increase in compressive strength as the confining pressure is increased. He tested Cwmtillery and Barnsley Hard coals and found that at higher pressures their strengths tend to a similar value in the range 103.4 to 137.9 MPa (15 000 to 20 000 lbf/in²) (at 27.58 MPa (4 000 lbf/in²) confining pressure) although their uniaxial compressive strengths are in the ratio of 5 : 1. Thus the strength of weaker coal (Cwmtillery) rises at a faster rate with the confining pressure.

HOBBS (1964) reported the results of laboratory measurements of the effect of a confining pressure on the compressive strength of a number of distinct coals. At atmospheric pressure the mean fracture strengths range from

2.21 to 51.37 MPa (320 to 7450 lbf/in²) and at a confining pressure of
34.48 MPa (5000 lbf/in²) the mean fracture strengths range, with the ex-
ception of anthracite from 109.77 to 144.86 MPa (15920 to 21010 lbf/in²).

SCHWARTZ (1964) tested specimens of granite, sandstone, limestone and
marble and found that the effect of confining pressure on shear strength
$(\sigma_1-\sigma_3)/2$ is much greater for granite and sandstone as compared with
limestone and marble. Strength of rock increases by greatest increment
under initial confining pressure. As confining pressure increases further,

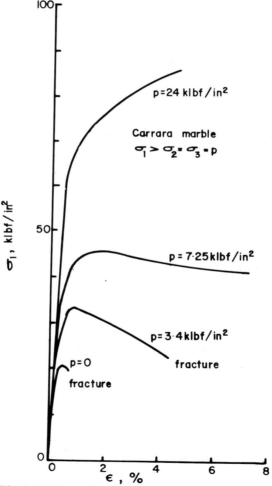

Fig. 5-11. The results of triaxial tests on Carrara marble
(after VON KARMAN, 1911).

the corresponding increase in strength becomes less and less. At high confining pressures, the strength of limestone is nearly constant.

EVANS and POMEROY (1966) reached similar conclusions from the tests on coal specimens. They reported that compressive strength increases with confining pressure for all coals but the manner of increase varies from coal to coal. Some of the results are given in Fig. 5-12.

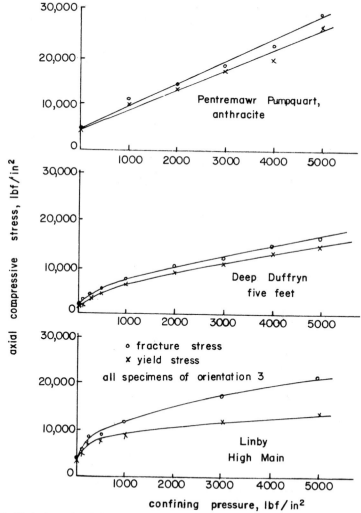

5-12. Variation of axial compressive yield and fracture stress with confining pressure (after EVANS and POMEROY, 1966).

They also reported that differential stress at failure $(\sigma_1-\sigma_3)$ also increases with confining pressure. For Linby coal, however, the increase in differential stress at confining pressures above 6.9 MPa (1 000 lbf/in^2) is small.

The pressure dependence of rock strength in the 'brittle' domain (Fig. 5-13) has been graphically categorised into three zones by MOGI (1966). These zones are

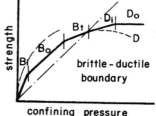

Fig. 5-13. A typical strength-pressure curve of dry rocks at room temperatures (after MOGI, 1966).

(i) B_i – The strength vs pressure curve is nonlinear and concave downward. The breaking strength increases while the rate of the increase decreases with the addition of confining pressure.

(ii) B_0 – The strength increases linearly with pressure.

(iii) B_t – The slope of the strength vs pressure curve is gradually decreasing. This zone represents the transition between purely brittle and brittle – ductile behaviour.

While these zones are typical of brittle rocks, some rock types such as quartzite consist primarily of B_0 and lack the B_i zone. Other rock types such as granite tend to change continuously from B_i to B_t. However, for small values of confining pressure, carbonate rocks do display a linear strength-pressure relation.

The pressure dependency of failure stress is different in different types of failure, brittle fracture and ductile flow (MOGI, 1970). In brittle fracture, the breaking strength greatly increases with the increasing pressure, but the yield stress in ductile flow approaches to constant values.

The relationship between confining pressures (σ_3) and axial stress (σ_1) at failure is linear (Figs. 5-14 to 5-16) for many rocks and can be represented by the equation

$$\sigma_1=\sigma_c+m\,\sigma_3 \qquad (5.1)$$

where σ_c = uniaxial compressive strength for a specimen having $\dfrac{h}{d}$ ratio 2
and
m = constant.

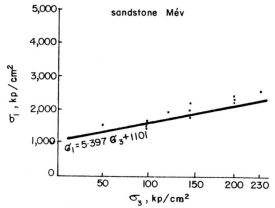

Fig. 5-14. Relationship between principal stresses at failure, obtained with sandstone specimens $(\sigma_1-\sigma_3)$
(after BODONYI, 1970).

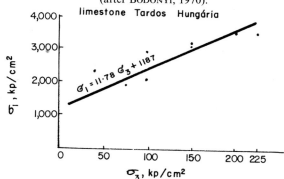

Fig. 5-15. Relationship between principal stresses at failure, obtained with crystalline limestone specimens $(\sigma_1-\sigma_3)$
(after BODONYI, 1970).

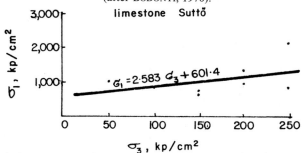

Fig. 5-16. Relationship between principal stresses at failure, obtained with loose-textured limestone specimens $(\sigma_1-\sigma_3)$
(after BODONYI, 1970).

RYABININ, BERESNEV and MARTINOV (1971), after performing many experiments on the pressure effect on plasticity and strength of various kinds of solids pointed out the following:

Brittle rupture takes place only up to a definite pressure called the 'threshold pressure'. At pressures higher than this threshold, the substance converts from the brittle state into the plastic one. Further pressure increases the plasticity.

One of the causes of increased plasticity is that the additional pressure tends to change the stressed state. As a result, the main normal stress values acting in a sliding plane under the definite hydrostatic pressure become compressed instead of stretched. The possible formation and development of specimen microcracks is thereby suppressed, and the plastic deformation process is promoted.

The second cause of increased plasticity is that deformation under high pressure cures the microcracks that earlier existed.

The third cause is that under pressure changes occur in the physical nature of the processes that are the basis for plastic deformation. The high pressure greatly affects the dislocation phenomena, making more active the process of low temperature overcreeping of dislocations during the deformation, which results in further plastic flow.

They have investigated deformation properties of such rocks as gabbro, granitoid, diabase, granite, and eclogite. The results of the experiments performed at room temperature under pressure of 1 GPa (145033 lbf/in²) (10 kbar) are given in Fig. 5-17. The rocks that undergo brittle rupture under atmospheric pressure, at high pressure, acquire the possibility of large deformations without rupture. This points to the fact that under high pressure the rocks become plastic. It is only granite and eclogite that break brittle, but at the excess stresses under atmospheric pressure. For the possibility of plastic deformation, they need to be pressed at more than 1 GPa (145033 lbf/in²) (10 kbar).

Their experiments showed that under high pressure the brittle substances undergo profound 'strength increasing', the more brittle the substance the stronger the strength – increasing effect under pressure. Fig. 5-18 illustrates the igneous rock strength as a function of pressure in the strengthening region at deformations up to 1–2%. With pressure rising from atmospheric to 1 GPa (145033 lbf/in²) (10 kbar) the igneous rock strength increases by 4 or 5 times.

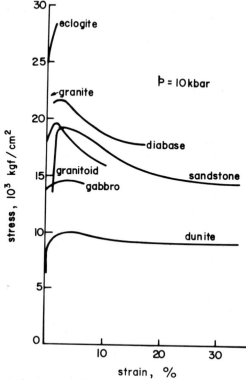

Fig. 5-17. Deformation curves of various rocks under pressure of 10 kbar
(after RYABININ et al., 1971).

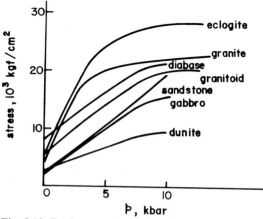

Fig. 5-18. Rock strength as a function of pressure
(after RYABININ et al., 1971).

With the deformation above the specified limit, the strengthening process converts into discontinuity strengthening, the dislocation accumulation being due to enormous stress concentration near the boundary interface. The dislocation accumulation causes such a state when the forming micro-crack amount exceeds the microcrack value curing in the deformation process under pressure. Further deformation results in the specimen rupture.

In summary, it may be said that the effect of confining pressure on triaxial strength varies from rock to rock. Although the compressive strength increases with the confining pressure, the rate of increase depends upon the rock type as well as upon the level of confining pressure.

Effect of h/d ratio on triaxial compressive strength:

In a study of end effects in the conventional triaxial compression test, MOGI (1966) showed that end effects markedly disappear with increasing confining pressure. One of the results is reproduced in Fig. 5-19. The failure strength at 1 atmosphere (0.1 MPa) (14.71 lbf/in²) is greatly affected by the height/ diameter ratio of a cylindrical rock specimen, but under high confining pressure it becomes independent of the ratio. The result shows that the end effect of the dolomite specimen connected to the steel end-pieces by epoxy cement is negligible under the confining pressure of a few hundred bars (tens of MPa) (thousands of lbf/in²) and over.

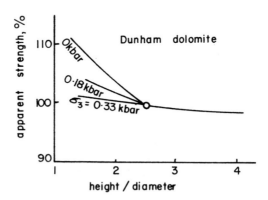

Fig. 5-19. Relation between apparent compressive strength under confining pressure and height/diameter ratio of cylindrical specimens in Dunham dolomite. The relative strength is recalculated for the strength at height/diameter = 2.5. Numerals for each curve indicate the confining pressure
(after MOGI, 1966).

Effect of shape on triaxial compressive strength of rock:

BYERLEE (1967) used two specimen configurations while measuring the fracture strength of granite under confinement. One was a straight cylinder 1.58 cm (0.62 in) in diameter and 3.8 cm (1.5 in) long; the other was 1.58 cm (0.62 in) in diameter and 5.08 cm (2.00 in) long, but having a central 3 cm (1.18 in) section reduced to a diameter of 1.11 cm (0.44 in). Stress concentrations were avoided at the ends of the reduced section by fillets of 0.3 cm (0.12 in) radius of curvature. In Fig. 5-20 the axial stress σ_1 at fracture is plotted against confining pressure σ_3. The open circles are the results from specimens with a reduced central section; there is no appreciable effect due to differences in configuration of the specimens.

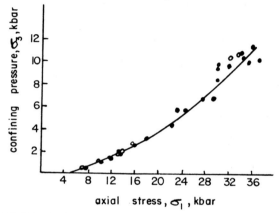

Fig. 5-20. Principal stresses at fracture for virgin samples of granite (after BYERLEE, 1967).

Effect of loading path on strength of rock:

Two different loading procedures are commonly used for triaxial testing: proportional loading and constant confining stress loading. In proportional loading, the confining stress and the axial stress on the specimen are applied in a fixed ratio. This can be achieved by a simple mechanical-hydraulic system, or by a more sophisticated electrical-hydraulic closed-loop servo-controlled system. In constant confining stress loading, the confining stress is applied completely, before any significant axial stress has been applied, and then is kept constant as the specimen is loaded axially. The confining stress can be kept constant by manually controlling a hydraulic pressure generator, or by using a precision relief valve or a closed-loop servo-mechanism (CROUCH, 1972a).

SWANSON and BROWN (1971) investigated the effect of stress loading path on fracture or maximum stress for several rocks. For this study, a special testing apparatus was constructed. This uses conventional cylindrical specimens under pressures up to 0.7 MPa (101.5 lbf/in²), but with the unique features that the ratio of the two independent principal stresses could be controlled by means of electro-hydraulic servo-systems, thus controlling the stress loading path. The fundamental result observed is that the maximum stresses in all rocks tested are independent of the stress loading path. Typical results are given in Figs. 5-21 and 5-22. The loading paths employed are illustrated in these figures. It can be seen that a consistent and smooth curve can be passed through the data independent of the path used to arrive at the failure locus. CROUCH (1972a) also confirmed this after conducting experiments on a South African norite.

Effect of temperature on triaxial compressive strength

HANDIN and HAGER (1957, 1958) conducted a number of experiments on various sedimentary rocks under confining pressures at room and high temperatures. Figs. 5-23 and 5-24 show changes in ultimate strength of different sedimentary rocks with increase in depth of occurrence.

GRIGGS, TURNER and HEARD (1960) tested a number of rocks at various temperatures. Their results are given in Fig. 5-25. It is seen that the effect of rise in temperature on different types of rocks is different. The effect is more pronounced on calcite than on silicate igneous rocks. Dolomite remains almost unaffected by rise in temperature. At 800 °C (1472 °F) dolomite is considerably stronger than basalt though at lower temperatures (below 500 °C (932 °F)) basalt is stronger than dolomite.

SERDENGECTI and BOOZER (1961) also showed that at constant confining pressure and strain rate, the effect of increase in temperature is to decrease the strength of rocks.

SEIFERT (1969) determined the strength of Adirondack anorthosite in triaxial compressive tests for temperatures from 400 to 1000 °C (752 to 1832 °F) and for confining pressures between 440 and 1480 MPa (63814 and 214648 lbf/in²). The strength increases with increasing confining pressure and with decreasing temperature ranging from 2.5 GPa (362582 lbf/in²) at 400 °C (752 °F) and 1.48 GPa (214648 lbf/in²) to less than 200 MPa (29007 lbf/in²) at 1000 °C (1832 °F), and 440 MPa (63814 lbf/in²) for 8 per cent strain.

From these results, it can be said that the strength decreases with rise in temperature, although the effect is different on different types of rocks.

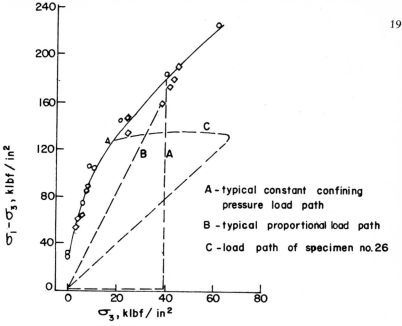

A - typical constant confining
    pressure load path

B - typical proportional load path

C - load path of specimen no. 26

Fig. 5-21. Failure locus for Westerly granite
(after SWANSON and BROWN, 1971).

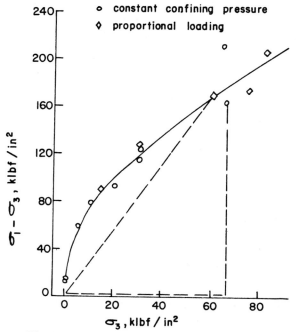

Fig. 5-22. Failure locus for Cedar City tonalite
(after SWANSON and BROWN, 1971).

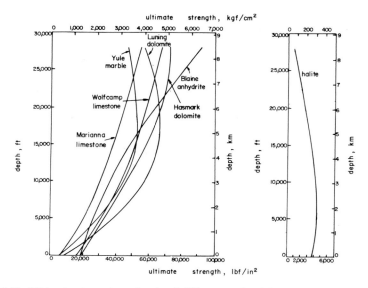

Fig. 5-23. Ultimate strength *vs* depth of different rocks deformed dry in compression
at confining pressures from 0 to 2000 bars at temperatures from 24° to 300 °C
(after HANDIN and HAGER, 1958).

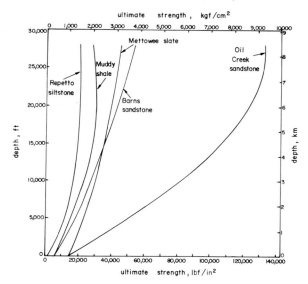

Fig. 5-24. Ultimate strength *vs* depth of different rocks deformed dry in compression
at confining pressures from 0 to 2000 bars at temperatures from 24° to 300 °C
(after HANDIN and HAGER, 1958).

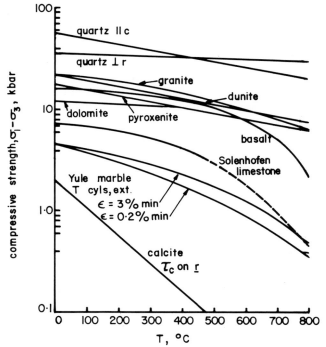

Fig. 5-25. Strength of rocks and minerals at 5 kbar. Note logarithmic scale of ordinate;
2, 3, and 5 are accented on each decade
(after GRIGGS, TURNER and HEARD, 1960).

Effect of pore pressure on strength of rock

Some of the early work in triaxial testing was done by GRIGGS in 1936 with unjacketed specimens of rock. In these tests the pore pressure tended to become equal to the confining pressure. A brittle-type failure was observed at 405.6 MPa (58 840 lbf/in²) in Solenhofen limestone and in marble. With higher confining pressures, GRIGGS observed plastic flow. In subsequent work, GRIGGS and his co-workers (GRIGGS, 1940; HANDIN and GRIGGS, 1951), jacketed their specimens, and most of the rocks were tested with pore pressure equal to zero. The results of this work demonstrated that the strength of the rock and the mode of the failure are dependent on the confining pressure. Comparison of the two types of tests, unjacketed and jacketed, indicated that the application of pore pressure changed the properties of rocks.

ROBINSON (1959) studied the effect of pore pressure on limestone, sandstone and shale specimens. He tested cylindrical specimens (1.91 cm (0.75 in) in diameter and 3.81 cm (1.5 in) long) at a constant strain rate of 0.038 mm/s (0.0015 in/s). He found that yield strength (yield strength represents the stress at which an increase in strain does not produce an accompanying increase in stress) increases as the pore pressure decreases (Figs. 5-26 and 5-27). From the study of the effect of pore pressure on yield strength of Indiana limestone, he found that when the confining and pore pressures are almost equal a slight decrease in pore pressure results in a large increase in yield strength (Fig. 5-28). These results present evidence that the strength of porous rocks is a function of the "effective confining pressure" (confining pressure – pore pressure).

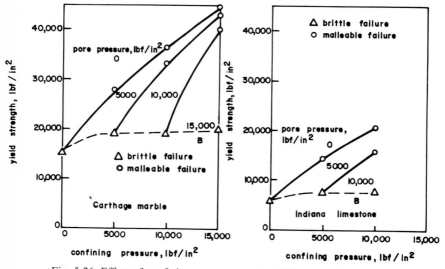

Fig. 5-26. Effect of confining pressure on the yield strength of limestone (after Robinson, 1959).

Serdengecti and Boozer (1961) carried out extensive tests on different rocks to study the effect of pore pressure on triaxial strength. They also found that the yield strength is a function of the effective confining pressure rather than the absolute values of the confining and interstitial pressures. According to them, the effective confining pressure concept is valid both for mineral oil and water saturated specimens.

Handin, Hager, Friedman and Feather (1963) tested Berea sandstone, Marianna limestone, Hasmark dolomite, Repetto siltstone and Muddy shale in triaxial compression in which the external confining pressures and internal pore pressures (to 200 MPa (29006.5 lbf/in^2)) are applied and measured independently.

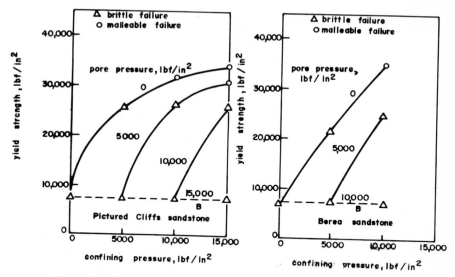

Fig. 5-27. Effect of confining pressure on the yield strength of sandstone
(after ROBINSON, 1959).

The ultimate strength of porous rocks is found to depend on effective confining pressure – the difference between external and internal pressures when the pore fluid is chemically inert, the permeability is sufficient to insure pervasion and uniform pressure distribution, and the configuration of pore space is such that the interstitial hydrostatic (neutral) pressure is transmitted fully throughout the solid framework. One typical result is given in Fig. 5-29.

The effects of pore pressure on ultimate compressive strength are illustrated with better geological perspective by plotting these parameters against depth of burial (Fig. 5-30). In Figs. 5-23 and 5-24, ultimate compressive strengths of dry rocks as functions of depth are given.

SCHWARTZ (1964) studied the effect of pore pressure on the triaxial strength of limestone, sandstone, granite and marble. The void ratio of limestone and sandstone specimens is approximately 0.20 whereas granite and marble specimens have values of approximately 0.02. The first two rocks are, therefore, very porous while the other two rocks are more or less impervious. Tests were conducted for pore pressures of 6.9 MPa, 20.7 MPa and 34.5 MPa (1 000 lbf/in^2, 3 000 lbf/in^2 and 5 000 lbf/in^2). The maximum differential stress ($\sigma_1 - \sigma_3$) is compared to the average strength of the dry specimens which are confined by pressure equal to the difference between pore and confining pressures applied to the saturated specimens. Results indicate that strength of the porous rocks is essentially the same, whether tested dry or saturated, when compared using the concept of "effective confining pressure" (Fig. 5-31). On the other hand, the strength of the impervious rocks show no correlation with the "effective confining pressure" (Fig. 5-32).

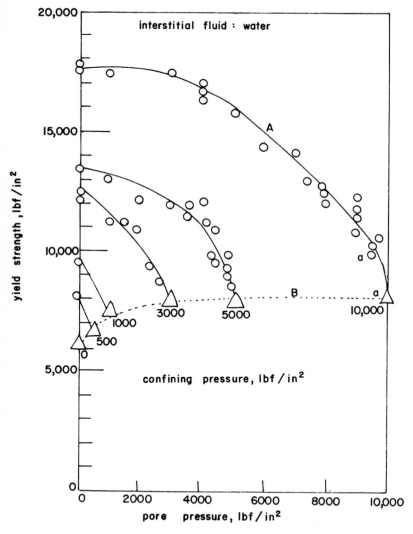

Fig. 5-28. Effect of pore pressure on the yield strength of Indiana limestone (after ROBINSON, 1959).

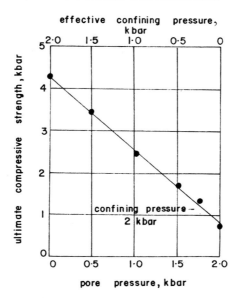

Fig. 5-29. Ultimate compressive strength of Berea sandstone at 24 °C, 2 kilobars confining
pressure as function of pore pressure and effective confining pressure
(after HANDIN et al., 1963).

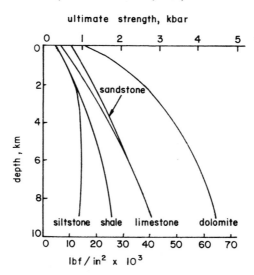

Fig. 5-30. Ultimate compressive strengths of water-saturated rocks as functions of depth.
Effects of confining (overburden) pressure, temperature (30 °C/km), and "normal"
formation (pore) pressure included
(after HANDIN et al., 1963).

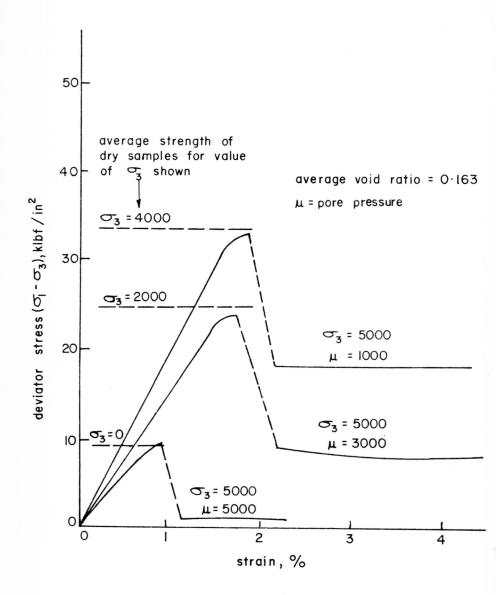

Fig. 5-31. Pore pressure tests for Pottsville sandstone
(after SCHWARTZ, 1964).

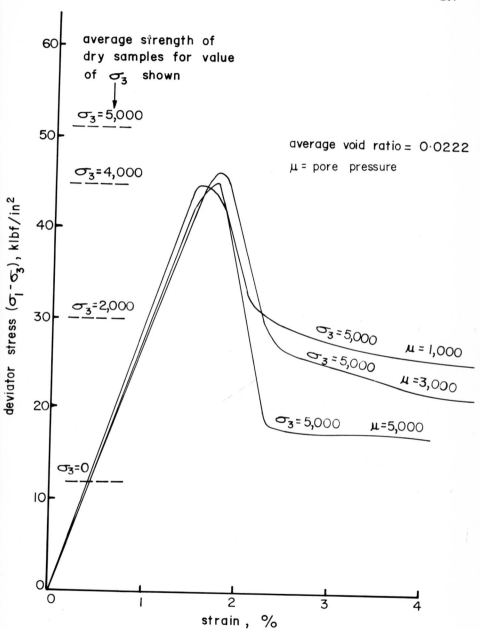

Fig. 5-32. Pore pressure tests for Stone Mountain granite
(after SCHWARTZ, 1964).

Brace and Martin (1968) conducted triaxial experiments on a variety of crystalline silicate rocks of low porosity (0.001–0.03) at strain rates from about 10^{-3} to $10^{-8}/s$ to test the law of effective stress. Comparison of the fracture strengths at different pore pressures revealed that the law of effective stress held for these rocks only when loading rate was less than some critical value which depended on permeability of the rock, viscosity of the pore fluid and specimen geometry. For example, in their experiments with water, it was about $10^{-7}/s$ for cylindrical specimens of granite several centimetres long. In experiments at loading rates greater than the critical value, the rock was as much as 50 per cent stronger than at zero pressure.

TABLE 23

Comparison of drained tests on Berea sandstone at equal effective confining pressures

(after Aldrich, 1969)

Effective confining pressure		Chamber pressure		Pore pressure		Maximum differential stress	
MPa	(lbf/in²)	MPa	(lbf/in²)	MPa	(lbf/in²)	MPa	(lbf/in²)
0	(0)	0	(0)	0	(0)	60.0	(8700)
		34.5	(5000)	34.5	(5000)	56.7	(8220)
20.7	(3000)	20.7	(3000)	0	(0)	172.9	(25070)
		34.5	(5000)	13.8	(2000)	169.5	(24580)
		44.8	(6500)	24.1	(3500)	166.8	(24190)
		69.0	(10000)	48.3	(7000)	167.1	(24240)
34.5	(5000)	34.5	(5000)	0	(0)	205.6	(29820)
		48.3	(7000)	13.8	(2000)	210.8	(30570)
		69.0	(10000)	34.5	(5000)	212.5	(30820)
55.2	(8000)	55.2	(8000)	0	(0)	253.9	(36820)
		69.0	(10000)	13.8	(2000)	250.4	(36320)

Aldrich (1969) investigated the effects of pore pressure on Berea sandstone deformed at room temperature and 0 to 55.2 MPa (0 to 8000 lbf/in²) effective confining pressure. "Drained" tests, in which the applied pore pressure is kept constant at a preselected level, and "undrained" tests, in which applied pore pressure is allowed to fluctuate during loading, were conducted. Several tests were also conducted on air-dry specimens.

The drained tests show that the effective stress theory is applicable to Berea sandstone, and that wet specimens are approximately 11 per cent weaker than air-dry specimens at all pressure levels (Tables 23 and 24).

Peak strength (strength at failure) of an undrained test specimen is controlled by the effective confining pressure at failure, and the magnitude of pore pressure rise in the specimen is governed by the initial effective confining pressure.

TABLE 24
Summary data for drained tests
(after ALDRICH, 1969)

Chamber pressure		Applied pore pressure		Effective confining pressure		Maximum differential stress	
MPa	(lbf/in²)	MPa	(lbf/in²)	MPa	(lbf/in²)	MPa	(lbf/in²)
0	(0)	0	(0)	0	(0)	59.8	(8680)
34.5	(5000)	34.5	(5000)	0	(0)	58.4	(8470)
34.5	(5000)	34.5	(5000)	0	(0)	55.0	(7980)
13.8	(2000)	6.9	(1000)	6.9	(1000)	106.0	(15380)
13.8	(2000)	6.9	(1000)	6.9	(1000)	103.6	(15020)
20.7	(3000)	0	(0)	20.7	(3000)	171.0	(24800)
20.7	(3000)	0	(0)	20.7	(3000)	174.7	(25330)
34.5	(5000)	13.8	(2000)	20.7	(3000)	167.8	(24330)
34.5	(5000)	13.8	(2000)	20.7	(3000)	169.1	(24520)
34.5	(5000)	13.8	(2000)	20.7	(3000)	171.8	(24920)
44.8	(6500)	24.1	(3500)	20.7	(3000)	166.7	(24180)
69.0	(10000)	48.3	(7000)	20.7	(3000)	159.4	(23120)
69.0	(10000)	48.3	(7000)	20.7	(3000)	174.9	(25360)
34.5	(5000)	0	(0)	34.5	(5000)	212.6	(30840)
34.5	(5000)	0	(0)	34.5	(5000)	206.6	(29960)
34.5	(5000)	0	(0)	34.5	(5000)	201.7	(29260)
69.0	(10000)	34.5	(5000)	34.5	(5000)	213.6	(30980)
69.0	(10000)	34.5	(5000)	34.5	(5000)	213.6	(30980)
69.0	(10000)	34.5	(5000)	34.5	(5000)	210.2	(30490)
48.3	(7000)	13.8	(2000)	34.5	(5000)	212.1	(30760)
48.3	(7000)	13.8	(2000)	34.5	(5000)	211.1	(30620)
48.3	(7000)	13.8	(2000)	34.5	(5000)	209.2	(30340)
55.2	(8000)	0	(0)	55.2	(8000)	254.6	(36920)
55.2	(8000)	0	(0)	55.2	(8000)	253.1	(36710)
69.0	(10000)	13.8	(2000)	55.2	(8000)	247.0	(35830)
69.0	(10000)	13.8	(2000)	55.2	(8000)	250.9	(36390)
69.0	(10000)	13.8	(2000)	55.2	(8000)	253.3	(36740)

In summary, it may be said that the effect of pore pressure depends upon the porosity of the rock, viscosity of pore fluid, specimen size and rate of straining. Usually, the increase in pore pressure decreases the strength. The effective confining pressure concept is valid when loading rate is less than some critical value which depends upon permeability of the rock, viscosity of pore fluid and specimen size.

Effect of chemical nature of pore fluids on the strength of rocks

BOOZER et al. (1962), in addition to studying the effect of the pressure of pore fluids on the strength of rocks under triaxial compression, also studied the chemical effects of the fluids (absorption, etc.). They found that chemically active fluids (water, oleic acid) reduced the strengths of the rocks below the values obtained when similar specimens saturated with an inactive fluid (n-hexadecane) were tested under otherwise identical conditions.

ROBINSON (1967) studied the effect of hardness reducers on failure characteristics of rock. The tests on Indiana limestone indicate that chemical additives in the pore fluids can increase or decrease the strength in malleable, but not brittle, failure. Tests using a series of the sodium salts of dicarboxylic acids show that odd-numbered carbon-atom chains decrease the yield strength as much as 20.7 MPa (3×10^3 lbf/in^2), and even-numbered carbon-atom chains increase the strength as much as 6.2 MPa (9×10^2 lbf/in^2). The most effective chemical, sodium citrate, decreased the strength of Indiana limestone from 110.3 to 82.7 MPa (16×10^3 to 12×10^3 lbf/in^2).

Effect of strain rate on triaxial compressive strength

The effect of higher strain rate (higher rate of loading) is to increase the strength of rocks. The effect of strain rate was investigated by SERDENGECTI and BOOZER (1961) on Solenhofen limestone and gabbro. They have clearly demonstrated that ultimate strength increases with an increase in confining pressure and/or rate of loading.

LOGAN and HANDIN (1970) reported results of quasi-dynamic triaxial compression tests at confining pressures to 700 MPa (101 523 lbf/in^2). In the case of Westerly granite, which was deformed at confining pressures to 700 MPa (101 523 lbf/in^2), room temperature, and axial strain rates of 10^{-2} to 1/s, an increase of ultimate strength with confining pressure was found as expected. The ultimate strength was also found to vary directly with increasing strain rate, the rate of rise increasing with confining pressure (Fig. 5-33).

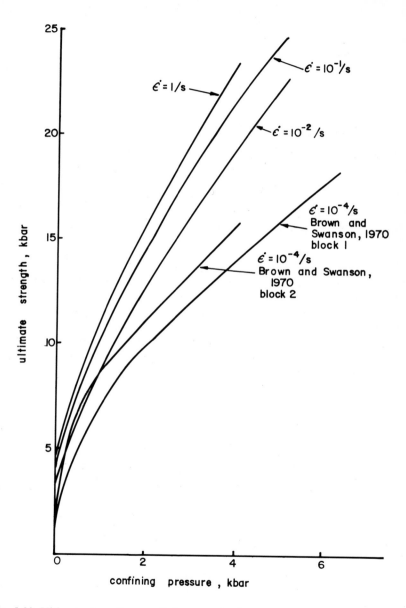

Fig. 5-33. Ultimate strength *vs* confining pressure for Westerly granite at strain rates of 10^{-2} to $1/s$. Data at a strain rate of $10^{-4}/s$ is from BROWN and SWANSON (after LOGAN and HANDIN, 1970).

DONATH and FRUTH (1971) reported results for 69 triaxial compression tests run on a marble, a lithographic limestone, a very fine-grained sandstone, and a siltstone at room temperature, dry, confining pressures of 100 and 200 MPa (14503 and 29007 lbf/in^2), and at strain rates of 10^{-3}, 10^{-4}, 10^{-5}, 10^{-6}, and 10^{-7}/s. A decrease in strain rate from 10^{-3} to 10^{-7}/s at 200 MPa (29007 lbf/in^2) confining pressure caused a decrease in strength at 2 percent strain of about 33 percent for the marble and 8.4 percent for the sandstone, but had no significant effect on either the sandstone or siltstone. Similar results were obtained for the tests run at 100 MPa (14503 lbf/in^2). Over the same range of strain rates, the strength at 10 percent strain decreased by about 10 percent for the marble at 200 MPa (29007 lbf/in^2), but increased slightly more than 11 percent at 100 MPa (14503 lbf/in^2). The limestone showed a small increase at 200 MPa (29007 lbf/in^2). Again, there was no significant change for the sandstone and siltstone at either confining pressure.

In summary, it may be said that the strength usually increases with an increase in rate of loading. Also, the rate of rise increases with confining pressure. Depending upon the rock, there may not be any significant effect also.

Post-failure behaviour of rock

As is usual in the triaxial tests, there is an increase in the compressive strength (ultimate load bearing capacity of the specimen) with increase in the lateral pressure in the triaxial tests. But it is of interest to note that the onset of the pronounced non-linear part of the stress-strain curve is considerably insensitive to the value of the confining pressure (Fig. 5-34).

The post-failure curves, in general, may be characterised by regions of sudden drop in load bearing capacity followed by more gentle slopes when tested at low confining pressures. At higher confining pressures, the brittle to ductile transition takes place and the sudden drop slowly disappears. This is very clearly seen for the rocks with class I behaviour (Tennessee marble II, Fig. 5-34). But for rocks with class II behaviour, say Westerly granite (Fig. 5-35) this behaviour persists up to very high confining pressure, but there exists evidence that at high pressure this transition will take place.

At confining pressures, a behaviour similar to one given in Fig. 2-49 (Chapter 2) exists except that at higher confining pressures slabbing is eliminated and the regions VI and VII become wider associated with multiple shear fractures. The angle of fracture increases from almost vertical (slabbing) to angles greater than 30° to the direction of greatest compression.

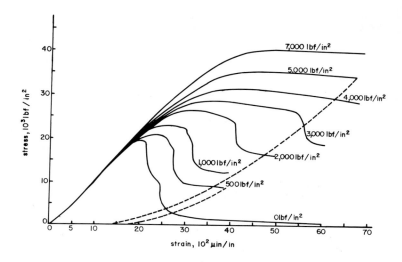

Fig. 5-34. Complete stress-strain curves for unconfined and confined Tennessee marble II
(after WAWERSIK and FAIRHURST, 1970).

The post-failure behaviour of rocks is sensitive to the changes in the stress
state and is stress-path dependent. CROUCH (1972a, b) conducted some
interesting tests on post-failure stress-strain path dependence of South
African norite. The ultimate strength of norite is very nearly independent
of the manner in which the axial and confining stresses are applied, but
the post-failure $\sigma - \varepsilon$ locus is confining stress path dependent (Fig. 5-36).
In this figure, curves B and C are obtained at the same confining stress
10.0 MPa (1 450 lbf/in²) except that C was obtained by keeping lateral stress
constant while in B, the stress was changed on failure from 6.9 to 10.0 MPa
(1 000 to 1 450 lbf/in²).

Hydraulic extension test

MURRELL (1962) carried out experiments on a sandstone in which dumb-bell
shaped specimens were subjected to an axial tension and a confining pressure.
The specimens fractured across a plane normal to the tension. The results
are given in Table 25. Over the range studied it can be seen that fracture
occured at an approximately constant value of the tensile minor principal
stress.

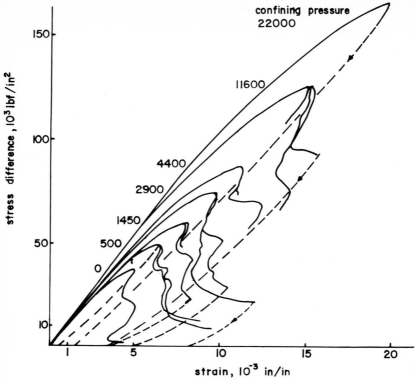

Fig. 5-35. Stress-strain curves of Westerly granite in uniaxial and triaxial compression (after WAWERSIK and BRACE, 1971).

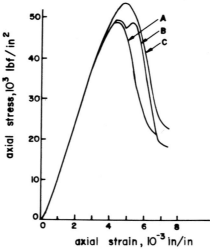

Fig. 5-36. Axial stress-axial strain curves for norite between 1 000 and 1 450 lbf/in² confining stress:

(A) – 1 000 lbf/in² confining stress (constant);
(B) – 1 000 lbf/in² confining stress (constant); increased to 1 450 lbf/in² and kept constant
(C) – 1 450 lbf/in² confining stress (constant)
(after CROUCH, 1972 a).

TABLE 25

Hydraulic extension test results

(after MURRELL, 1962)

Tensile stress MPa	(lbf/in²)	Confining pressure MPa	(lbf/in²)	
2.5	(365)	0.6	(85)	[6]
3.1	(450)	1.6	(225)	[8]
3.3	(480)	3.1	(445)	[13]
3.1	(450)	4.5	(650)	[11]
3.3	(485)	10.3	(1500)	[16]

Numbers of specimens tested given in brackets [ ]

TABLE 26

Results of extension tests under confining pressures

(after BRACE, 1963)

Rock	Fluid pressure MPa	(lbf/in²)	Axial stress at failure MPa	(lbf/in²)
Webatuck	24	(3481)	− 8	(− 1160)
Webatuck	93	(13488)	− 2	(− 290)
Webatuck	239	(34663)	+ 10	(+ 1450)
Blair	11	(1595)	− 34	(− 4931)
Blair	19	(2756)	− 36	(− 5221)
Blair	223	(32342)	− 43	(− 6236)
Diabase	25	(3626)	− 43	(− 6236)
Diabase	50	(7252)	− 39	(− 5656)
Diabase	146	(21175)	− 40	(− 5801)
Diabase	265	(38434)	+147	(+21320)
Diabase	277	(40174)	+ 77	(+11168)
Diabase	253	(36693)	+ 13	(+ 1885)
Diabase	265	(38434)	− 30	(− 4351)
Quartzite	15	(2175)	− 24	(− 3481)
Quartzite	60	(8702)	− 31	(− 4496)
Quartzite	261	(37854)	− 22	(− 3191)
Granite	30	(4351)	− 21	(− 3046)
Granite	151	(21900)	− 12	(− 1740)
Granite	159	(23060)	− 12	(− 1740)
Granite	239	(34663)	+ 5	(+ 725)

BRACE (1963) conducted hydraulic extension tests on specimens of Webatuck dolomite, Blair dolomite, Frederick diabase, Cheshire quartzite and Westerly granite. The specimens used are of shape more or less similar to that given in Fig. 1-2 (Chapter 1) with a test length of 2.54 cm (1 in) (at throat) and of diameter 1.27 cm (0.5 in). The heads are of 2.54 cm (1 in) diameter. The total length is 15.24 cm (6 in). The specimen is set in a usual triaxial testing machine and axial load and fluid pressure applied. If the axial load on the specimen is F_1 and radial pressure p_3 and d_1 and d_2 the head and throat diameters, respectively, then tensile stress acting at test section of the specimen can be given by

$$\sigma_t = - \left[\frac{4F_1}{\pi d_2^2} - \frac{p_3 \left(\dfrac{\pi d_1^2}{4} - \dfrac{\pi d_2^2}{4} \right)}{\dfrac{\pi d_2^2}{4}} \right] \tag{5.2}$$

Results obtained by him are given in Table 26. These indicate that tensile strength is not dependent upon the hydrostatic pressure applied.

HANDIN, HEARD and MAGOUIRK (1967) also came to the same conclusion that tensile strength is essentially constant from triaxial extension tests.

5.3.5. Modes of Failure of Rocks

There are two modes of failure occuring in rocks depending on the amount of the deformation before failure. Rocks are described as brittle if they fail without large deformation, or ductile if they deform appreciably before failure, that is, if they deform plastically. True brittle fracture, by definition, is a process which produces no permanent change in the material other than its separation into parts. Two basic processes generally operate together in ductile microscopic behaviour: dissipative processes such as gliding and viscous flow, and processes such as frictional gliding or rotation of grains about one another.

Rocks are usually considered as brittle materials, but they may be ductile and sometimes show the transition from brittle to ductile behaviour resulting from changes in their physical environment. The reaction of the rock to deformation depends upon its structure and upon the magnitude of the confining pressure, temperature, rate of loading and the presence and nature of interstitial solutions.

TERZAGHI (1945) classified rock failure into splitting, shear, and pseudo-shear, depending on the inclination of the failure planes. Splitting may be recognised by cracks appearing parallel to the direction of the axial load which seems to indicate that the bonds between grains fail by tension. This tension between adjacent grains is caused by the wedging action of inter-mediate grains. On the other hand, shear failure can occur when bonded grains are displaced along a glide plane (shear plane). The pseudo-shear failure represents a combination of tension and shear fracture to produce a 'zig-zag' failure.

GRIGGS and HANDIN (1960) described the macroscopic deformation of rocks and minerals deformed at high confining pressures in the laboratory (that is, in triaxial compression tests) in terms of three principal categories of behaviour – extension fractures, faults, and uniform flow. They defined the extension fractures as separation of a body across a surface normal to the direction of maximum principal stress. In faults, the shear surface may be inclined at from 45° to a few degrees to the direction of the maximum

principal stress. In this case, there may or may not be total loss of cohesion, actual separation, release of stored elastic energy, or loss of resistance to differential stress. Uniform flow denotes macroscopically homogeneous de-formation. In Fig. 5-37 schematic representation of the spectrum from brittle fracture to ductile flow, with typical strains before fracture and stress-strain curves for uniaxial compression and extension is given.

ROBINSON (1959) analysed thin sections of Indiana limestone subjected to high confining pressures and found that crystals twin and then fail by shear fracture. He further concluded that when confining pressure is equal to the pore pressure, failure takes place along one shear plane passing through the specimen. But when differential pressure is 3.4 MPa (500 lbf/in^2) and confining pressure 69.0 MPa (10 000 lbf/in^2), two or three shear planes pass through the specimen and produce two or three or more sections. When the pore pressure is zero and confining pressure 69.0 MPa (10 000 lbf/in^2), shear planes are of much shorter length and the surface has a mottled appearance because of the great number of shear planes. Thus the number of shearing surfaces increases with increase in differential pressure and high confining pressures.

SERDENGECTI and BOOZER (1961) found that the type of failure of rock in triaxial compression is dependent upon confining pressure, temperature and rate of deformation. Rock failure occurs in a brittle manner at low confining pressures, low temperatures and high rates of deformation. On the other hand, ductile failure is favoured at high confining pressures, high temperatures and low deformation rates.

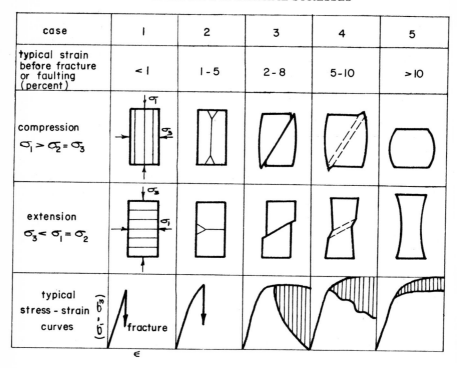

σ_1 , σ_2 , σ_3 , are maximum, intermediate, and
minimum principal stresses, respectively.

Fig. 5-37. Schematic representation of the spectrum from brittle fracture to ductile flow, with typical strains before fracture and stress-strain curves for uniaxial compression and extension. The ruled portions of the stress-strain curves indicate the variation within each case and the overlap between cases 3, 4, and 5 (after GRIGGS and HANDIN, 1960).

BOOZER, HILLER and SERDENGECTI (1962) further reported that the pore pressure fluid affects the mode of failure. At a confining pressure of 6.9 MPa (1 000 lbf/in²) Indiana limestone fails in a brittle manner regardless of the saturation fluid. As the confining pressure is increased, it begins to yield and deform in a ductile manner. Specimens saturated with oleic acid continue to fail in a brittle manner at higher confining pressures than specimens saturated with n-hexadecane or water. Microscopic observations showed that the ductile behaviour of Indiana limestone is the result of intercrystalline gliding and some twinning of the calcite matrix.

SCHWARTZ (1964) observed failure surface under binocular microscopes and studied micrographs. Transition from brittle to ductile failure occurs when confining pressure is increased from 0 to 69.0 MPa (0 to 10000 lbf/in²) for limestone and marble while no ductile failure is observed for granite and sandstone at confining pressures up to 69.0 MPa (10000 lbf/in²). The mode of failure progresses slowly from tension to pseudo-shear and finally shear.

The angle of the plane of failure varies with the confining pressure. An increase in the angle of failure has been observed with increase in confining pressures (EVANS and POMEROY, 1966).

RAMEZ (1967) conducted triaxial tests on Darley Dale sandstone under dry conditions and at room temperature. All specimens failed along shear fracture surfaces. In addition, 3 types of intragranular fractures were observed: A – Tensile fractures parallel to the compression axis, B – Shear fractures parallel to the megascopic shear fracture surface, C – Strain release fractures normal to the axis of compression which becomes more significant as the confining pressure is increased.

5.4. Polyaxial Test*

The fracture behaviour of rocks has been intensively studied under triaxial compression with two of the principal stresses equal. However, owing to experimental difficulties, few investigations of failure under general triaxial stress systems, in which all three principal stresses are different, have been made.

In principle, triaxial homogeneous stresses, $\sigma_1 > \sigma_2 > \sigma_3$, can be obtained by loading a rectangular parallelopiped across its three pairs of mutually perpendicular surfaces. If stresses are applied through steel end-pieces, friction between end-pieces and specimens and stress concentration at the ends of specimens could introduce marked errors.

HOJEM and COOK (1968) applied lateral stresses (σ_2 and σ_3) by thin copper flat-jacks, and an axial stress (σ_1) by steel end-pieces of the same cross-section as that of the specimen. The specimen is in the shape of a rectangular prism measuring 2.54 cm (1 in) square by 7.62 cm (3 in) in length. The flat-jacks react against segmental, tapered brass spacers confined in a steel cylinder. By using different fluid pressures in each of the pairs of flat-jacks, states of polyaxial stress are achieved within specimen.

---

* The term 'polyaxial' has been chosen to describe tests in which the value of the three principal stresses differs from one another.

BIENIAWSKI, DENKHAUS and VOGLER (1969) developed equipment for stiff multiaxial compression tests on rock. Longitudinal loading is done in a 4.98 MN (1 120 000 lbf) press. Two separate hydraulic circuits, independent of the circuit of the press, are used to supply pressure for lateral loading of the specimen under conditions of $\sigma_2 \neq \sigma_3$.

MOGI (1971 a, b) designed a new triaxial cell for the general triaxial compression test in which all three principal stresses are different. The most important difference in structure from conventional triaxial cells is the lateral pistons for independent application of σ_2. The pistons are connected to a 298 920 N (30 ton) jack. The axial pistons for application of σ_1 are connected to a 697 481 N (70 ton) jack. The high pressure vessel is a thick-walled hollow cylinder with a diametrical hole for the lateral pistons. A confining pressure σ_3, of up to 800 MPa (116 026 lbf/in²) can be applied in this vessel.

Another character in this design is direct measurements of axial and lateral loads by load cells inside the pressure vessel. The load cells embody electric resistance strain gauges. Strain was also measured directly by an electric resistance strain gauge mounted on the specimen.

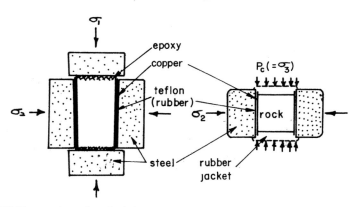

Fig. 5-38. Test specimen for triaxial compression tests. Left: front section; right: horizontal section (after MOGI, 1971 b).

The test specimen is shown in Fig. 5-38. It is a rectangular prism 1.5 cm (0.59 in) square by 3.0 cm (1.18 in) long. The end-pieces on the top and bottom of the specimen are connected to a specimen with epoxy and the lateral end-pieces are connected to the sides of the specimen through a lubricant (teflon sheets), by which the frictional effect of lateral surfaces was effectively reduced. To avoid intrusion of teflon into the specimen, the sides of specimen were jacketed by thin copper sheets. The length of the lateral end-pieces is slightly shorter than the length of rock specimen to allow the compression of the rock. The specimen is jacketed by silicon rubber to prevent intrusion of the pressure medium (oil) into the specimen (Fig. 5-38).

The confining pressure was first applied, and the lateral load was increased to a constant value; then, the axial load was increased with constant strain rate (10^{-4}/s) until failure occurred. Measurement of confining pressure was made both by a manganin gauge and a Heise Bourdon tube gauge.

5.4.1. Results

HOJEM and COOK (1968) studied the influence of the intermediate principal stress on the strength and fracture of specimens of Karroo dolerite using their polyaxial cell. Their results given in Fig. 5-39, show that the value of the intermediate principal stress has a significant and regular effect on the compressive strength. Under conditions of polyaxial stress, failure produces two roughly plane fractures lying in the direction of the intermediate principal stress and inclined at a narrow angle to the direction of the major principal stress. In triaxial compression – that is, with equal pressures in each pair of flat-jacks – failure produces an axially symmetric conical fracture with an included angle similar to that between the plane fractures in the case of polyaxial stress.

A comparison between the triaxial strengths of circular and square section specimens of Karroo dolerite, measured in the triaxial and polyaxial cells respectively, shows them to be identical, provided that the axial load is reduced by an amount corresponding to that borne by the copper flat-jacks at a stress equal to their yield strength.

MOGI (1970) studied the failure behaviours of rocks under general triaxial stress state in which all three principal stresses are different. Examples of stress-strain curves of Dunham dolomite for different σ_2 values under a constant σ_3 are shown in Fig. 5-40. The ultimate strength under constant σ_3 increases slightly with increasing σ_2.

Fig. 5-41 shows the limiting value of the maximum principal stress σ_1, which is the maximum stress achieved during an experiment, as a function of the intermediate principal stress σ_2, for various minimum principal stresses σ_3. The σ_2 effect is large at low σ_2 and gradually decreases with the increase of σ_2. That is, the σ_1 vs σ_2 curves are concave downward.

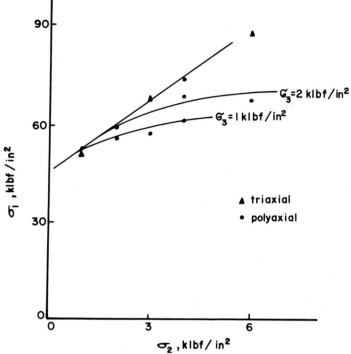

Fig. 5-39. Effect of intermediate principal stress on strength of Karroo dolerite
(after HOJEM and COOK, 1968).

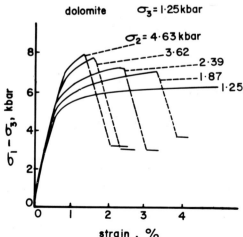

Fig. 5-40. Stress-strain curves of Dumham dolomite for different σ_2 values ($\sigma_3 = 1.25$ kbar)
(after MOGI, 1970).

In a later publication (MOGI, 1971a) details of studies on other rocks –
Solenhofen limestone, Yamaguchi marble, Mizuho trachyte, Orikabe
monzonite, Inada granite and Manazuru andesite – are given. The results
are very similar to the ones reported here for Dunham dolomite.

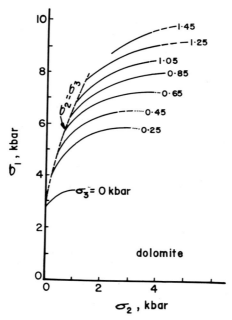

Fig. 5-41. Failure stress (σ_1) as a function of σ_2 and σ_3
(after MOGI, 1970).

5.5. Miscellaneous Tests

5.5.1. Torsion of Solid Cylinders under Compression

BOKER (1915) used VON KARMAN apparatus for torsional studies under
confining pressures with super-position of longitudinal compression on
this state. The torque is transmitted to the square end of the specimen
through the piston.

HANDIN, HIGGS and O'BRIEN (1960) devised a set up for investigating rocks
under torsion under conditions of longitudinal loading and confining
pressures up to 269 MPa (39050 lbf/in²) and at temperatures up to 300 °C

(572 °F). To the basic components of the Handin apparatus, they added
the following:

(a) An electric motor for providing the rotary movement of the cylinder
    with the upper piston and the specimen remaining fixed as before

(b) A bridge circuit of the sensing device for the electrical resistance strain
    gauge attached to the piston for the determination of torque and

(c) Equipment for measuring the angle of rotation of the cylinder.

Jacketed cylindrical specimens of Yule marble and calcite single crystals
have been twisted at a constant rate of 0.1 radian per minute under confining
pressures of 100 to 269 MPa (14 200 to 39 050 lbf/in²), at temperatures
from 24 to 300 °C, (75.2 to 572 °F), and under axial loads of 0 to 100 MPa
(0 to 14 200 lbf/in²). Permanent twists of as much as 1.6 rad/cm (4.1 rad/in)
have been obtained. The yield stress and ductility of the marble increase
with confining pressure and are further enhanced by an axial compressive
load. The yield stress decreases, and the ductility increases as the temperature
is raised. Torsion under confining pressure alone leads to tensile fracture
across a helical surface which is everywhere normal to the least principal
stress, a tension of about 19.6 MPa (2 840 lbf/in²). In specimens under an
axial compressive load, failure is by shear fracturing approximately parallel
to the plane of maximum shearing stress.

5.5.2. Punching under Confining Pressure

Punching experiments on discs of rock subjected to confining pressure give
an approximate value for the variation of shear strength with confining
pressure. They were conducted by ROBERTSON (1955), who reported a
considerable strengthening effect of confining pressure on Solenhofen
limestone. JAEGER (1962) reported the results of the tests on marble, slate
and sandstone. For marble and slate, confining pressure has a considerable
strengthening effect, but for sandstone this effect is very small.

5.5.3. Brazilian Test under Confining Pressure

The method of testing is same as described in section 3.3 except that the
specimen is placed in a high pressure cell and hydrostatic pressure applied
to the whole surface of the disc. The stress state can be represented by the
following equations:

1. Tensile stress acting perpendicular to the loaded diameter and parallel to the face of the disc

$$\sigma_t = -\left[\frac{F}{\pi r_0 t} - p_1\right] \qquad (5.3)$$

2. Compressive stress acting along the diameter

$$\sigma_c = \frac{F}{\pi r_0 t}\left[\frac{1}{r_0 - y} + \frac{1}{r_0 + y} - \frac{1}{2r_0}\right] + p_1 \qquad (5.4)$$

where F = force applied on the disc
r_0 = radius of the disc
t = thickness of the disc
p_1 = confining pressure and
y = distance along the diameter from the centre.

Results obtained by EVANS and POMEROY (1966) are given in Table 27. These indicate that tensile strength is not dependent upon the hydrostatic pressure applied. Results of disc test on Barnsley Hard show, however, that tensile strength parallel to the bedding plane increases with increase in confining pressure.

HANDIN, HEARD and MAGOUIRK (1967) also conducted Brazilian tests on Solenhofen limestone. The discs 1.3 cm (0.51 in) thick and 1.3 cm (0.51 in) in diameter were jacketed by epoxy cement and loaded under confining pressure in HANDIN's triaxial apparatus. The breaking stresses (Table 28) appear to increase slightly from about 20 MPa (2900 lbf/in²) at atmospheric pressure to about 26 MPa (3771 lbf/in²) at 500 MPa (72516 lbf/in²) confining pressure. At 800 MPa (116026 lbf/in²) the values are much higher.

5.5.4. Hollow Cylinders under Compression

In most of the triaxial tests, the lateral stresses σ_2, and σ_3 are equal and the effect of variation of σ_2 or σ_3 on the triaxial strength has not been widely investigated. MAZANTI and SOWERS (1965) used hollow cylinders of granite to determine the effect of the intermediate principal stress ($\sigma_2 \neq \sigma_3$). The cylinders were subjected to both internal and external pressure.

The magnitudes of the stresses at a point depend upon the values of the applied pressures, the diameter of the cylinder, the wall thickness of the cylinder, and the radial distance from the centre of the cylinder to the point

TABLE 27

The effect of compressive principal stresses on tensile strength measurements

(after Evans and Pomeroy, 1966)

Direction of tensile stress	Hydrostatic pressure, MPa (lbf/in²)		Coal			
			Barnsley Hards		Pentremawr anthracite	
			Minimum compressive stress MPa (lbf/in²)	Tensile stress MPa (lbf/in²)	Minimum compressive stress MPa (lbf/in²)	Tensile stress MPa (lbf/in²)
Parallel to bedding planes	0	(0)	7.2±0.8 (1050±120)	2.4±0.3 (350± 40)	5.6±0.4 (810± 60)	1.9±0.1 (270± 20)
	1.7	(250)	—	—	14.8±1.4 (2140±210)	2.6±0.5 (380± 70)
	3.4	(500)	19.8±1.4 (2870±210)	2.0±0.5 (290± 70)	20.4±2.3 (2960±330)	2.2±0.8 (320±110)
	5.2	(750)	31.6±3.1 (4590±450)	3.7±1.0 (530±150)	—	—
	6.9	(1000)	35.6±3.5 (5170±510)	2.7±1.2 (390±170)	28.2±2.7 (4090±390)	0.2±0.9 (30±130)
Perpendicular to bedding planes	0	(0)	4.8±0.6 (690± 90)	1.6±0.2 (230± 30)	6.2±0.4 (900± 60)	2.1±0.1 (300± 20)
	1.7	(250)	17.4±2.3 (2530±330)	3.5±0.8 (510±110)	14.5±1.4 (2110±210)	2.6±1.0 (370±140)
	6.9	(1000)	16.2±3.9 (2350±570)	3.1±1.3 (450±190)	29.9±3.3 (4330±480)	0.8±1.1 (110±160)

The discs were 2.54 cm (1 in) in diameter and 0.85 cm (0.33 in) thick in question. For a cylinder loaded uniformly over the inner and outer surfaces, the stresses existing can be given by

$$\sigma_\theta = \frac{r_i^2 r_0^2 (p_0 - p_i)}{(r_0^2 - r_i^2) r^2} - \frac{r_i^2 p_i - r_0^2 p_0}{r_0^2 - r_i^2} \tag{5.5}$$

and

$$\sigma_r = -\frac{r_i^2 r_0^2 (p_0 - p_i)}{(r_0^2 - r_i^2) r^2} - \frac{r_i^2 p_i - r_0^2 p_0}{r_0^2 - r_i^2} \tag{5.6}$$

where σ_θ = circumferential stress
$\quad\ \sigma_r$ = radial stress
$\quad\ r_i$ = inner radius
$\quad\ r_0$ = outer radius
$\quad\ r$ = radial distance to point in question
$\quad\ p_0$ = external pressure and
$\quad\ p_i$ = internal pressure.

Using these expressions, they calculated the three principal stresses and the effect of the intermediate principal stress was investigated. They conducted a series of tests with the minor principal stress, σ_3, as zero (radial stress at the inner surface of the hollow cylinder) and caused the specimens to fail by increasing σ_2 (calculated circumferential stress at the inner surface) and σ_1 (the axial stress). They found that the principal stress difference $(\sigma_1 - \sigma_3)$ increased with increasing ratio of σ_2/σ_1 up to a point, after which it decreased. Their results are shown in Fig. 5-42. The maximum stress difference for $\sigma_3 = 0$ appears to occur at $\frac{\sigma_2}{\sigma_1} = 0.5$.

HOSKINS (1969) also performed a series of experiments on thick-walled cylinders of five different types of isotropic rock. Figures 5-43 to 5-45 are graphs of σ_1 vs σ_2 for various ratios of σ_3/σ_2 for the three main materials tested. The σ_3/σ_2 ratio of 1.0 represents the conventional triaxial compression tests. The other curves represent tests conducted on hollow cylinders with the applied pressures arranged so that $\sigma_3 < \sigma_2$ by various amounts. In practice, the experiments are performed with $p_i \neq p_0$, the principal stresses at failure are calculated and plotted and smooth curves are interpolated among the experimental results. The magnitude of the intermediate principal stress appears to have a marked and regular effect on the strength of these rocks.

TABLE 28

**Results of Brazilian tests on Solenhofen
limestone at room temperature**

(after HANDIN, HEARD and MAGOUIRK, 1967)

Confining pressure		Minimum principal (tensile) stress σ3,	
MPa	(lbf/in²)	MPa	(lbf/in²)
0	(0)	− 20.5	(− 2973)
0	(0)	− 19.5	(− 2828)
0	(0)	− 21.5	(− 3118)
200	(29007)	− 22.0	(− 3191)
200	(29007)	− 23.5	(− 3408)
500	(72516)	− 25.0	(− 3626)
500	(72516)	− 27.0	(− 3916)
500	(72516)	− 26.0	(− 3771)
800	(116026)	− 42.0	(− 6091)
800	(116026)	− 71.5	(−10370)
800	(116026)	− 35.5	(− 5149)
800	(116026)	− 63.5	(− 9210)

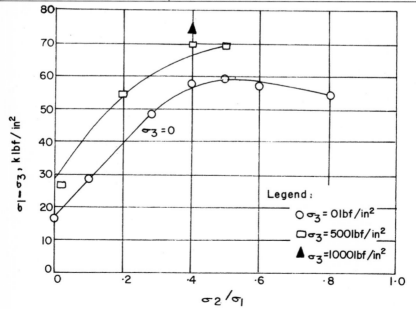

Fig. 5-42. Variation of principal stress difference with σ_2/σ_1 ratio for granite hollow
cylinders (after MAZANTI and SOWERS, 1965).

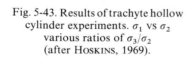

Fig. 5-43. Results of trachyte hollow cylinder experiments. σ_1 vs σ_2 various ratios of σ_3/σ_2 (after Hoskins, 1969).

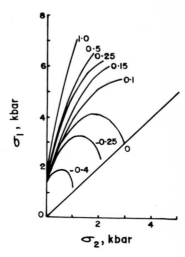

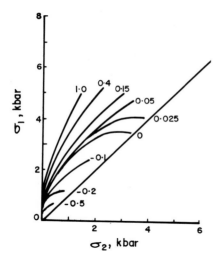

Fig. 5-44. Results of marble hollow cylinder experiments. σ_1 vs σ_2 for various ratios of σ_3/σ_2 (after Hoskins, 1969).

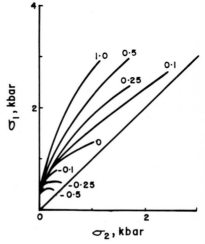

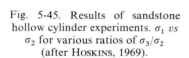

Fig. 5-45. Results of sandstone hollow cylinder experiments. σ_1 *vs* σ_2 for various ratios of σ_3/σ_2 (after Hoskins, 1969).

HANDIN, HEARD and MAGOUIRK (1967) conducted tests on hollow cylinders. They tried to jacket the hollow cylinders by merely coating them with epoxy. However, such specimens failed by extension fracture at positive (compressive) values of σ_3 in excess of 100 MPa (14503 lbf/in²) and they were compelled to develop the scheme for inside and outside copper jacketing.

5.6. Strength of Rock under Biaxial Stress

The difference in biaxial and triaxial testing of rock is that in the former case, the stress applied along one of the axes (e.g. one of the horizontal axes) is kept at zero. Lateral stress applied along one of the horizontal axes is sometimes termed as intermediate stress, for stress along the second horizontal axis is zero.

The measurement of biaxial strength is done either

1. By subjecting hollow cylinders to external hydrostatic pressure and axial force or

2. By compressing cubes simultaneously between two pairs of their faces.

5.6.1. Hollow Cylinder Subjected to External Hydrostatic Pressure and Axial Force

HOBBS (1962) determined the strength of coal under biaxial compression using hollow cylinder subjected to external hydrostatic pressure and axial force. He used the N.C.B. apparatus.

The stresses induced in a hollow cylinder with inner and outer radii of r_i and r_0, respectively, subjected to an external hydrostatic pressure p_0 and axial force F in a triaxial cell can be calculated from the theory of elasticity. The stresses at the inner radius are biaxial and the principal stresses, axial, σ_z, tangential, σ_θ, and radial, σ_r, at this surface of the cylinder are

$$\sigma_z = \frac{F}{\pi\,(r_0^2 - r_i^2)} + \frac{p_0\,r_0^2}{r_0^2 - r_i^2} \tag{5.7}$$

$$\sigma_\theta = \frac{2p_0\,r_0^2}{(r_0^2 - r_i^2)} \tag{5.8}$$

$$\sigma_r = 0 \tag{5.9}$$

If $F > \pi r_0^2 \, p_0$, then $\sigma_z > \sigma_\theta$. Thus by applying various hydrostatic pressures it is possible to vary the magnitude of the intermediate (tangential) stress.

When the inner and outer surfaces of the cylinder are not concentric, the value of maximum tangential stress at the inner surface would not be the same. HOBBS (1962) calculated the effect of eccentricity on maximum tangential stress for various values of centre distance, d, internal radius, r_i, and external radius, r_0, for the case $d < 1/2 \, r_i$ (Table 29) and found that the effect is marginal.

TABLE 29

Effect of eccentricity on maximum tangential stress

(after HOBBS, 1962)

Internal radius	External radius	Centre distance	Maximum tangential compressive stress/hydrostatic pressure p_0
0.5	1.0	0.00	2.67
0.5	1.0	0.05	2.75
0.5	1.0	0.10	2.85
0.65	1.65	0.00	2.37
0.65	1.65	0.10	2.41
0.65	1.65	0.20	2.46

5.6.2. Cube Compressed Simultaneously between Two Pairs of Its Faces

The apparatus used by HOBBS (1962) is given in Fig. 5-46. Three spherical seatings are incorporated in the apparatus to align the four platens with the surface of the cube as accurately as possible and thus correct for non-parallelism of the specimen faces. The four faces of the cube are loaded simultaneously until the intermediate stress reaches its required value; the major stress is then allowed to increase until failure occurs.

5.6.3. Results

HOBBS (1962) tested hollow cylinders of Barnsley Hards and Garw coals of internal diameter 1.7 cm (0.66 in), external diameter 4.2 cm (1.64 in) and length 4.9 cm (1.94 in) with bedding and main cleat planes parallel to their axes by first applying a hydrostatic pressure and then superimposing an additional axial force until failure occurred. His results are given in Fig. 5-47.

At the lower values of the tangential stress the axial stress increases rapidly with increasing tangential stress. At higher values of the tangential stress, the axial stress tends to fall.

He also tested cubes and the results of these tests are given in Fig. 5-48. The fracture stress increases with initial increase in the intermediate stress and a decrease in the fracture stress occurs at the higher values of the intermediate stress.

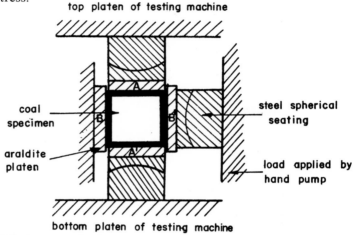

Fig. 5-46. Apparatus for fracturing cubes of coal under biaxial compression (after Hobbs, 1962).

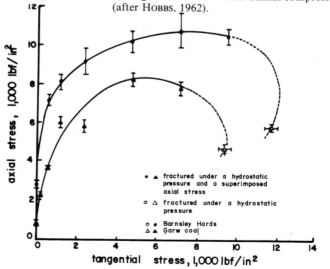

Fig. 5-47. Variation of the axial stress at failure with the tangential stress at failure (after Hobbs, 1962).

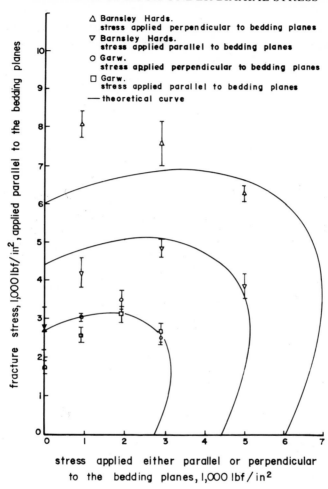

Fig. 5-48. Results of biaxial experiments on cubes of coal
(after HOBBS, 1962).

5.7. Determination of Shear Strength from Triaxial Tests

For the determination of the shear strength of rock from triaxial tests, a
series of tests are conducted and the strength values (σ_1) are obtained for
different values of confining pressures (σ_3). The value σ_1 will always vary
for different values of σ_3 and will be higher for higher values of σ_3. This
data is then represented on a $\tau - \sigma$ plane (Fig. 4-30 in Chapter 4) by plotting
a family of MOHR's circles and common tangents are drawn giving the

MOHR envelope. The point where the enveloping curve cuts the τ-axis gives the shear strength of the rock. The slope (ϕ) of the enveloping curve gives the angle of internal friction of the rock (Fig. 5-49).

This enveloping curve is linear for many rocks and can be represented by

$$\tau_\theta = \pm(\tau_t + \sigma_\theta \tan \phi)$$

Since $\tan \phi = \cot 2\theta$

$$\tau_\theta = \pm(\tau_t + \sigma_\theta \cot 2\theta)$$

where σ_θ = normal stress acting on the failure plane
τ_t = shear strength of the rock and
$\tan \phi$ = the slope of the envelope curve.

When the enveloping curve is curved, the envelope can be expressed in terms of σ_1 and σ_3 (BALMER, 1952). From triangle ADH (Fig. 5-49)

$$\left(\frac{\sigma_1 + \sigma_3}{2} - \sigma_\theta\right)^2 + \tau_\theta^2 = \left(\frac{\sigma_1 - \sigma_3}{2}\right)^2 \tag{5.10}$$

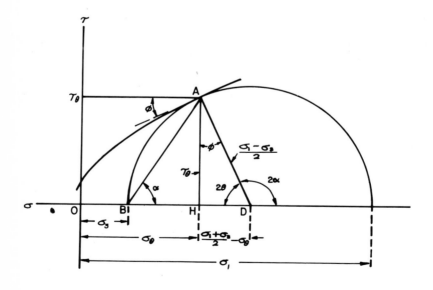

Fig. 5-49. Designation of the stresses and angles in a MOHR's representation (after BALMER, 1952).

Taking partial derivative of σ_1 with respect to σ_3 and solving for σ_θ

$$\sigma_\theta = \sigma_3 + \frac{\sigma_1 - \sigma_3}{\left(\dfrac{\partial \sigma_1}{\partial \sigma_3} + 1\right)} \tag{5.11}$$

Substituting this in equation (5.10), and solving for τ_θ

$$\tau_\theta = \left[\frac{\sigma_1 - \sigma_3}{\dfrac{\partial \sigma_1}{\partial \sigma_3} + 1}\right] \left(\frac{\partial \sigma_1}{\partial \sigma_3}\right)^{1/2} \tag{5.12}$$

Equations (5.11) and (5.12) represent MOHR's envelope in terms of σ_1 and σ_3. From these two equations and triangle A H B in Fig. 5-49, we have

$$\tan \alpha = \frac{\tau_\theta}{\sigma_\theta - \sigma_1} = \left(\frac{\partial \sigma_3}{\partial \sigma_1}\right)^{1/2} \tag{5.13}$$

The slope (ϕ) of the enveloping curve can be given by

$$\frac{\partial \tau_\theta}{\partial \sigma_\theta} = \tan \phi \tag{5.14}$$

As $2\alpha = \phi + 90$ and $\tan \phi = -1/\tan 2\alpha$, and by means of identity $\tan 2\alpha = \dfrac{2 \tan \alpha}{1 - \tan^2 \alpha}$, the equations (5.13) and (5.14) can be combined to give

$$\frac{\partial \tau_\theta}{\partial \sigma_\theta} = \tan \phi = \frac{\tan^2 \alpha - 1}{2 \tan \alpha} = \frac{\dfrac{\partial \sigma_1}{\partial \sigma_3} - 1}{2 \left(\dfrac{\partial \sigma_1}{\partial \sigma_3}\right)^{1/2}} \tag{5.15}$$

Equation (5.15) shows that the slope of the MOHR's envelope $\dfrac{\partial \tau_\theta}{\partial \sigma_\theta}$ and the slope of the axial-radial stress curve $\dfrac{\partial \sigma_1}{\partial \sigma_3}$ are related. If the $\sigma_1 - \sigma_3$ curve is linear, then

$$\frac{\partial \sigma_1}{\partial \sigma_3} = \tan \beta \tag{5.16}$$

and from equation (5.15), MOHR's envelope is also linear and the respective slopes are related by

$$\tan \phi = \frac{\tan \beta - 1}{2 \tan^{1/2} \beta} \tag{5.17}$$

$$\tan \beta = \frac{\sin \phi + 1}{\sin \phi - 1} \tag{5.18}$$

For a linear MOHR's envelope, the relationship between σ_c and τ_t can be represented

$$\sigma_c = \frac{2 \tau_t \cos \phi}{1 - \sin \phi} \tag{5.19}$$

5.8. Failure Criteria

A material is considered to have failed if it is permanently deformed or fractured into two or more parts. Failure is caused by a combination of stresses. If a material is completely free of stress, there is no reason for it to fail.

Materials may be categorised into 1. brittle and 2. ductile. If the resistance to sliding (shearing) is greater than the resistance to separation (tension), the material is brittle; whereas, if the resistance to separation is greater than the resistance to sliding, the material is ductile. In general, materials are rarely exclusively brittle or ductile. Failure of brittle materials is generally associated with tensile stresses and failure of ductile materials is caused by shear stresses.

The state of stress at any point within a solid can be specified in terms of three principal stresses: σ_1, σ_2, σ_3, where $\sigma_1 > \sigma_2 > \sigma_3$; i.e., maximum, intermediate, and least compressive stresses, respectively. The set of σ_1, σ_2, σ_3 values at which failure occurs in an element of a solid can be represented by a point in σ_1, σ_2, σ_3 space, and the totality of these points describes the failure surface.

$$f(\sigma_1, \sigma_2, \sigma_3) = 0 \tag{5.20}$$

Such a relation is called a criterion of failure. Essentially, experimental measurements under different conditions should provide the form of this surface. Discussion will be confined to the region $\sigma_1 \geqslant 0$. Fig. 5-50 shows the information commonly available about this surface, namely, the uniaxial tensile strength $\sigma_3 = -\sigma_t$, $\sigma_1 = \sigma_2 = 0$; the uniaxial compressive strength $\sigma_1 = \sigma_c$, $\sigma_2 = \sigma_3 = 0$; and values obtained in the conventional triaxial test $\sigma_1 > \sigma_2 = \sigma_3 > 0$ which lie on a curve $\sigma_c T$.

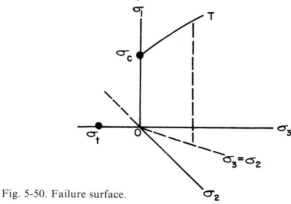

Fig. 5-50. Failure surface.

Various empirical assumptions about the form of the criterion for failure have been made. Of these, the simplest are the following:

(i) Maximum tensile stress: The material is assumed to fail by brittle fracture in tension if the least principal stress σ_3 is equal to the minus uniaxial tensile strength,

$$\sigma_3 = -\sigma_t \qquad (5.21)$$

This is, in fact, adequate under certain restricted conditions.

(ii) Maximum shear stress: The material is assumed to fail when the maximum shear stress reaches a specific value τ_t, which is referred to as the shear strength.

That is

$$\sigma_1 - \sigma_3 = 2\tau_t \qquad (5.22)$$

The failure occurs on a plane bisecting the angle between the two extreme principal stresses. For example, in a triaxial test, the plane of failure should be at 45° to the axial load, a conclusion that is not borne out by experiment. Rather, this direction varies with the applied loads and from one rock type to another. For specimens that fail in compression, the failure surface makes an angle less than 45° to the direction of the larger (compressive) stress, and, for specimens that fail in extension, the failure surface makes an angle about 90° to the direction of the minimum stress.

This criterion, known as COULOMB's, is definitely not strictly true, but is frequently useful as a special case of the COULOMB-NAVIER criterion.

(iii) Maximum octahedral shear stress: The material is assumed to fail when the octahedral shear stress τ_{oct} reaches a value k characteristic of the material, that is,

$$\tau_{oct} = \frac{1}{3}\{(\sigma_1-\sigma_2)^2+(\sigma_2-\sigma_3)^2+(\sigma_3-\sigma_1)^2\}^{1/2}=k \qquad (5.23)$$

This criterion involves all the principal stresses.

The criteria for failure which have proved most useful have not been obtained, as above, from simple mathematical assumptions, but rather as the expressions of simple physical hypotheses. These are the COULOMB-NAVIER, MOHR, and GRIFFITH criteria, which will be discussed below.

5.8.1. Coulomb-Navier Criterion

NAVIER modified the COULOMB (maximum shear stress) criterion by assuming that the normal stress acting across the plane of failure increases the shear resistance of the material by an amount proportional to the magnitude of the normal stress. Considering the two-dimensional case (Fig. 5-51), if σ_θ and τ_θ are the normal and shear stresses acting on the failure plane, this criterion stipulates that failure will occur when the magnitude of the shear stress acting up on the failure plane reaches a value

$$|\tau_\theta|=\tau_t+\mu\sigma_\theta \qquad (5.24)$$

where τ_t is the shear strength of the material. As $\mu\sigma_\theta$ is analogous to the frictional force on an inclined plane due to a normal reaction, μ is referred to as the coefficient of internal friction.

This criterion in a triaxial or biaxial test can be written in terms of the normal and shear stresses,

$$\sigma_\theta=\frac{\sigma_1+\sigma_3}{2}-\frac{\sigma_1-\sigma_3}{2}\cos 2\theta \qquad (5.25)$$

and

$$\tau_\theta=-\frac{1}{2}(\sigma_1-\sigma_3)\sin 2\theta \qquad (5.26)$$

Thus

$$\tau_t = |\tau_\theta| - \mu\sigma_\theta = -\frac{\mu}{2}(\sigma_1 + \sigma_3) + \frac{1}{2}(\sigma_1 - \sigma_3)(\sin 2\theta + \mu \cos 2\theta) \quad (5.27)$$

This equation has a maximum value with respect to θ when

$$\tan 2\theta = \frac{1}{\mu} \quad (5.28)$$

and the magnitude of τ_t at this angle is

$$\tau_t = \frac{\sigma_1}{2}\left((\mu^2 + 1)^{1/2} - \mu\right) - \frac{\sigma_3}{2}\left((\mu^2 + 1)^{1/2} + \mu\right) \quad (5.29)$$

Equation (5.28) indicates that $\theta < \frac{\pi}{4}$ (the plane of failure passes through the axis of the intermediate principal stress), which is in agreement with experimental evidence, although, for a given rock type, the value of μ and the corresponding angle may vary considerably with the applied load. If μ is a constant for a given material, equation (5.29) indicates that the σ_1, σ_3 failure curve should be a straight line. This condition is reasonably well satisfied for most igneous and other hard crystalline rocks. However, for the evaporite minerals, shales and carbonates, the slope of the σ_1, σ_3 relationship usually decreases as σ_3 increases.

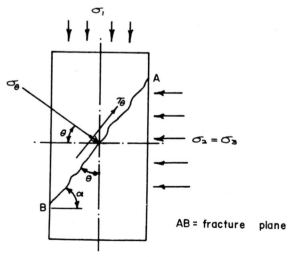

Fig. 5-51. Principal stresses applied to a triaxial compressive test specimen.

This criterion for failure can be expressed in terms of σ_t and σ_c, the tensile and compressive strength of the material, by first making $\sigma_1 = 0$ and $\sigma_3 = -\sigma_t$ in Eq. (5.29) so that

$$2\tau_t = \sigma_t \left((\mu^2 + 1)^{1/2} + \mu \right) \tag{5.30}$$

which corresponds to failure in tension, and then by making $\sigma_1 = \sigma_c$ and $\sigma_3 = 0$ so that

$$2\tau_t = \sigma_c \left((\mu^2 + 1)^{1/2} - \mu \right) \tag{5.31}$$

which corresponds to failure in compression. Thus, combining Eqs. (5.30) and (5.31),

$$\frac{\sigma_c}{\sigma_t} = \frac{(\mu^2 + 1)^{1/2} + \mu}{(\mu^2 + 1)^{1/2} - \mu}$$

This criterion predicts that the compressive strength is greater than the tensile strength, but the ratio is not as large (10 to 50) as found in practice. For a nominal value of $\mu = 1.0$, the ratio $\sigma_c/\sigma_t = 5.8$.

Substituting Eqs. (5.30) and (5.31) into Eq. (5.29) gives

$$1 = \frac{\sigma_1}{\sigma_c} - \frac{\sigma_3}{\sigma_t} \tag{5.32}$$

which is the relationship for the line AB of Fig. 5-52. For σ_1, σ_3 values lying to the left of AB, the material will fail, and σ_1, σ_3 values to the right

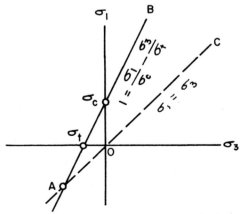

Fig. 5-52. Representation of the Coulomb-Navier criterion of failure.

of AC are excluded because $\sigma_1 < \sigma_3$. Hence, the σ_1, σ_3 values for which the material will not fail must lie in the area bounded by the lines AB and AC.

Since μ is constant, the angle of failure given by $\dfrac{1}{2} \tan^{-1}\left(\dfrac{1}{\mu}\right)$ is the same for tension and compression failure. In compression the angle of failure is relatively constant for most rock types, but in tension the failure surface is usually normal to the direction of the tensile stress. This theory assumes shear fracture, so that σ_t should not be the actual (brittle) tensile strength but the value at which shear failure in tension would take place if in fact brittle failure did not occur in practice before this value is reached. The difference in the appearance of the fracture surfaces created in tension and shear also indicate that the mechanism of failure is not the same in the two cases.

If the normal stress across the fracture plane is negative, the concept of an internal friction becomes meaningless, as this would tend to separate the fracture surfaces; hence, the COULOMB-NAVIER criterion should not be expected to hold for failure at extension.

From Table 21, Chapter 4, it can be seen that the value of μ varies from 1.0 to 2.5. In that case the shear strength (from Eq. (5.31)) would be about 0.2 to 0.1 times the compressive strength of rocks.

5.8.2. MOHR's Criterion

A material may fail through plastic slip or by fracture when either the shear stress τ_θ in the plane of slip or fracture has increased to a certain value which in general will depend also on the normal stress σ_θ active across the same plane or when the numerically largest tensile principal stress has reached a limiting value σ_t dependent on the properties of the material. Thus at failure either

$$\tau_\theta = f(\sigma_\theta) \tag{5.33}$$

or

$$\sigma_3 = -\sigma_t \tag{5.34}$$

The functional relationship $\tau_\theta = f(\sigma_\theta)$ must be determined experimentally and is represented by a typical curve A $\sigma_t \tau_t$ B (Fig. 5-53). As this curve is the envelope to the MOHR's circles for the values of $\sigma_3 \sigma_1$ at failure, its physical significance is as follows: For any state of stress represented by a MOHR's circle lying completely within the envelope, the material will not fail, whereas, if any part of the circle lies outside of the envelope, the critical stresses will be exceeded. For the circle tangent to the envelope, the material will fail on the plane making the angle θ with respect to the larger principal stress. MOHR's criterion further implies that the intermediate principal stress σ_2 has no influence on failure.

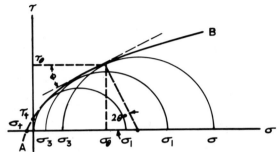

Fig. 5-53. Representation of MOHR's criterion of failure.

This criterion of failure not only specifies the state of stress at failure but predicts the direction of the failure plane. For specimens tested in triaxial compression, τ_θ increases monotonically with σ_θ. Hence MOHR's criterion implies that a material will not fail in hydrostatic compression, a consequence that is consistent with experimental fact. The envelope curves, if projected into the $-\sigma$ quadrants, do not predict the correct magnitude or angle of failure in tension. In these quadrants, the maximum tensile stress criterion is assumed; i.e. failure will occur when σ_3 reaches a critical value $-\sigma_t$, and the failure plane will be normal to the direction of failure stress.

For the special case when the envelope curves are straight lines

$$\tau_\theta = \pm(\tau_t + \sigma_\theta \tan\phi) \tag{5.35}$$

and recalling that $\tan\phi = \cot 2\theta = \mu$

$$\tau_\theta = \pm(\tau_t + \mu\sigma_\theta) \tag{5.36}$$

Hence, for this case, the COULOMB-NAVIER and MOHR theories are identical. Some information regarding MOHR's criterion has already been given in article 5.7.

5.8.3. GRIFFITH's Criterion

This criterion (GRIFFITH, 1921) postulates the presence of microscopic cracks within the material. When the material is stressed, large tensile stress concentrations occur around the tips of the GRIFFITH cracks. When the tensile stress at or near the tip attains a certain critical value, the crack starts extending, ultimately contributing to failure. The theory has been substantiated by experimental work on glass.

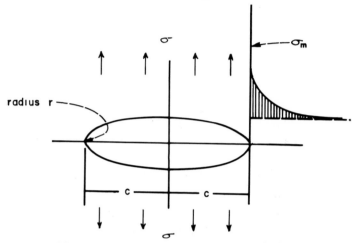

Fig. 5-54. Stress distribution at end of elliptical hole.

The maximum tensile stress σ_m in a flat plate of unit thickness containing an elliptical hole of major axis $2c$ and subjected to an average tensile stress σ in a direction perpendicular to the major axis (Fig. 5-54) is given by (INGLIS, 1913)

$$\sigma_m = 2\sigma \left(\frac{c}{r}\right)^{1/2} \tag{5.37}$$

where r is the radius of curvature at the ends of the major axis. The maximum stress occurs at the ends of the major axis, and as $r \to 0$, the ellipse tends to a flat crack, the stress tends to infinity. Crack length may be assumed to be the longest grain boundary. The crack will spread if σ_m equals the stress which the material can sustain without cracking. To estimate this, the process of cracking must be considered. When a crack begins propagating, elastic energy is released. However, a certain amount of energy is gained as surface energy due to the creation of new crack surface area. The elastic strain energy released by the spreading of a crack in a thin plate is given by

$$W_e = \frac{\pi c^2 \sigma^2}{E} \tag{5.38}$$

and the surface energy gained by the creation of the crack is

$$W_s = 4c\sigma_s \tag{5.39}$$

where σ_s is the surface tension.

Hence the crack has decreased the total energy by

$$W = W_e - W_s = \frac{\pi c^2 \sigma^2}{E} - 4c\sigma_s \tag{5.40}$$

According to GRIFFITH, such a crack will just propagate or just not propagate and produce brittle failure if $\dfrac{\partial W}{\partial c} \geqslant 0$, that is, if the net total energy tends to maximum. That is

$$\sigma = \left(\frac{2\sigma_s E}{\pi c}\right)^{1/2} \geqslant \sigma_t \tag{5.41}$$

where σ_t is the tensile strength of the material.

·In this equation, the stress necessary to cause brittle fracture varies inversely with the length of the existing cracks. Hence the tensile strength of a completely brittle material is determined by the largest crack existing prior to loading.

GRIFFITH (1924) also showed that tensile stresses develop near the tip of cracks oriented at angles other than normal to the applied stress, and for compressive as well as tensile loading.

If $\sigma_3/\sigma_1 < -\frac{1}{3}$,* fracture will occur when the minor principal stress equals the uniaxial tensile strength, i.e., when $\sigma_3 = -\sigma_t$ and, in this case, the angle of failure $\theta = 0$. If $\sigma_3/\sigma_1 > -\frac{1}{3}$, fracture will occur when

$$\frac{(\sigma_1 - \sigma_3)^2}{(\sigma_1 + \sigma_3)} = 8\sigma_t$$

and at an angle given by

$$\cos 2\theta = \frac{1}{2} \frac{(\sigma_1 - \sigma_3)}{(\sigma_1 + \sigma_3)}$$

If $\sigma_3 = 0$ and $\sigma_1 = \sigma_c$, it follows that $\sigma_c = 8\sigma_t$. Thus, GRIFFITH's criterion of fracture predicts that the magnitude of the compressive stress should be

---

* Recalling that compression is positive and $\sigma_1 > \sigma_2 > \sigma_3$.

exactly eight times the tensile stress, a condition that is not consistent with observation, as the compressive strength of most rock varies from 10 to 50 times the tensile strength.

Once fracture is initiated as a result of the applied stress attaining the value

$$\left(\frac{2\sigma_s E}{\pi c}\right)^{1/2}$$

the stage of fracture propagation is reached. Two types of fracture propagation exist, namely, stable and unstable.

The fracture propagation is stable, so long as there is a definite relationship between the half-length c of the crack and the applied stress σ and the condition

$$\sigma > \left(\frac{2\sigma_s E}{\pi c}\right)^{1/2}$$

is maintained.

Fracture propagation is unstable when unique relationship between c and σ ceases to exist, that is, when other quantities, e.g., the crack growth velocity, also play a role and fracture propagation cannot be controlled any more by the applied load.

While in stable propagation the crack growth can be stopped by stopping load increases, this does not hold for unstable fracture propagation; the fracture then propagates uncontrollably although the stress may be kept constant. Stable fracture propagation is usually a slow process while unstable fracture propagation is fast.

If energy is available and the crack exceeds the maximum speed, then the crack will branch out and follow several paths.

MURRELL (1962) showed that this fracture criterion corresponds to a MOHR's envelope at failure given by

$$\tau_\theta^2 + 4\sigma_t \sigma_\theta = 4\sigma_t^2 \tag{5.42}$$

Thus, GRIFFITH's comparatively simple model of a brittle material containing microcracks of a specified length leads to a failure criterion represented by a parabolic MOHR envelope. Although some of the sedimentary rocks (limestone, sandstone, and carbonaceous rocks) have a nonlinear MOHR envelope, it is common for the more brittle rocks such as granite and quartzite to have a linear MOHR envelope in compression. Moreover, as the stress concentration around a GRIFFITH crack is calculated on the basis of elastic theory, this mechanism of failure should be time-independent and hence would not account for variation in strength with stress or strain rate.

MCCLINTOCK and WALSH (1962) extended the GRIFFITH criterion for the case of high biaxial conditions, where the compression stresses are sufficient to close the crack and thereby allow the action of friction forces on the crack surfaces. This midified GRIFFITH's criterion includes two critical quantities, namely, the critical tensile stress at the tip, expressed by the value of uniaxial tensile strength of the material (as in the original GRIFFITH criterion) and the coefficient of friction between crack surfaces. Failure occurs when

$$\sigma_1 \left((1+\mu^2)^{1/2} - \mu \right) - \sigma_3 \left((1+\mu^2)^{1/2} + \mu \right)$$
$$= 4\sigma_t (1+\sigma_{cr}/\sigma_t)^{1/2} - 2\mu\sigma_{cr} \tag{5.43}$$

where μ is the coefficient of friction for the crack surface and σ_{cr} is the stress normal to the crack required to close it. It should be noted that the coefficient of friction of the crack surface is not the same as the coefficient of internal friction that appears in MOHR's criterion of failure, although these quantities may be related.

BRACE (1963) pointed out that σ_{cr} is small and can be neglected. Hence the above equation becomes

$$\sigma_1 \left((1+\mu^2)^{1/2} - \mu \right) - \sigma_3 \left((1+\mu^2)^{1/2} + \mu \right) = 4\sigma_t \tag{5.44}$$

and the relationship between σ_1 and σ_3 is linear as in the COULOMB-NAVIER criterion. If $\sigma_1 = \sigma_c$ and $\sigma_3 = 0$ are the conditions for simple compression, the ratio of the compression to tensile strength is

$$\frac{\sigma_c}{\sigma_t} = \frac{4}{\left((1+\mu^2)^{1/2} - \mu \right)} \tag{5.45}$$

For $\mu = 1$, the ratio of the compression to tensile strength is approximately 10, which is an improvement over the COULOMB-NAVIER predicted ratio of 5.8; but lower than generally observed values.

The treatment of GRIFFITH's theory given here is based on a two-dimensional model, i.e., on a crack in a thin plate. SACK (1946) extended the theory to three dimensions considering a penny-shaped crack and determined that the maximum and minimum boundary stresses and the surface energy differ from the two-dimensional case by only a few percent. Fracture occurs by a crack growing in a plane normal to the principal stress and parallel to the intermediate stress. This implies that crack growth and strength are not affected by the magnitude of the intermediate stress.

5.9. Summary and Conclusions

The recommendations concerning the testing equipment have been given in the text itself.

A number of investigators studied the effect of confining pressure on the strength of rocks. The strength was found to increase in all cases with the confining pressure, the rate of increase depending upon the rock type as well as the level of confining pressure.

The strength of rocks decreases with rise in temperature, the effect being different on different types of rocks.

The effect of pore pressure depends upon the porosity of the rock, viscosity of pore fluid, specimen size and rate of straining. Usually, the increase in pore pressure decreases the strength. The effective confining pressure concept is valid when loading rate is less than some critical value which depends upon the permeability of the rock, viscosity of pore fluid and specimen size.

Usually, the strength increases with increase in rate of loading. However, there have been cases where the opposite effect was observed. In the case of some rocks, no significant effect was found.

The importance of testing under general triaxial stress systems has long been recognised. However, owing to experimental difficulties, few investigations have been carried out. Recently (HOJEM and COOK, 1968; MOGI, 1971a, b) equipment has been designed and built for the general triaxial compression test. The results of tests clearly indicate that the value of the intermediate stress influences the strength of the rocks.

A number of failure criteria have been given in this chapter. The COULOMB-NAVIER and MOHR criteria provide relationships between the applied stresses at failure and these relationships can be evaluated empirically by testing each rock type under consideration. These theories do not assume any internal mechanisms leading to fracture, and terminal failure cannot be related to other physical data. GRIFFITH's criterion, on the other hand, provides an internal mechanism and a mathematical model that relates fracture to basic physical data, but, because these data are difficult to measure for rock, an empirical approach must be taken, namely, that of evaluating this criterion in terms of compressive and tensile strengths and the coefficient of friction for the crack surfaces.

References

1. ALDRICH, M. J.: Pore pressure effects on Berea sandstone subjected to experimental deformation. Geol. Soc. Am. Bull., Vol. 80, No. 8, Aug., 1969, pp. 1577–1586.
2. A.S.T.M.: Standard method of test for triaxial compressive strength of undrained rock core specimens without pore pressure measurements. A.S.T.M. Designation: D 2664-67, A.S.T.M. Standards Part II, 1968, pp. 822–826.
3. BAIDYUK, B. V.: Mechanical properties of rocks at high temperatures and pressures. Translated from Russian by J. P. Fitzsimmons. New York, Consultants Bureau, 1967, 75 p.
4. BALMER, G.: A general analytic solution for Mohr's envelope. A.S.T.M. Proc., Vol. 52, 1952, pp. 1260–1271.
5. BIENIAWSKI, Z. T., DENKHAUS, H. G. and VOGLER, U. W.: Failure of fractured rock. Int. J. Rock Mech. Min. Sci., Vol. 6, No. 3, May, 1969, pp. 323–341.
6. BODONYI, J.: Laboratory tests of certain rocks under axially-symmetrical loading conditions. Proc. 2nd Cong. Int. Soc. Rock Mech., Belgrade, 1970, Vol. 1, pp. 389–397.
7. BOKER, R.: Die Mechanik der bleibenden Formänderung in kristallinisch aufgebauten Körpern. Ver. dt. Ing. Mitt. Forsch., Vol. 175, 1915, pp. 1–51.
8. BOOZER, G. D., HILLER, K. H. and SERDENGECTI, S.: Effects of pore fluids on the deformation behaviour of rocks subjected to triaxial compression. Proc. 5th Symp. Rock Mech., Minneapolis, Minn., 1962, pp. 579–624.
9. BRACE, W. F.: Brittle fracture of rocks. Proc. Int. Conf. State of Stress in the Earth's Crust, Santa Monica, California, 1963, pp. 110–174.
10. BRACE, W. F. and MARTIN, R. J.: A test of the law of effective stress for crystalline rocks of low porosity. Int. J. Rock Mech. Min. Sci., Vol. 5, No. 5, Sept., 1968, pp. 415–426.
11. BRADY, B. T.: The effect of confining pressure on the elastic stress distribution in a radially end-constrained circular cylinder. Int. J. Rock Mech. Min. Sci., Vol. 8, No. 2, March, 1971, pp. 153–164.
12. BYERLEE, J. D.: Frictional characteristics of granite under high confining pressure. J. Geophys. Res., Vol. 72, No. 14, July 15, 1967, pp. 3639–3648.
13. CROUCH, S. L.: A note on post-failure stress-strain path dependence in norite. Int. J. Rock Mech. Min. Sci., Vol. 9, No. 2, March, 1972a, pp. 197–204.
14. CROUCH, S. L.: The post-failure behaviour of norite in triaxial compression. Eng. Geol., Vol. 6, 1972b, pp. 19–30.

REFERENCES 249

15. DONATH, F. A. and FRUTH, L. S.: Dependence of strain-rate effects on deformation mechanism and rock type. J. Geol., Vol. 79, No. 3, May, 1971, pp. 347–371.
16. EHRGOTT, J. Q.: Development of a dynamic high pressure triaxial test device. Proc. 12th Symp. Rock Mech., Rolla, Missouri, 1970, pp. 195–219.
17. EVANS, I. and POMEROY, C. D.: The strength, fracture and workability of coal. London, Pergamon Press, 1966, 277 p.
18. GRIFFITH, A. A.: The phenomena of rupture and flow in solids. Phil. Trans. Roy. Soc. London, Series A, Vol. 221, 1921, pp. 163–198.
19. GRIFFITH, A. A.: The theory of rupture. Proc. 1st Int. Cong. Appl. Mech., Delft, 1924, pp. 55–63.
20. GRIGGS, D. T.: Deformation of rocks under high confining pressures. I. Experiments at room temperature. J. Geol., Vol. 44, No. 5, July-Aug., 1936, pp. 541–577.
21. GRIGGS, D.: Experimental flow of rocks under conditions favouring recrystallisation. Geol. Soc. Am. Bull., Vol. 51, 1940, pp. 1001–1022.
22. GRIGGS, D. and HANDIN, J.: Observations on fracture and a hypothesis of earthquakes. Geol. Soc. Am. Mem. 79, 1960, pp. 347–364.
23. GRIGGS, D. and MILLER, W. B.: Deformation of Yule marble: Part 1 – Compression and extension experiments on dry Yule marble at 10000 atmospheres confining pressure, room temperature. Geol. Soc. Am. Bull., Vol. 62, 1951, pp. 853–862.
24. GRIGGS, D. T., TURNER, F. J. and HEARD, H. C.: Deformation of rocks at 500° to 800 °C. Geol. Soc. Am. Mem. 79, 1960, pp. 39–104.
25. HANDIN, J.: An application of high pressure in geophysics: Experimental rock deformation. Trans. A.S.M.E., Vol. 75, 1953, pp. 315–324.
26. HANDIN, J. W. and GRIGGS, D.: Deformation of Yule marble: Part 2 – Predicted fabric changes. Geol. Soc. Am. Bull., Vol. 62, 1951, pp. 863–885.
27. HANDIN, J. and HAGER, R. V.: Experimental deformation of sedimentary rocks under confining pressure: Tests at room temperature on dry samples. Bull. Am. Assoc. Pet. Geol., Vol. 41, No. 1, Jan., 1957, pp. 1–50.
28. HANDIN, J. and HAGER, R. V.: Experimental deformation of sedimentary rocks under confining pressure: Tests at high temperature. Bull. Am. Assoc. Pet. Geol., Vol. 42, No. 12, Dec., 1958, pp. 2892–2934.
29. HANDIN, J., HAGER, R. V., FRIEDMAN, M. and FEATHER, J. N.: Experimental deformation of sedimentary rocks under confining pressure: Pore pressure tests. Bull. Am. Assoc. Pet. Geol., Vol. 47, No. 5, May, 1963, pp. 717–755.
30. HANDIN, J., HEARD, H. C. and MAGOUIRK, J. N.: Effects of the intermediate principal stress on the failure of limestone, dolomite, and glass at different temperatures and strain rates. J. Geophys. Res., Vol. 72, No. 2, Jan. 15, 1967, pp. 611–640.
31. HANDIN, J., HIGGS, D. V. and O'BRIEN, J. K.: Torsion of Yule marble under confining pressure. Geol. Soc. Am. Mem. 79, 1960, pp. 245–274.
32. HEARD, H. C.: Transition from brittle fracture to ductile flow in Solenhofen limestone as a function of temperature, confining pressure, and interstitial fluid pressure. Geol. Soc. Am. Mem. 79, 1960, pp. 193–226.
33. HECK, W. J.: Suggested method of test for triaxial compressive strength of undrained rock core specimens with induced pore pressure measurements. In Special Procedures for Testing Soil and Rock for Engineering Purposes. A.S.T.M. Special Technical Publication No. 479, 1970, pp. 604–612.
34. HOBBS, D. W.: The strength of coal under biaxial compression. Coll. Eng., Vol. 39, 1962, pp. 285–290.

35. HOBBS, D. W.: The strength and the stress-strain characteristics of coal in triaxial compression. J. Geol., Vol. 72, No. 2, March, 1964, pp. 214–231.

36. HOEK, E. and FRANKLIN, J. A.: Simple triaxial cell for field or laboratory testing of rock. Trans. Inst. Min. Metall., Vol. 77, Sec. A, 1968, pp. A22–A26.

37. HOJEM, J. P. M. and COOK, N. G. W.: The design and construction of a triaxial and polyaxial cell for testing rock specimens. S. African Mech. Eng., Vol. 18, No. 2, Sept., 1968, pp. 57–61.

38. HOSKINS, E. R.: The failure of thick-walled hollow cylinders of isotropic rock. Int. J. Rock Mech. Min. Sci., Vol. 6, No. 1, Jan., 1969, pp. 99–125.

39. INGLIS, C. E.: Stresses in a plate due to the presence of cracks and sharp corners. Trans. Royal Inst. Naval Architects, Vol. 55, 1913, pp. 219–230.

40. JAEGER, J. C.: Punching tests on discs of rock under hydrostatic pressure. J. Geophys. Res., Vol. 67, No. 1, Jan., 1962, pp. 369–373.

41. KOTTE, J. J., BERCZES, Z. G., GRAMBERG, J. and SELDENRATH, TH. R.: Stress-strain relations and breakage of cylindrical granitic rock specimens under uniaxial and triaxial loads. Int. J. Rock Mech. Min. Sci., Vol. 6, No. 6, Nov., 1969, pp. 581–595.

42. LOGAN, J. M. and HANDIN, J.: Triaxial compression testing at intermediate strain rates. Proc. 12th Symp. Rock Mech., Rolla, Missouri, 1970, pp. 167–194.

43. MAZANTI, B. B. and SOWERS, G. F.: Laboratory testing of rock strength. Proc. Symp. Testing Techniques for Rock Mech., Seattle, Wash., 1965, pp. 207–227.

44. MCCLINTOCK, F. A. and WALSH, J. B.: Friction on Griffith cracks in rocks under pressure. Proc. 4th U.S. Nat. Cong. Appl. Mech., Berkeley, California, 1962, Vol. 2, pp. 1015–1021.

45. MOGI, K.: Some precise measurements of fracture strength of rocks under uniform compressive stress. Rock Mech. Eng. Geol., Vol. 4, 1966, pp. 41–55.

46. MOGI, K.: Effect of the triaxial stress system on rock failure. Rock Mech. in Japan, Vol. 1, 1970, pp. 53–55.

47. MOGI, K.: Fracture and flow of rocks under high triaxial compression. J. Geophys. Res., Vol. 76, No. 5, Feb. 10, 1971 a, pp. 1255–1269.

48. MOGI, K.: Effect of the triaxial stress system on the failure of dolomite and limestone. Tectonophysics, Vol. 11, No. 2, Feb., 1971 b, pp. 111–127.

49. MURRELL, S. A. F.: The strength of coal under triaxial compression. Proc. Conf. Mech. Prop. Non-metallic Brittle Materials, London, 1958, pp. 123–145.

50. MURRELL, S. A. F.: A criterion for brittle fracture of rocks and concrete under triaxial stress, and the effect of pore pressure on the criterion. Proc. 5th Symp. Rock Mech., Minneapolis, Minn., 1962, pp. 563–577.

51. NEFF, T. L.: Equipment for measuring pore pressure in rock specimens under triaxial load. Proc. Symp. Testing Techniques for Rock Mech., Seattle, Wash., 1965, pp. 3–17.

52. OBERT, L.: An inexpensive triaxial apparatus for testing mine rock. U.S.B.M.R.I. 6332, 1963, 10 p.

53. PRICE, N. J.: A study of rock properties in conditions of triaxial stress. Proc. Conf. Mech. Prop. Non-metallic Brittle Materials, London, 1958, pp. 106–122.

54. RAMEZ, M. R. H.: Fractures and the strength of a sandstone under triaxial compression. Int. J. Rock Mech. Min. Sci., Vol. 4, No. 3, July, 1967, pp. 257–268.

55. ROBERTSON, E. C.: Experimental study of the strength of rocks. Geol. Soc. Am. Bull., Vol. 66, 1955, pp. 1275–1314.

56. ROBINSON, L. H.: The effect of pore and confining pressure on the failure process in sedimentary rock. Proc. 3rd Symp. Rock Mech., Golden, Colo., 1959, pp. 177–199.

57. ROBINSON, L. H.: Effect of hardness reducers on failure characteristics of rock. Soc. Pet. Eng. J., Vol. 7, No. 3, Sept., 1967, pp. 295–298.

58. RYABININ, YU. N., BERESNEV, B. I. and MARTINOV, E. D.: Mechanical properties and processes in solids under high pressure. J. Geophys. Res., Vol. 76, No. 5, Feb. 10, 1971, pp. 1370–1375.

59. SACK, R. A.: Extension of Griffith's theory of rupture to three dimensions. Proc. Phys. Soc. London, Vol. 58, 1946, pp. 729–736.

60. SAUCIER, K.: Use of laboratory dynamic triaxial tests to develop criteria for design of concrete stems for field cratering tests. Proc. 1st Cong. Int. Soc. Rock Mech., Lisbon, 1966, Vol. 1, pp. 651–653.

61. SCHWARTZ, A. E.: Failure of rock in the triaxial shear test. Proc. 6th Symp. Rock Mech., Rolla, Missouri, 1964, pp. 109–151.

62. SEIFERT, K. E.: Strength of Adirondack anorthosite at elevated temperatures and pressures. Geol. Soc. Am. Bull., Vol. 80, No. 10, Oct., 1969, pp. 2053–2059.

63. SERDENGECTI, S. and BOOZER, G. D.: The effects of strain rate and temperature on the behaviour of rocks subjected to triaxial compression. Proc. 4th Symp. Rock Mech., Univ. Park, Penn., 1961, pp. 83–97.

64. SWANSON, S. R. and BROWN, W. S.: An observation of loading path independence of fracture in rock. Int. J. Rock Mech. Min. Sci., Vol. 8, No. 3, May, 1971, pp. 277–281.

65. TERZAGHI, K.: Stress conditions for the failure of saturated concrete and rock. A.S.T.M. Proc., Vol. 45, 1945, pp. 777–792.

66. VON KARMAN, TH.: Festigkeitsversuche unter allseitigem Druck. (Strength tests with triaxial compression.) Z. Ver. dt. Ing., Vol. 55, 1911, pp. 1749–1757.

67. WAWERSIK, W. R. and BRACE, W. F.: Post-failure behaviour of a granite and diabase. Rock Mech., Vol. 3, 1971, pp. 61–65.

68. WAWERSIK, W. R. and FAIRHURST, C.: A study of brittle rock fracture in laboratory compression experiments. Int. J. Rock. Mech. Min. Sci., Vol. 7, No. 5, Sept., 1970, pp. 561–575.

APPENDIX

Stiff Testing Machines

Concept of Stiff Testing Machines

The first clear explanation of the influence of the machine stiffness on the failure of test specimens was given by WHITNEY (1943) who stated that during failure of concrete cylinders, the elastic movement of the testing machine head imposes a large additional strain on the specimen which may be considerably greater than the total strain up to the time that failure starts. As a result, a large amount of elastic energy is stored in the machine and the specimen, the release of which causes the breakdown of the specimen.

SALAMON (1970) has given a very clear concept of the failure of specimens in the post-failure region. When a specimen is loaded in a testing machine, the system can be represented by two springs of stiffness k_m (machine) and k_s (specimen) placed between two rigid supports R and R' (Fig. 1a) which move in relation to the junction 0 in the positive and negative directions (Fig. 1b). If both the springs are supposed to be linear, the force-displacement relationship for the machine and the specimen can be represented by Fig. 1c, and can be given by

$$\left. \begin{array}{l} F_m = -k_m \delta_m \\[2mm] F_s = k_s \delta_s \end{array} \right\} \tag{A.1}$$

where F = force (compressive force $+ve$)
δ_m = displacement of the machine ($-ve$) and
δ_s = displacement of the specimen ($+ve$)

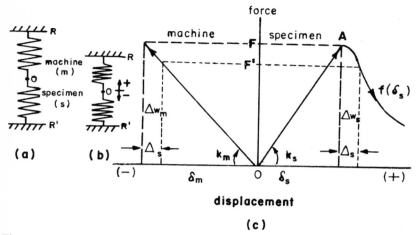

Fig. 1. Representation of machine-specimen testing system, (a) and (b), with linear
force-displacement curve (c)
(after HUDSON, CROUCH and FAIRHURST, 1972).

The system is in equilibrium as long as the following condition holds good:

$$F_m = F_s$$

or

$$-k_m \delta_m = k_s \delta_s$$

(A.2)

In case when the specimen behaviour is non-linear, then $F_s = f(\delta_s)$ and the
equilibrium condition becomes

$$-k_m \delta_m = f(\delta_s)$$

(A.3)

This equilibrium condition of the system is maintained as long as the spring
(machine) is not able to cause further deformation of the specimen without
the addition of external energy. Now if the points R and R' remain relatively
fixed and if any strain is introduced in the specimen as a result of its failure
at the point A (Fig. 1c), the virtual work required to be done by the spring
(ΔW_m) to introduce this displacement in the specimen Δ_s equivalent to the
work ΔW_s, the equilibrium condition shall be maintained as long as the
following condition holds good:

$$\Delta W_s - \Delta W_m > 0$$

(A.4)

This will lead to drop in the force from F to F'.

The work done by the machine on the specimen during the virtual displacement can be given by

$$\Delta W_m = (F' + \tfrac{1}{2} \Delta F_m) \Delta_s \qquad (A.5)$$

and the work absorbed by the specimen to deform itself

$$\Delta W_s = (F' + \tfrac{1}{2} \Delta F_s) \Delta_s \qquad (A.6)$$

The values of ΔF_m and ΔF_s are dependent upon the stiffness of the machine and the specimen. The machine stiffness remaining linear, the stiffness of the rock specimen in the post-failure case may not be linear. Therefore,

$$\left. \begin{aligned} \Delta F_m &= -k_m \Delta_s \\ \Delta F_s &= f(\delta_s) \, \Delta_s = \lambda \Delta_s \end{aligned} \right\} \qquad (A.7)$$

where λ represents the slope of the force-displacement curve of the specimen in the post-failure region at the point where the failure just occurs.

Substituting Eq. A. 7 into Eqs. A. 5 and A. 6, we get

$$\Delta W_m = (F' - \tfrac{1}{2} k_m \Delta_s) \Delta_s \qquad (A.8)$$

$$\Delta W_s = (F' + \tfrac{1}{2} \lambda \Delta_s) \Delta_s \qquad (A.9)$$

Putting these values of ΔW_m and ΔW_s into the equilibrium condition, Eq. A. 4, we get

$$\lambda + k_m > 0 \qquad (A.10)$$

The slope of the force-displacement of the machine is $+ve$ and fixed $(+k_m)$ and that of the specimen changes from a positive value to a negative value at the point of failure. The condition (Eq. A. 10) indicates that the equilibrium will be stable throughout the pre-failure and in the post-failure regions as long as the value of $\lambda > k_m$. If the stiffness of the machine is superimposed on the post-failure curve of the specimen (Fig. 2), the unstable condition occurs at the point where this forms tangent to the force-displacement of the specimen and at this point violent failure will occur. If the stiffness of the machine is high $(+k_m')$, this instability condition may never be reached. The failure of the specimen will be controlled and the displacement of the specimen shall take place only under an application of external energy.

A machine can be called stiff relative to the specimen when numerically $k_m > \lambda$, otherwise the machine is soft. The stiffness of most of the testing machines is 196 M N/m (1.1×10^6 lbf/in).

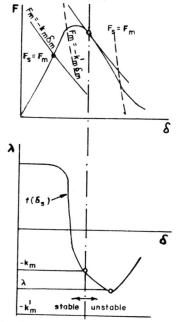

Fig. 2. Criterion for instability in terms of $f(\delta)$ and $f(\delta_s)$ or λ
(after SALAMON, 1970).

Stiffness of a Testing Machine

The usual testing machines consist of hydraulic or screw driven loading system, loading frames and movable cross-heads. Besides in testing of rock specimens several times, end pieces, steel cylinders as load gauges and spacers are used. The stiffness of the testing system, therefore, is dependent upon the stiffness of the components.

The composite stiffness of N components placed in series such that they are subjected to the same force is given by the reciprocal of the sum of the reciprocals of their stiffness.

$$k_m = 1 \left/ \left[\sum_{i=1}^{i=N} \frac{1}{k_i} \right] \right. \tag{A.11}$$

The stiffness of the members placed in parallel is given by the sum of the stiffness of these elements.

$$k_m = k_1 + k_2 + k_3 + \ldots + k_N \qquad (A.12)$$

The overall stiffness of the testing system, obviously, depends upon the machine design and the test method (use of spacers, etc.).

The stiffness of an element means the force required for unit displacement. Thus the stiffness of an elastic component of length L, cross-sectional area A and modulus of elasticity E when subjected to uniaxial compression can be given by

$$k = \frac{AE}{L} \qquad (A.13)$$

The stiffness of such a member shall therefore be higher when the modulus of elasticity is increased, or its area of cross-section is increased or its length is decreased. The frame of a testing machine, the spacers placed between the specimen and the platens, the load cell, etc., are subjected to simple compression. Their stiffnesses can be increased by increasing their cross-sectional areas and decreasing their lengths.

The stiffness of the cross-heads and the loading platens is dependent upon the area upon which the load is applied. The major factor influencing the stiffness is probably the indentation of the platens particularly when the cross-heads are thick. TIMOSHENKO and GOODIER (1951) have given the displacement of a rigid circular punch of diameter d indenting a flat surface as

$$w = F(1 - v^2)/dE \qquad (A.14)$$

where w = displacement
  F = load
  v = POISSON's ratio
  d = diameter of the punch or die (in this case the rock specimen) and
  E = YOUNG's modulus of the flat surface.

This means that the stiffness of two ridigly connected platens can be very nearly given by $\frac{1}{2} dE$. If the diameter of the specimen (acting as a punch) is 2.54 cm (1 in), then the stiffness of the steel platens will be of the order of 2.6 GN/m (15×10^6 lbf/in) (HUDSON, BROWN and FAIRHURST, 1971a).

The platen indentation effect is important in case of very strong rocks and may be reduced by using load spreader of truncated shape made from tungsten carbide.

The stiffness of the hydraulic loading system is governed by the compression of the hydraulic fluid as well as the expansion of the cylinder, tubing, gauges, valves, etc. The stiffness of a column of fluid of height H, bulk modulus K and cross-sectional area A can be given by

$$k = \frac{AK}{H} \tag{A.15}$$

The stiffness, therefore, can be increased by decreasing the column of the fluid, increasing its cross-sectional area while at the same time decreasing the length of the pipes, using stronger cylinders and pipes and using less compressible fluids such as mercury (SPAETH, 1935; TURNER and BARNARD. 1962).

COOK and HOJEM (1966) have analysed a 0.49 MN (50 tonf) commercial testing machine which had a rigidity of 95 MN/m (0.54×10^6 lbf/in). They found that the rigidity is distributed among the major structural components in the following order:

Piston rod	=	4.380 GN/m (25 $\times 10^6$ lbf/in)
Cross-head	=	1.472 GN/m (8.4 $\times 10^6$ lbf/in)
Cylinder wall	=	1.332 GN/m (7.6 $\times 10^6$ lbf/in)
Tie bolts	= 648	MN/m(3.7 $\times 10^6$ lbf/in)
Hydraulic oil	= 133	MN/m(0.76 $\times 10^6$ lbf/in)

The rigidity of the machines, therefore, could be improved by minimising the compressibility of the hydraulic oil, reducing the stresses in the members by increasing their cross-section, reducing the length of the members, reducing the number of load-bearing interfaces between the components and by ensuring that all interfaces fit as accurately as possible.

Recently, a number of stiff testing machines with servo-controlled systems have been built and used very successfully. In these machines, the displacement of the platens, the rate of displacement of the platens, load or the rate of loading can be controlled by the feed back control system. The important factor in these machines is not the stiffness of the loading frame or the hydraulic system, etc., but the correct choice of the feed back signal and the response time of the closed loop. The principle of the closed loop servo-controlled testing machine is given in Fig. 3. Say, for example, when the test is run on displacement control as the control variable, the signal from the displacement transducer mounted in between the two platens of the loading frame (or on the specimen) is fed to the servo-controller where it is compared with the signal from the programmer which has been programmed to give a constant rate increased voltage signal representing constant rate of displacement (e. g. electro-mechanical function generator, or electronic function generator). The servo-controller supplies a control signal to the servo-valve that is proportional to the magnitude and polarity of the difference between the feed back and programme signal. When the two signals are equal, the experiment corresponds to the programme and hence the servo-valve remains stationary, but if there is a difference, the valve operates reducing or increasing the pressure in the cylinder so as to bring the experiment to correspond to the programme condition. If, for example, the strain is high, as it happens in the post-failure region, the servo-valve so opens that the pressure in the cylinder is reduced thereby decreasing load on the cylinder.

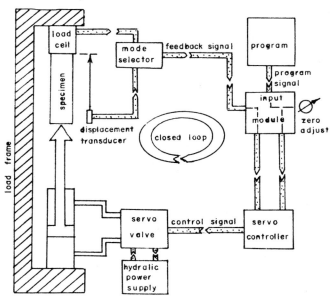

Fig. 3. Schematic of fast-response, closed-loop, servo-controlled testing system
(after HUDSON, BROWN and FAIRHURST, 1971 b)

The sequence of events that occur in a servo-controlled machine in arresting free run of any instability that occurs is schematically shown in Fig. 4. When a specimen is deformed at any constant rate of deformation $\dot{x}$ following the line JK (Fig. 4) such that any instability as a result of crack initiation or propagation occurs at the point K, the servo system acts as a soft machine allowing it to deform to the point L when the servo-system reacts dropping the force while in the mean time the instability continues due to the kinetic energy developed by it till it is arrested at the point N. During this period, if the time elapsed between the initiation of the instability K and its arrest

N is t, such that $\dot{x}\,t = \Delta X_p$, the system will further unload since the specimen is over deformed (to ΔX_N) and this will follow the residual elastic curve to the point P. At this point, the system will start loading again and the specimen will follow the path PNQ until the failure locus Q is reached. The cycle is again repeated. The system thus gives a curve $JKLMNQ$ instead of the actual curve. $JKMQ$.

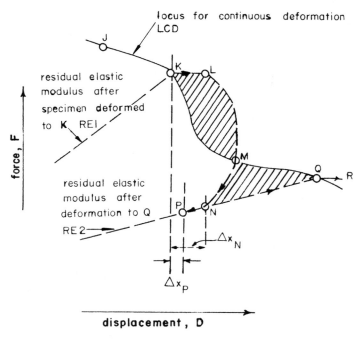

Fig. 4. Idealised response of the servo-system to a rapidly generated instability (after RUMMEL and FAIRHURST, 1970).

The response time of the system, i.e., time that elapses between the detection of the error and the correction of the error is important. If this time is large, it may so happen that the crack that is initiated may run through before the pressure is reduced. Studies conducted on the rate of crack growth on rocks (BIENIAWSKI, 1968) have shown that the crack velocity increases slowly and that it increases from almost zero to a few centimetres per second in the initial phase and this permits the control. The response time of the servo-controlled units is about 5 milliseconds and the crack initiates but in this short period do not propagate to any significant distance if the proper feed back signal is used.

The feed back signal usually used in rock testing is the displacement and optimised control is obtained when the feed back transducer is located for maximum sensitivity in detecting failure. The placing of the feed back transducer for a variety of tests is given in Fig. 5. The important point that should be kept in view is that the feed back signal should increase monotonically as the programme signal. In many cases the axial displacement in the direction of maximum load may not increase monotonically and in general it is advisable to place the feed back signal in the direction of least principal stress.

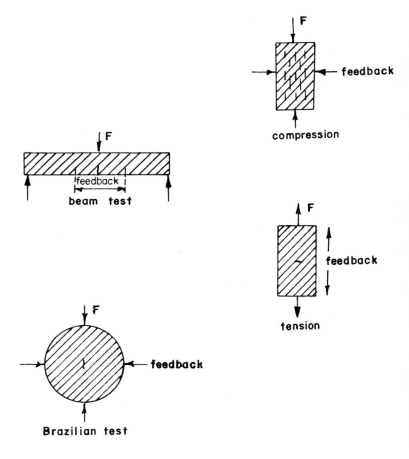

Fig. 5. Feedback for optimum displacement control in varuious situations
(after HUDSON, BROWN and FAIRHURST, 1971a).

Development of Stiff Machines for Testing of Rocks

The first complete stress-strain curve under compression extending to the post-failure region was obtained by KIENDL and MALDARI (1938) while testing 15.24 cm (6 in) diameter and 30.48 cm (12 in) long concrete specimens in a Riehle testing machine in which the displacement of the head was controlled at 0.15 cm/min (0.06 in/min). Subsequent work on concrete was done by WHITNEY (1943), BLANKS and MCHENRY (1949), RUSCH (1960), BROCK (1962), TURNER and BARNARD (1962), HINDE (1964), HUGHES and CHAPMAN (1966).

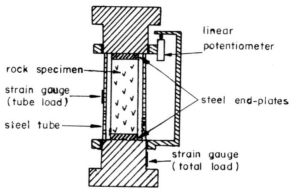

Fig. 6. A device for determining the strain-stress characteristics of rock specimens and for increasing the stiffness of a compression testing machine
(after COOK, 1965).

The work on the post-failure behaviour of rocks started sometimes in 1965 by PAULDING (1965a, b) who loaded granite specimens through a simply supported steel beam and was able to observe crack growth as the compressive strength approached near. COOK (1965) loaded rock specimens of Tennessee marble and St. Cloud granite and steel tube parallel to their long axes (Fig. 6) which allowed increase in the resilience of the machine from 2.7×10^{11} to 13.5×10^{11} dynes/cm (1.56×10^{10} to 7.8×10^{10} lbf/in) and was able to obtain a partial post-failure curve. The first complete stress-strain curve was perhaps obtained by BIENIAWSKI (1966) who used steel columns loaded in parallel with the specimen in a 1.00 MN (100 tonf) loading machine. The arrangement used by him is given in Fig. 7 and the stiffness of the machine could be varied between 105 MN/m to 1.804 GN/m (0.6×10^6 lbf/in to 10.3×10^6 lbf/in) depending upon the stiffening column diameter and height. COOK and HOJEM (1966) designed the first stiff compression machine (Fig. 8) which consists of 3, 33.0 cm (13.0 in) diameter,

3.8 cm (1.5 in) thick mild steel cross-heads mounted on 3, 6.4 cm (2.5 in) diameter, 58.4 cm (23.0 in) long aluminium alloy pillars. The top and bottom cross-heads are fixed while the middle cross-head is movable. The specimen is placed between the top and middle cross-head and preloaded by a 298.92 k N (30 tonf) hydraulic jack and locked during the course of which hot water is circulated through the aluminium columns. At the final stages of loading, cold water is circulated to contract the columns. They achieved the rigidity of the machine of the order of 1.577 G N/m (9.0×10^6 lbf/in) and the maximum capacity of the machine is 1.00 M N (100 tonf).

WAWERSIK (1968) and WAWERSIK and FAIRHURST (1970) utilised the same principle and constructed a machine having stiffness of 1.542 G N/m (8.8×10^6 lbf/in) using 1.00 M N (100 tonf) cylinder instead of a 597.841 k N (60 tonf) with heavier aluminium pillars having 5 central holes for cooling. This machine had many refinements so that the parallelism of the cross-heads was continually checked by 3 dial gauges and adjusted by regulating flow of water. The rate of strain was about 10^{-5}/s. The method of loading the specimens was slightly modified. The specimen was loaded to approximately 50–75% of maximum load carrying capacity by the 1.00 M N (100 tonf) hydraulic cylinder. The cross-heads were locked and cold water was circulated through the aluminium columns to increase load. Whenever the recorder trace indicated that the post-failure curve of the rock tended to become steeper than the unloading characteristics of the machine, the 1.00 M N (100 ton f) jack was actuated to create force in opposition to that exerted by the cooling aluminium columns resulting in decreasing the load on the specimen. The failure of the specimen was thus halted as soon as the remaining energy associated with fracture propagation was used up. Once the failure was stopped, the sample was reloaded until the failure curve was reached again and fracture propagation commenced.

The use of servo-machines has now become widespread in the study of the post-failure behaviour of rocks. The principle underlying these machines has already been described.

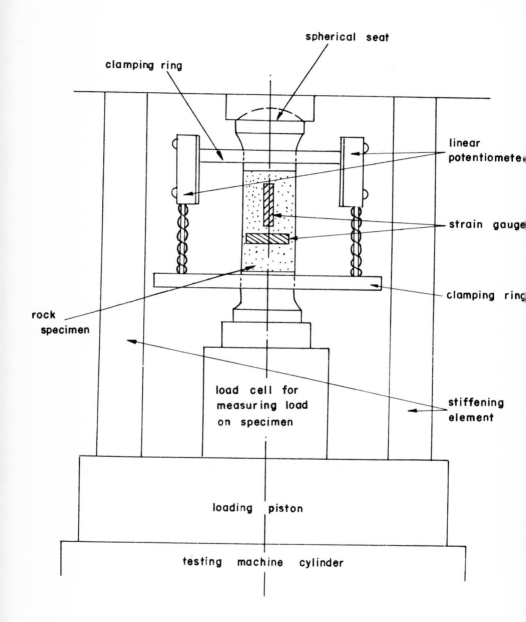

Fig. 7. Increasing stiffness of a testing machine by stiffening elements
(after BIENIAWSKI, 1966).

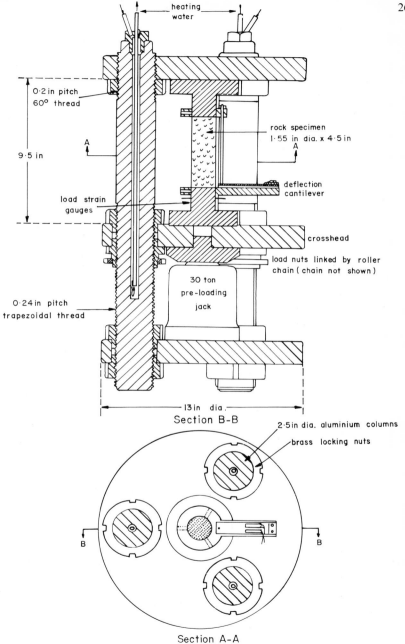

Section B-B

Section A-A

Fig. 8. A 100 ton thermally-controlled stiff machine
(after Cook and Hojem, 1966).

References

1. BIENIAWSKI, Z.T.: Mechanism of rock fracture in compression. Rep. S. African C.S.I.R., No. MEG 459, 1966, 75 p.
2. BIENIAWSKI, Z.T.: The phenomenon of terminal fracture velocity in rock. Rock Mech. Eng. Geol., Vol. 6, 1968, pp. 113–125.
3. BLANKS, R.F. and McHENRY, D.: Plastic flow of concrete relieves high-load stress concentrations. Civ. Eng., Vol. 19, No. 5, May, 1949, pp. 40–42.
4. BROCK, G.: Concrete: Complete stress-strain curves. Engineering, Vol. 193, 1962, pp. 606–608.
5. COOK, N.G.W.: The failure of rock. Int. J. Rock Mech. Min. Sci., Vol. 2, No. 4, Dec., 1965, pp. 389–403.
6. COOK, N.G.W. and HOJEM, J.P.M.: A rigid 50-ton compression and tension testing machine. S. African Mech. Eng., Vol. 16, No. 4, Nov., 1966, pp. 89–92.
7. HINDE, P.B.: Testing machine stiffness problem. The Engineer, Vol. 217, No. 5657, 26 June, 1964, pp. 1124–1127.
8. HUDSON, J.A., BROWN, E.T. and FAIRHURST, C.: Optimising the control of rock failure in servo-controlled laboratory tests. Rock Mech., Vol. 3, 1971a, pp. 217–224.
9. HUDSON, J.A., BROWN, E.T. and FAIRHURST, C.: Shape of the complete stress-strain curve for rock. Proc. 13th Symp. Rock Mech., Urbana, Illinois, 1971b, pp. 773–795.
10. HUDSON, J.A., CROUCH, S.L. and FAIRHURST, C.: Soft, stiff and servo-controlled testing machines: A review with reference to rock failure. Eng. Geol., Vol. 6, 1972, pp. 155–189.
11. HUGHES, B.P. and CHAPMAN, G.P.: The complete stress-strain curve for concrete in direct tension. Bull. RILEM, No. 30. March, 1966, pp. 95–97.
12. KIENDL, O.G. and MALDARI, J.A.: Comparison of physical properties of concrete made of three varieties of coarse aggregates. B.S. Thesis, Univ. Wisconsin, Madison, Wisconsin, 1938.
13. PAULDING, B.W.: Crack growth during brittle fracture in compression. Ph.D. Thesis, M.I.T., Cambridge, Mass., 1965a, 214 p.
14. PAULDING, B.W.: Techniques used in studying the fracture mechanics of rock. Proc. Symp. Testing Techniques for Rock Mech., Seattle, Wash., 1965b, pp. 73–86.
15. RUMMEL, F. and FAIRHURST, C.: Determination of the post-failure behaviour of brittle rock using a servo-controlled testing machine. Rock Mech., Vol. 2, 1970, pp. 189–204.
16. RUSCH, H.: Researches toward a general flexural theory for structural concrete. Proc. Am. Conc. Inst., Vol. 57, 1960, pp. 1–28.
17. SALAMON, M.D.G.: Stability, instability and design of pillar workings. Int. J. Rock Mech. Min. Sci., Vol. 7, No. 6, Nov., 1970, pp. 613–631.
18. SPAETH, W.: Einfluß der Federung der Zerreißmaschine auf das Spannungs-Dehnungs-Schaubild. Arch. Eisenhüttenwesen, Vol. 6, 1935, pp. 277–283.
19. TIMOSHENKO, S. and GOODIER, J.N.: Theory of elasticity. 2nd edition, New York, McGraw-Hill, 1951, 506 p.
20. TURNER, P.W. and BARNARD, P.R.: Stiff constant strain rate testing machine. The Engineer, Vol. 214, No. 5557, 27 July, 1962, pp. 146–148.
21. WAWERSIK, W.R.: Detailed analysis of rock failure in laboratory compression tests. Ph.D. Thesis, Univ. Minnesota, Minneapolis, Minn., 1968, 165 p.

22. WAWERSIK, W. R. and FAIRHURST, C.: A study of brittle rock fracture in laboratory compression experiments. Int. J. Rock Mech. Min. Sci., Vol. 7, No. 5, Sept., 1970, pp. 561–575.

23. WHITNEY, C. S.: Discussion on the paper "The plasticity ratio of concrete and its effect on the ultimate strength of beams" by Jensen, V. P. J. Am. Conc. Inst., Vol. 14, 1943, pp. 584-2 to 584-6.

ABOUT THE AUTHORS

V. S. *Vutukuri* was born in India on September 22, 1937. In 1960 he received the Degree of Bachelor of Science in Mining Engineering from Banaras Hindu University. He received the Degree of Master of Science in Mining Engineering from University of Wisconsin in 1965.

Between 1960 and 1964 he held the post of Lecturer in Mining Engineering at Banaras Hindu University. He then went to University of Wisconsin on study leave for postgraduate studies on a Wisconsin Alumni Research Foundation Fellowship. After completing the requirements for M. S. Degree, he joined the staff of White Pine Copper Company and was engaged with them for 6 months, in rock mechanics and rock breaking research. In 1966, he returned to Banaras Hindu University. He was promoted to Reader in 1966. In 1970 he emigrated to Australia and has been Lecturer in Mining Engineering, University of New South Wales, Broken Hill Division since that time. His special interests are in rock mechanics and rock fragmentation.

He is a Member of the Mining, Geological and Metallurgical Institute of India, a Member of the American Institute of Mining, Metallurgical and Petroleum Engineers, a Member of the International Society for Rock Mechanics and an Associate Member of the Australasian Institute of Mining and Metallurgy.

R. D. *Lama* was born in India on April 1, 1940 and received the Degree of Bachelor of Science (with merit) from the Punjab University in 1957 and the Degree of Bachelor of Science in Mining Engineering in 1961 from the Banaras Hindu University standing First Class First throughout.

He worked for one year in the Research Department of the Bengal Coal Co. and then left for higher studies to Poland on a Govt. of India Scholarship. During the period 1962–66 he worked in the Academy of Mining and Metallurgy, Cracow, Poland and obtained the Degree of Doctor of Technical Science in 1966 with a thesis on rock bursts and mechanical behaviour of coal seams in-situ.

In 1967 he joined Banaras Hindu University as a Reader in Coal Mining where he had been engaged in the teaching of Rock Mechanics, and Ground Movement to the post-graduate and under-graduate students.

In 1971, he worked for six months with the Institute of Underground Mining, Akademia Górniczo-Hutnicza, Cracow, on the problems associated with the prediction of cracking and crack density around tunnels and since December 1971 he is working in the Institute of Soil Mechanics and Rock Mechanics, University of Karlsruhe on certain aspects of jointed rock masses.

Dr. *Lama* was awarded Banaras Hindu University Gold Medal, Nand Lal Gold Medal of the Banaras Hindu University and Roberton Medal of the Mining, Geological and Metallurgical Institute of India for his outstanding academic record. He is a member of the International Society of Rock Mechanics, Canadian Institute of Mining and Metallurgy, Association of the Mining Engineers and Technicians Poland and the Mining, Geological and Metallurgical Institute of India.

S. S. *Saluja* was born in India on April 15, 1925 and obtained the Associateship of the Indian School of Mines in 1950. He worked for several years in the mining industry first as a mining engineer and later occupying the position of a mine manager in 1955.

In 1954 he worked as a Columbo-plan fellow in the Post-graduate School of Mining, University of Sheffield and in 1957 joined the Banaras Hindu University as Professor of Mining. In 1959 he travelled widely in Europe, Asia and Australia under the Nuffield Foundation travelling fellowship in engineering visiting various research organisations and in 1960 he left for U.S.A. on a USAID fellowship when he obtained his M.S. from the University of Illinois in 1961 and Ph.D. from the University of Wisconsin with a thesis on mechanics of rock blasting.

In 1965, he was appointed as Head of the Department of Mining and Principal of the College of Mining and Metallurgy. He was the Dean of the Faculty of Engineering and since 1971 is working as a Director of the Institute of Technology, Banaras Hindu University.

Dr. *Saluja* is a member of the Mining, Geological and Metallurgical Institute of India, Institution of Engineers (India), Institution of Mining Engineers (U.K) and several other expert committees in mining and allied fields in the country.

Author Index

Volkov, V. A.	(see Smorodinov, M. I., 61)
v. Karman, Th.	175, 181, 189, 190, 223
Voropinov, J.	144, 145, 171
Vutukuri, V. S.	115, 121, 122
Walsh, J. B.	246
Wawersik, W. R.	63, 64, 65, 66, 213, 214, 263
Whitney, C. S.	253, 262
Wiid, B. L.	51, 52, 53, 57, 58
Windes, S. L.	37, 47, 50, 80, 88, 89, 91, 97, 98
Wright, P. J. F.	134
Wuerker, R. G.	5, 89, 166
Yamaguchi, U.	8
Yarovaya, L. I.	(see Alekseev, A. D., 33, 43, 44, 49)
Yu, Y. S.	91, 110, 134
Zahary, G.	194
Zaruba, Q.	50
Zhuravlev, V. I.	(see Alekseev, A. D., 33, 43, 44, 49)
Znanski, J.	21, 31

Subject Index

ADVERTISER'S INDEX

ELECTRICAL MEASUREMENT OF MECHANICAL QUANTITIES

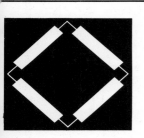

sensing

with HBM-Transducers for

Force	$0 \ldots 1{,}5 \cdot 10^6$ pounds
Pressure	$0 \ldots 50\,000$ psi
Torque	$0 \ldots 35\,000$ lb-ft
Strain	$0 \ldots \pm 10^5$ micro-in/in
Displacement	$0 \ldots 400$ mm
Acceleration	$0 \ldots 250$ g
Amplitude	$0 \ldots \pm 25$ mm

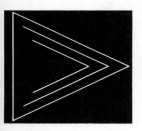

conditioning

with HBM

**Amplifiers
Indicators
Complementary and
Special Instrumentation
Measuring Point Selectors**

display

with

**Analog/Digital Indicators
Recorders
UV-Oscillographs
Oscilloscopes
XY-Plotter
Magnetic Tape Recorder
Digital-Printer**

HOTTINGER BALDWIN MESSTECHNIK GMBH

D 61 Darmstadt · W-Germany · Postbox: 4151 · Telephone: 06151 8031 · Telex: 0419341 · Telegrams: Messtechnik Darmstadt

Specialized Servo-Hydraulic Rock and Soil Mechanics Testing Systems

MFL

Prüf- und Meßsysteme GmbH
D 68 Mannheim, Box 1502
W.-Germany

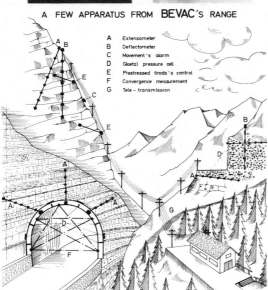

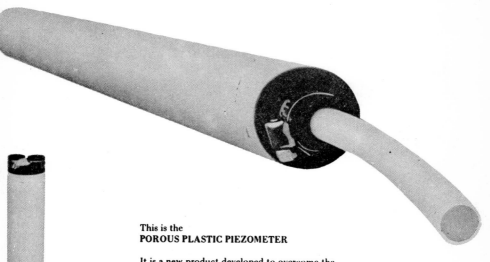

This is the
POROUS PLASTIC PIEZOMETER

It is a new product developed to overcome the
deficiencies of its predecessors.

Answering previous field assembly problems,
the pre-assembled porous plastic unit only
requires attaching to the lead-in tubing. The
unit is robust and relatively immune to rough
field handling.

The porous plastic has an average pore size of
50 microns. This small pore size enables the
material to be used in direct contact with silt or
clay with no worries about clogging. The great
profusion of pores results in high permeability.
Stability of the plastic is ensured within the
temperature range normally encountered. As
constructed the piezometer has a negative
buoyancy for ease of installation.

Model PFF is available for circulating de-airing
water through the unit.

Same day air express shipment
from our factory.

TERRATEST PIEZOMETERS
90 Milvan Drive
Weston (Toronto) Ontario
Canada
1-416-749-1294

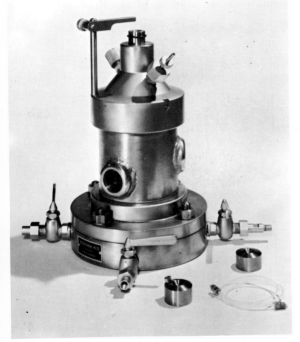

Series on Rock and Soil Mechanics
Vol. 1 (1971/74) No. 1

Bins and Bunkers for Handling Bulk Materials

— Practical Design and Techniques —

By **W. Reisner, M. v. Eisenhart Rothe** and **H. Colijn**

1971, reprinted 1974, 280 pages, 333 references, 15 tables, 178 illustrations
Price: US $ 24.00 paperback

International Standard Book No: 0-87849-001-9
Library of Congress Catalog Card No: 74-149275

Contents:

Handling and storing of bulk materials has become increasingly important in recent years to the mining, mineral processing, chemical, railroading, shipping and farming industries. This is primarily due to the ever increasing capacities of individual plants and installations.

This book is the first attempt to gather the widely scattered literature on the subject of bins and bunkers and gives a survey of the state of the art. The text treats the theoretical considerations of bulk solids in bins, bunkers and silos, but concentrates on the practical aspects.

"It is, in effect, a design handbook incorporating a large number of figures and diagrams illustrating designs and listing 61 equipment manufacturers engaged in the production of bins, bunkers and ancilliary equipment As such, the book should prove a useful tool for engineers in industry who are concerned with bulk materials handling."

Solid Liquid Flow Abstracts

"The planning and design engineer will appreciate this survey, and also the possibility of being able to quickly locate publications which deal with his special problems in more detail."

The Australien Concrete Journal

Series on Rock and Soil Mechanics
Vol. 1 (1971/74) No. 2

The Science of Rock Mechanics

PART 1
STRENGTH PROPERTIES
OF ROCKS

By Prof. Dr. **W. Dreyer,** Technical University Clausthal, Germany

1972, reprinted 1973, 500 pages, 200 references, 86 tables, 137 figures,
price: US $ 30.00 hard cover

International Standard Book Number: 0-87849-002-7.
Library of Congress Catalog Card Number: 78-149276.

The present volume is the first — in itself complete — part of the monography "The Science of Rock Mechanics". It comprises primarily the relationship between state of stress, strength of rocks and their determining textural data. As the description of the mechanical behavior of rocks under compressive load is extremely incomplete without adequate consideration of the petrographic parameters such as mineral composition, mineral interlocking, granulation, grain density and porosity, the author has treated the mineral content of all investigated rock samples quantitatively and formulated them mathematically.

The operation of caverns in salt deposits for the purpose of storage requires intimate knowledge of stability and convergence behavior of an underground system. The solution to this highly complex rock mechanics problem is discussed in a special chapter.

"Originality in its true and good sense of the word is the great advantage of this book. Here, a professor has not written a seventh book out of six others, but a researcher has presented his field of interest and especially the results of his own studies, extending over almost two decades, among them many to be published for the first time.

ERZMETALL

"Une part importante de l'ouvrage est réservée aux methodes des mesure et aux essais sur la portance des roches soumises à des charges homogènes et hétérogènes, aux études de convergence des excavations minières, et aux conditions de stabilité des réservoirs souterrains. Cet ouvrage constitue en fait une excellente introduction aux problèmes de la méchanique des roches, et pour le practicien, une source de renseignements précieux."

Industrie Minérale

Series on Rock and Soil Mechanics
Vol. 1 (1971/74) No. 4

E X P L O S I V E S

for

North American Engineers

By Dr. **Cedric E. Gregory,** Professor of Mining Engineering,
University of Idaho, USA

1973, 276 pages, 80 figures, 15 tables, 130 references,
price: US $ 24.00 hard cover.

International Standard Book Number: ISBN 0-87849-007-8
Library of Congress Catalog Card Number: LC 72-96512

Contents

"The author does a fine job of covering his subject without overwhelming the reader with limited prior knowledge of the field."

Contractors & Engineers Magazine

"The author's aim was to write a textbook primer that is both readable and understandable, and this book has achieved that admirably. It should, however, also be of substantial benefit to operators in the field and also to those engaged in improving blasting methods and materials. Blasting is one of the more fascinating aspects of mining which many tend to stay clear of due to the difficulties of 'getting to grips' with the subject. This book provides a first-rate textbook written by an authoritiy on the subject in a clear and straightforward way. It is to be firmly recommended to both students and practising engineers not only in North America but throughout the world."

Mining Magazine

Series on Rock and Soil Mechanics
Vol. 1 (1971/74) No. 3

FOUNDATION INSTRUMENTATION

By **Dr. Thomas H. Hanna,** Professor of Civil and Structural Engineering, University of Sheffield, England

1973, 372 pages, 251 figures, 520 references, price: US $ 35.00 hard cover

International Standard Book Number: ISBN 0-87849-006-x
Library of Congress Catalog Card Number: LC 72-90015

Contents

"The book represents a fine help and a welcome treasury of methods and devices for every civil and structural engineer concerned with the design and construction of civil engineering works, since the ground always affects the stability and performance of these structures. It can be recommended warmly to students and civil engineers in the field of design, construction and research."

Applied Mechanics Reviews

"This most interesting book includes a very large number of references and a list of instrument suppliers. It will probably become one of the most widely used tools for soil and foundation engineers who understand the need for performance evaluation."

Canadian Geotechnical Journal

"The book can obviously be recommended to all people dealing with foundations, earth and rockfill dams, tunnels, and soil mechanics in general."

Water Power